THE LIFE OF SCIENCE LIBRARY 45

Nobel Prize
Winners
in
MEDICINE
and
PHYSIOLOGY
1901-1965

Nobel Prize Winners in MEDICINE and PHYSIOLOGY

1901-1965

by THEODORE L. SOURKES

B.Sc., M.Sc., Ph.D.

Professor of Biochemistry, McGill University

Revision of earlier work by
LLOYD G. STEVENSON, M.D., Ph.D.

Abelard-Schuman

London New York Toronto

16605

LONDON	NEW YORK	TORONTO
Abelard-Schuman	Abelard-Schuman	Abelard-Schuman
Limited	Limited	Canada Limited
8 King St. WC2	6 West 57th St.	896 Queen St. W.

Printed in the United States of America

FROM THE PREFACE TO THE FIRST EDITION

A HALF-CENTURY OF ACHIEVEMENT IN MEDICAL SCIENCE IS reflected in the awards of the Nobel Prize for Physiology and Medicine. One-fifth of the interest on Alfred Nobel's fortune is to be given annually "to the person who shall have made the most important discovery" in this domain. Winners are selected by the Caroline Medico-Chirurgical Institute in Stockholm. Each Nobel laureate is judged to have made a personal contribution of first-rate importance. Behind and around him there is always a constellation of scientists who have taken part in the same work. Their preliminary researches have made it possible, or their subsequent efforts have made it more fruitful. The winner of the Prize is therefore not only a discoverer in his own right, but a representative—by virtue of his outstanding contribution—of those who have worked toward the same or a similar goal. The configuration of the heavens may be roughly indicated by mapping the principal stars, but the sky would be dim indeed without the rest.

In the following pages each Prize Winner is represented, first, by a short biographical sketch; second, by a passage in which he describes the Prize discovery in his own words; and third, by a brief editorial explanation of the meaning and importance of the work. For the most part the quotation is an excerpt from the Nobel Lecture delivered in Stockholm at the time of the presentation of the Prize.

These Lectures are given to general audiences and should therefore be suitable for general readers, as many of them are. Unfortunately this is not always the case. When the Lecture has been very technical in form, some less complicated version of the same story has been sought for elsewhere in the author's works. Sought for, but not always found. Happily there are only a few cases—Professor Gullstrand's is one—in which the very nature of the discovery requires that the reader should have extensive background knowledge before he can hope for a competent understanding. These few instances must be left to those who can grasp them. The majority of the discoveries are easy to comprehend in outline. No more than this is aimed at here.

Occasionally, too, the Prize Winner has grown bored with his own discovery long before reaching Stockholm—he may have described it already fifty times—and has chosen to talk about something else. Pavlov and Florey are examples: both of them preferred to speak of more recent work. Again, a modest laureate may devote most of his time to expounding the related discoveries of other scientists. In all such cases it is obvious that the Nobel Lecture would have been an unsuitable choice for the present purpose. Actually most of these Lectures are precisely what is needed. Sometimes, too, the choice has been determined by the way in which the work of one Prize Winner can be linked with that of another: as they are here represented, Sherrington's physiological discovery leads on from an anatomical finding by Golgi; there are also other examples. . . .

Lloyd G. Stevenson, M.D.

October, 1952

PREFACE TO THE SECOND EDITION

SINCE 1901 THE NOBEL PRIZE has been awarded on 56 occasions to 90 scientists working in the broad area encompassed by the term "physiology and medicine." This new edition incorporates much of the material in the original volume as well as new chapters covering the period from 1951 to 1965. The text of the first edition has been revised to bring biographies up to date; the descriptions of the Prize-winning work have in a few cases been changed through selection of different material from the laureate's writings; and, as before, the assessments of the significance of the work take into account the new perspectives that current progress in science and medicine have brought. An appendix, in which the Nobel laureates are listed by the subjects of their research, has been added; together with the index, it may be of assistance to the general reader as well as to teachers who use the book for didactic purposes. Although I have revised some material, I have also preserved extensive sections from the original volume and, in many cases, have retained complete chapters. I worked with the conviction that, in the interests of the reader, Dr. Stevenson's fine exposition had best be tampered with as little as possible.

It is my great pleasure to thank Dr. Stevenson, now Professor of the History of Science and Medicine at Yale University, who generously handed over to me the fruit of his earlier labour. His suggestion that I undertake the preparation of a new edition of *Nobel Prize Winners in Medicine and Physiology* led me into a fascinating project which, through the pressure of teaching and of laboratory research, necessarily became a part-time avocation during the last two and one-half years.

Theodore L. Sourkes, Ph.D.

Montreal, May 1966

CONTENTS

Nobel Prize Winners
in
MEDICINE
and
PHYSIOLOGY
1901-1965

1 9 0 1
EMIL VON BEHRING
(1854–1917)

"For his work on serum therapy, especially its application against diphtheria, by which he has opened a new road in the domain of medical science and thereby placed in the hands of the physician a victorious weapon against illness and death."

BIOGRAPHICAL SKETCH

EMIL ADOLF (VON) BEHRING WAS BORN IN DEUTSCH-EYLAU, Germany, in 1854 and studied in Berlin. He entered the Army Medical Corps and was lecturer in the Army Medical College, Berlin, in 1888. The following year he became assistant in Robert Koch's Institute of Hygiene. In 1891, when Koch became chief of the new Institute for Infectious Diseases, von Behring accompanied him. Meantime (1890) he had published his important papers on serum therapy. The consequences in medical practice were sensational and von Behring was soon famous. In 1894 he accepted the chair of hygiene in Halle, but a year later transferred to a similar position in Marburg. He received many distinctions and several monetary prizes. In Marburg he established works for the manufacture of antitoxins and a remedy for the tuberculosis of cattle. He died in 1917.

DESCRIPTION OF THE PRIZE-WINNING
WORK*

"As already proved by Löffler, then Roux and Yersin, there are animals naturally immune to diphtheria; I have confirmed by my own investigations that this is true of mice and rats, and that these animals tolerate, without appreciable damage to their health, inoculations with cultures which have a sure and deadly effect on much larger animals, such as the guinea pig, rabbit, and wether. . . .

"Furthermore, one can make animals immune which were originally very susceptible to diphtheria. . . .

"1. One of the immunization methods, which I can show to be very reliable on the ground of my own research, has been described exactly by Prof. C. Fränkel [1861-1915; an assistant of Koch's who became professor of hygiene at Halle and did much original work in bacteriology and immunology]. . . . It depends on the use of sterilized cultures, and with the help of this method one can make guinea pigs nonsusceptible in 10-14 days to inoculations that are certain death to normal guinea pigs. . . .

"2. [Von Behring next describes a method of his own, using in place of the sterilized cultures of Fränkel cultures weakened by the addition of iodine trichloride in small amounts. A feeble culture was succeeded by a more active one. Finally a fully virulent culture was tolerated.]

"In both the methods just mentioned, immunity is brought about by the metabolic products bred by diphtheria bacilli in cultures.

"3. But it is also possible to produce immunity through the same metabolic products engendered from diphtheria bacilli in the living animal organism. If one investigates animals dying of diphtheria, one finds an extremely abundant transudate in the pleural cavity. . . .

"In more than 50 separate cases investigated, this transudate never contained diphtheria bacilli; but it possesses properties poi-

---

* Translated from Emil von Behring, " Untersuchungen über das Zustandekommen der Diphtherie-Immunität bei Thieren," *Deutsche medizinische Wochenschrift,* Vol. 16 (December 11, 1890), pp. 1145-1148.

sonous for guinea pigs. The degree of toxicity is not always the same. . . .

"Those [few] guinea pigs which survive an injection of [10 to 15 c.c. of] transudate . . . are regularly sick for a long time; [here follows a description of their symptoms].

"Now when I awaited the complete recovery of those animals which displayed the symptoms just described to a pronounced degree, then . . . I could establish that they endured without harm inoculations that would kill healthy animals in 3 to 4 days. . . .

"4. An[other] immunization method, one not hitherto employed, can also be traced to the operation of the metabolic products of the diphtheria bacilli.

"*It consists in first infecting the animals and then doing away with the deleterious effect through therapeutic management.* [This was exceedingly difficult. Of the many drugs tried, most were useless. Mention is made, however, of certain compounds which appeared to have cured infected guinea pigs, notably iodine trichloride. Behring reported that treatment with this drug prior to infection did no good.]

"5. [It was reported that prior treatment with hydrogen peroxide seemed to confer some immunity. This alleged success had nothing to do with immune products resulting from the metabolism of bacilli.]

"All five of the methods of immunization against diphtheria thus far described are in my opinion not practicable—at least in the form I have given them—for humans.

"But from the scientific viewpoint, and . . . for the understanding of the occurrence of diphtheria immunity, they are capable of affording us worth-while service.

"That is to say, immunity having somehow occurred—and I do not exclude natural immunity—all diphtheria-immune animals have certain characteristics in common which distinguish them from non-immune animals.

"First of all, the living immune animals, as a whole, not only possess protection against infection with the living diphtheria bacilli but are also protected against the deleterious effect of the poisonous substances formed by the diphtheria bacilli in cultures and in the animal body.

"I have undertaken the proof of this in various ways. First I tried it with the solution of an albuminous substance which I separated from old cultures with acidified alcohol; however, I was unable to remove the acid from the resulting preparation without impairing the poisonous effect; I also think it no easily soluble problem . . . to separate other precipitating agents from the precipitate produced. But for the purpose in question I scarcely needed to go after the diphtheria poison, or, perhaps more correctly, the diphtheria poisons; filtrates of old cultures afforded me all I wanted.

"Using my cultures grown in alkaline bouillon, with 10 c.c. normal alkali per liter, I found that after 10 weeks they contained so much poisonous substance that, having been rendered germ-free by filtration, they already called forth characteristic symptoms of diphtheria poisoning with a dose of 1 c.c. in medium-sized guinea pigs; these symptoms did not entirely disappear for 3 to 4 weeks. Furthermore, 3 to 4 c.c. were enough to kill larger guinea pigs in 3 to 8 days . . .

"Now all guinea pigs with established diphtheria immunity . . . endured 3 to 5 c.c. without any discernible disease symptoms or local reaction whatever; on the other hand, guinea pigs that had still not quite recovered from an infection proved to be only very little more poison-resistant than they normally would be. . . . *It is very noteworthy that the immunity can be lost again through the subcutaneous injection of considerable and repeated quantities; this happens with all the more certainty, the less the immunity has been 'established.' At all events, guinea pigs under the influence of the poisonous, germ-free diphtheria culture fare as before against diphtheria infection under unfavorable conditions.*

"The first thought to arise could be this, that the resistance to poison here described depends on 'habituation,' as in the case of alcoholics, morphine addicts, arsenic eaters. . . .

"But such an interpretation is at once controverted by the fact that animals which have never had anything to do with diphtheria poison also possess diphtheria poison resistance.

"If we start out again with the 10-week culture rendered germ-free, then, calculating on the basis of body weight, it is deadly for guinea pigs in the ratio of about 1:100; but mice endure the poison without any harm when it is injected into them in the ratio of 1:20, and I have injected rats on several successive days with 4 c.c. at a time without the appearance of a reaction worth mentioning.

"A further argument against accepting habituation to the poison [as the explanation] is the circumstance that I have never succeeded, despite the most cautious increase in the dosage of poison from a quite harmless to a higher one, in protecting animals against the diphtheria poison, except insofar as they have later been able to endure a little more of it than they normally could.

"These observations and considerations led me to approach closer to the question whether the origin of the poison resistance really does not depend at all on a characteristic of the living cellular parts of the organism, but rather on a peculiar property of the blood, freed of living cells.

"In order to decide this question I withdrew blood from rats 3 hours after they had had large amounts of diphtheria poison injected into their abdominal cavities, and injected it, or the serum obtained from it, into the abdominal cavities of guinea pigs; no trace of the symptoms of poisoning occurred, whereas the blood of diphtheria-susceptible animals which had received the diphtheria poison, when injected into the abdominal cavity in like amount (4 c.c.), did not, indeed, kill the guinea pigs, yet clearly made them sick.

"For the future, then, I attach importance to the fact that the extravascular blood of diphtheria-immune guinea pigs also has the capacity of making the diphtheria poison harmless. To what extent this occurs, and to what extent therapeutic results can be obtained with the blood of immunized animals—on these points I propose to contribute later. . . ."

CONSEQUENCES IN THEORY AND PRACTICE

In No. 49 (December 4, 1890) of the *Deutsche medizinische Wochenschrift* (German Medical Weekly), von Behring and his Japanese colleague, Shibasaburo Kitasato (1852-1931) announced the discovery of tetanus antitoxin. It was shown that "immunity to this disease . . . depends on the capacity of the blood to render harmless the poisonous substances produced by the tetanus bacilli."

"In that work," wrote von Behring, "the same was also affirmed for diphtheria immunity, in just the same way as for tetanus, but without the communication of separate investigations, which had shown for diphtheria, too, the equivalent mechanism of the occurrence of immunity." The work had already been done in part by von Behring, and one week later, in No. 50 (December 11, 1890) of the same journal, there appeared the classic paper from which an excerpt is quoted above. It is interesting that a large part of this paper concerns preliminary investigations and relates the way in which von Behring reached the conclusion that the power of resisting the disease does not reside in the cellular constitution of the body but rather in the cell-free blood serum. (This contention was so amply proved a little later that Metchnikoff's discovery of the part played by white blood cells in combating infection was at first rather ill received. See below, pp. 49-50.)

As suggested by the last sentence of the longer quotation, much remained to be done in studying this phenomenon. About a year after publication of the quoted paper the first human case was treated with diphtheria antitoxin. This was a child in Bergmann's clinic in Berlin, Geissler making the injection on Christmas night, 1891. The method was soon widely used and its success was phenomenal. The death rate from diphtheria, as reported by one of the Berlin hospitals, fell from 48 percent to 13 percent, and even better results soon were achieved. Before the discovery of antitoxin the fatality rate in general was about 35 percent, and in laryngeal cases about 90 percent. Since this discovery, mortality has fallen to approximately 5 percent, and in laryngeal cases to 15 percent.

Ability to measure dosage was largely the result of the brilliant work of Paul Ehrlich (see below, pp. 52-55). Further progress was made when the Health Department of New York City adopted the use of cultures for diagnosis and for control of the period of isolation; this was done in 1893 under the direction of Park. In 1913 Schick described the intradermal toxin reaction (skin test) for the determination of individual immunity. In the same year von Behring introduced the use of injections of toxin-antitoxin mixtures in children for active immunization against diphtheria. This proved a most effective means of protection. In 1924, Ramon brought forward his formalized toxin or anatoxin, commonly known as toxoid, which has largely replaced toxin-antitoxin mixtures.

Not only did von Behring make the most important contributions to the conquest of diphtheria but his introduction of serotherapy opened a whole new field to medicine.

REFERENCES

BULLOCH, WILLIAM. *The History of Bacteriology* (London and New York: Oxford University Press, 1938), and the literature cited there, especially E. Wernicke, "Die Immunität bei Diphtherie," *Handbuch der pathogenen Mikroorganismen von Kolle-Wassermann*, 1913.

1 9 0 2

RONALD ROSS
(1857–1932)

*"For his work on malaria, by which he has shown
how it enters the organism and thereby has laid the
foundation for successful research on this disease
and how to combat it."*

BIOGRAPHICAL SKETCH

RONALD ROSS CAME OF A THREE-GENERATION ANGLO-INDIAN
family. He was born at Almora in the Kumaon hills, northwest
Nepal, on May 13, 1857, the eldest of ten children. His father was
General Sir Campbell Claye Ross. In 1874 Ronald Ross began the
study of medicine at St. Bartholomew's Hospital Medical School.
He obtained the M.R.C.S. diploma in 1879 and for a time traveled
between London and New York as a ship's surgeon. He then
entered the Madras Medical Service and took part in the Burma
War. On leave in 1888, he studied bacteriology in London under
Klein, and took the D.P.H. Returning to India, he began, in 1892,
to take especial interest in malaria; he had already studied mosquitoes on his first tour of service. In 1894 Patrick Manson, the great
pioneer of tropical medicine, showed him the malarial parasites
discovered by Laveran in 1880. Returning to India in 1895 after
his second home leave, Ross carried on an exhaustive study of the
problem of the transmission of malaria, constantly advised and
encouraged by Manson. A series of frustrations, due to the failure
of the authorities to support his work and their maddening tend-

ency to transfer him at crucial moments in his research, dogged him for years. He nevertheless achieved the great success described below. Ross was later sent to Assam to investigate kala-azar. In 1899 he was appointed lecturer in tropical medicine at the Liverpool School and retired from the Indian Medical Service; in 1902 he became professor. In 1912 he left Liverpool to act as physician for tropical diseases at King's College Hospital. He served in various capacities as a consultant during the First World War and after 1918 he practiced in London. He traveled widely, chiefly to advise on antimalaria measures. In addition to his scientific writings and his *Memoirs,* he published books of verse and several romances. In 1911 he became a Knight Commander of the Bath, and in 1918 Knight Commander of the Order of Saint Michael and Saint George. The Ross Institute and Hospital for Tropical Diseases, founded in his honor, was opened at Putney in 1926. He died there in 1932.

DESCRIPTION OF THE PRIZE-WINNING WORK*

"Towards the middle of August [1897] I had exhaustively searched numerous grey mosquitoes and a few brindled mosquitoes. [Unable to obtain literature on mosquitoes, Ross made a working classification of his own and invented simple names. His grey mosquitoes belonged to the genus *Culex,* his brindled mosquitoes to the genus *Stegomyia.*] The results were absolutely negative; the insects contained nothing whatever. . . .

"I had remembered the small dappled-winged mosquitoes [genus *Anopheles*], but as I could not succeed either in finding their larvae or in inducing the adult insects to bite patients, I could make no experiments with them. On the 15th August, however, one of my assistants brought me a bottle of larvae, many of which hatched out next day. Among them I found several dappled-winged mosquitoes, evidently of the same genus as those found about the barracks, but much larger and stronger. Delighted with this capture I fed them (and they proved to be very voracious) on

---

* From Ronald Ross, "Researches on Malaria," *Les Prix Nobel en 1902.*

a case with crescents in the blood. Expecting to find more in the breeding bottle and wishing to watch the escape of the motile filaments in this new variety, I dissected four of them for this purpose immediately after feeding. This proved to be most unfortunate, as there were no more of these insects in the bottle, and the results as regards the motile filaments were negative. I had, however, four of the gorged dappled-winged mosquitoes left; but by bad luck two of the dissections were very imperfect and I found nothing. On the 20th August I had two remaining insects both living. Both had been fed on the 16th instant. I had much work to do with other mosquitoes, and was not able to attend to these until late in the afternoon when my sight had become very fatigued. The seventh dappled-winged mosquito was then successfully dissected. Every cell was searched, and to my intense disappointment nothing whatever was found, until I came to the insect's stomach. There, however, just as I was about to abandon the examination, I saw a very delicate circular cell apparently lying among the ordinary cells of the organ, and scarcely distinguishable from them. Almost instinctively I felt that here was something new. On looking further, another and another similar object presented itself. I now focussed the lens carefully on one of these, and found that it contained a few minute granules of some black substance exactly like the pigment of the parasite of malaria. I counted altogether twelve of these cells in the insect, but was so tired with work and had been so often disappointed before that I did not at the moment recognize the value of the observation. After mounting the preparation I went home and slept for nearly an hour. On waking, my first thought was that the problem was solved; and so it was.

"Next morning . . . the eighth and last dappled-winged mosquito . . . was killed and dissected with much anxiety. *Similar bodies were present in it.* . . . The objects lay, not in the stomach cavity of the insects, but in the thickness of the stomach wall. . . .

"These two observations solved the malaria problem. They did not complete the story, certainly; but they furnished the clue. At a stroke they gave both of the unknown quantities—the kind of mosquito implicated and the position and appearance of the parasites within it."

CONSEQUENCES IN THEORY
AND PRACTICE

In July 1897 MacCallum discovered the sexual phase of the reproduction of the malarial parasite. Manson at once recognized that Ross's pigmented cells were the fertilized female cells, becoming motile after fertilization and burrowing into the insects' tissues for further development. In July 1898 Ross discovered the sporozoids of *Proteosoma,* a malarial parasite attacking birds, in the salivary glands of mosquitoes. The route of infection was thus revealed and the story was virtually complete. Grassi extended the discovery from bird malaria to human malaria, and Italian malariologists worked out most of what remained to be learned. Ross optimistically expected that his discoveries were "to save human life in the gross, perhaps to open continents to civilization," a confidence widely shared. It was largely doomed to disappointment, for the problem has turned out to be an enormously difficult one. Economics, agriculture, and the social conditions of great masses of people have proved important, and often intractable, factors in the control of malaria. Furthermore, there appear to be epidemiological considerations which are not well understood even today. For example, no entirely satisfactory explanation has yet been advanced for the almost complete disappearance of malaria in certain areas, such as parts of the United States and Canada, where Anopheles mosquitoes continue to thrive. Nevertheless the discovery made by Sir Ronald Ross has borne fruit in such measures as the drainage or oiling of swamps and in the "malaria discipline" which, properly inculcated and enforced, has been shown capable of providing a large measure of protection to armies fighting in the tropics. This has been of great value to other groups and individuals exposed to the same danger; combined with the use of quinine, and more recently with other drugs, especially atabrine, it has reduced, although by no means abolished, the greatest hazard of the malaria-infested regions of the globe. The introduction of DDT (see below, pp. 261-265) and other insecticides has given the malariologist new weapons against the mosquito. In several malarial districts, notably in Cyprus, the most recent results have been very encouraging.

One may be tempted to suggest that Ross's work inspired Walter Reed, Charles Nicolle, and later discoverers of insect vectors in disease; but it should be remembered that earlier workers, notably Theobald Smith and Manson, had already performed a similar service. It will not be forgotten that General W. C. Gorgas, by exterminating mosquitoes in the Panama region, was able to control both malaria and yellow fever.

REFERENCES

MEGROZ, R. L. *Ronald Ross, Discoverer and Creator* (London: Allen & Unwin, 1931).

ROSS, RONALD. *Memoirs: With a Full Account of the Great Malaria Problem and Its Solution* (London: J. Murray, 1923).

1 9 0 3
NIELS RYBERG FINSEN

(1860–1904)

"In recognition of his contribution to the treatment of diseases, especially lupus vulgaris, with concentrated light rays, whereby he has opened a new avenue to medical science."

BIOGRAPHICAL SKETCH

Niels Ryberg Finsen was born December 15, 1860, at Thorshavn, capital of the Faroe Islands, and received some of his early schooling at Reykjavik, Iceland. He studied at the University of Copenhagen for eight years and took his degree in medicine in 1890. In the same year he was appointed professor of anatomy in the Surgical Academy. As an undergraduate he had already become interested in the influence of light upon living organisms. His work followed researches of Downes and Blunt on the influence of light upon bacteria, and those of Widmark on the power of the actinic rays to cause inflammation of the skin. In 1893 he published his first essay on the red-light treatment of smallpox. This was followed by other papers on the biological effects of light, including accounts of his work on the treatment of lupus vulgaris, a form of tuberculosis affecting the skin, especially that of the face. In 1895 he established the first Light Institute, at Copenhagen, which received patients from many parts of the world. Originally built and supported by private philanthropy, this Institute was later assisted by the state. When awarded the Nobel Prize, Finsen placed half the prize money at interest for the benefit of his family and donated the other half to the Institute. He died at the age of forty-three, on September 24, 1904.

DESCRIPTION OF THE PRIZE-WINNING WORK*

"Thanks to the work of Downes and Blunt, of Duclaux, Arloing, Roux, Geissler, Buchner, etc., it is at present [1897] well established that light possesses an energetic bactericidal power. Thus everything argues, at least theoretically, in favor of the use of light in the treatment of superficial cutaneous diseases caused by bacterial infection, and yet this therapeutic procedure has remained unused . . . to this day. . . . [Finsen here reviews some references in the literature to earlier attempts to use light in this way in the treatment of lupus. In some cases this apparently had been conceived as nothing more than a form of heat treatment; in general, Finsen concludes, the light source had been too feeble, the treatments too short and too few.]

"These isolated instances of the use of light for the treatment of lupus are thus of little value and can scarcely provide a basis for further researches. Consequently I have thought it my duty to re-undertake the study of this important question from top to bottom.

"As light only exerts its bactericidal effects very slowly, it is necessary . . . to concentrate it by means of mirrors or lenses, at the same time excluding the heat rays of the spectrum, the infrared, red, orange, and yellow, because when concentrated they cause burning of tissues. This exclusion, moreover, curtails the bactericidal action of the light only a very little, for on examining the question more closely one finds that the majority of observers have asserted that the bactericidal qualities are due to the most refractive rays, a fact which my own experiments have confirmed. . . . [At this point Finsen describes the filters he used for this purpose, the means he employed for "straining" and concentrating sunlight, and the apparatus he devised for making use of artificial sources of light to produce "blue-violet" rays. His chief resource for filtering

---

* Translated from Niels Ryberg Finsen, *La Photothérapie* (Paris: G. Carré et C. Naud, 1899), pp. 85-96.

sunlight was a hollow planoconvex lens filled with an ammoniacal solution of copper sulfate; when he used an electric arc lamp, the rays were made parallel by two planoconvex lenses.]

"Before having this apparatus constructed and perfected, I assured myself by a series of experiments that the bactericidal action of light is really augmented in the degree that its rays are concentrated . . . I made use of flat, rectangular vessels, coating their walls inside with peptone-gelatin or peptone-agar which I sowed with pure cultures [of bacteria]. On the outside of each flask I stuck a sheet of paper, white on one side and black on the other, the white surface being turned to the light in order to prevent the absorption of heat rays, and the black surface applied to the glass to prevent the light from influencing the culture. In addition I cut round holes in this paper across which I wrote on the glass of the vessel . . . figures indicating the time in minutes during which these parts were subjected to the action of light.

"Two identical flasks prepared in this way were simultaneously exposed . . . one to direct sunlight, the other to concentrated sunlight. . . . [The cultures were allowed to grow in the dark for a day or two. It was then found that the concentrated light had had a greater inhibitory effect than direct sunlight. Finsen performed other experiments of a similar nature to test this point. He also found that his blue-violet rays, when passed through the pinna of the ear, had no effect on photographic paper; but that if the ear were compressed between plates of glass until partly exsanguinated —i.e., deprived of blood—the rays then seemed capable of penetrating it. For this reason he devised glass discs to be bound firmly with tapes to the surfaces he wished to expose; these were supposed to prevent blood from absorbing too much of the radiation by forcing it out of the areas under treatment.]

"I have employed the method of treatment by concentrated chemical rays in different infectious skin diseases, but above all in *lupus vulgaris,* an affection which presents particularly favorable conditions for putting this therapeutic procedure to work. It is known that lupus vulgaris is caused by the tubercle bacillus, that it is a local and quite superficial malady. On the other hand it is well established that light is capable of killing the tubercle bacillus. . . .

"When a plaque of lupus has been subjected for a long enough time to the action of concentrated chemical rays, its margins, previously elevated, become smooth, the redness progressively diminishes, the skin regains its normal color, and ulcerations, when they exist, are cicatrized."

CONSEQUENCES IN THEORY
AND PRACTICE

Finsen's use of concentrated radiation from the sun or an artificial light source, with the heat rays eliminated, made available the most refractive rays, the blue and especially the ultraviolet. Ultraviolet light continues to hold a place in the treatment of lupus vulgaris and a few other types of skin disease. The apparatus used and the details of treatment have changed, but the principle remains. X-ray treatment has been substituted in some cases of lupus, particularly in those with marked ulceration and hypertrophy, but the Finsen method, although time-consuming and costly, yields the least disfiguring scars. Sometimes both X rays and Finsen rays are used, and radium, too, has been employed. Local treatment with drugs and the surgical removal of severe localized lesions have been recommended, in combination with the systemic treatment of tuberculosis. Despite variations, a leading place is still reserved for ultraviolet irradiation. The approach to therapy has been altered, however, by the recent introduction of cortisone and ACTH.

The therapeutic use of other forms of irradiation has probably been inspired in part by Finsen's success. Ultraviolet light is now used for a variety of other purposes, including the partial sterilization of a limited, enclosed space; attempts have also been made to reduce the number of upper respiratory infections by ultraviolet irradiation of working places, but with limited and rather dubious success. (The importance of sunlight for health has been confirmed by the discovery that vitamin D_2 is produced by the ultraviolet irradiation of ergosterol, a substance derived from yeast and other plant sources, but also found in animal tissues, notably in the skin; hence the rarity of rickets in sunny climates.) Meanwhile, Bernhard, Rollier, and a number of later workers have extended the use of phototherapy in surgical cases and in several different forms of tuberculosis.

Finsen had earlier (1893) described a method for the prevention of pitting in smallpox by keeping the patient in a red-lighted room, the chemical rays at the other end of the spectrum being excluded. This procedure is now seldom mentioned in the textbooks.

1 9 0 4
IVAN PETROVICH PAVLOV
(1849–1936)

"In recognition of his work on the physiology of digestion, by which, in essential respects, he has transformed and enlarged our knowledge of this subject."

BIOGRAPHICAL SKETCH

IVAN PETROVICH PAVLOV, WHO CAME OF A FAMILY OF POOR country priests, was born September 26, 1849, in the city of Riazan, in Russia. He began his education in the church school and continued it in the theological seminary. Discovering an interest in the natural sciences, he left the seminary in 1870 and entered St. Petersburg University, where Mendeleev and Butlerov were among his teachers. Subsequently he entered the Medico-Chirurgical Academy and was graduated in 1879. The influence of Professor E. von Cyon and the fame of Sechenov are said to have determined his future career. After graduation he served as Professor S. P. Botkin's *chef de laboratoire* in the Clinic of Internal Medicine at the St. Petersburg Military Medical Academy, where he continued to study physiology and carry on research. In 1884 he went abroad to study, spending two years in further training, partly with Ludwig at Leipzig, partly with Heidenhain in Breslau. He returned to the Military Medical Academy in 1886. In 1888 he discovered the secretory nerves to the pancreas; in 1889 he described his experiments in sham feeding (see below). Not until 1890 did he obtain

20

a chair, becoming professor of pharmacology. A year later he was also appointed director of the Department of Physiology of the Institute of Experimental Medicine. In 1895 he gave up his chair of pharmacology for that of physiology in the Medico-Chirurgical Academy, which he retained until 1924. In 1902 Bayliss and Starling announced the discovery of secretin, the hormone which incites the pancreas to secrete its digestive juice. The discovery was confirmed in Pavlov's laboratories, but Pavlov himself had concentrated on nervous correlations and the introduction of a humoral (blood-stream) factor seems to have cooled his interest in digestion. At any rate he now turned to his famous work on the conditioned reflex. For the next thirty years he devoted himself to the reflex activity of the cerebral hemispheres. His death occurred in 1936.

DESCRIPTION OF THE PRIZE-WINNING WORK *

"In the year 1852 Bidder and Schmidt had observed that, under certain circumstances, one needs only to excite a dog by the sight of food in order to call forth a secretion of gastric juice. . . . In recent times the French physiologist Richet has had the opportunity of making observations on a patient on whom the operation of gastrotomy had been performed for an incurable stricture of the oesophagus [i.e., a permanent opening had been made from the stomach to the exterior to permit feeding]. Soon after the patient took anything sweet or acid into the mouth, Richet was able to perceive a secretion of pure gastric juice. . . . [These] observations prove . . . that the gastric glands are influenced through nerves by 'distant effect,' since the phenomenon comes to pass without any immediate contact between the food and the gastric mucous membrane. It only remained to make the experiment constant and simple; in other words, to facilitate its reproduction and seek out its proper interpretation.

"As a matter of fact, I am now able to demonstrate experiments to you which yield absolutely constant and unequivocal results. We

---

* From J. P. Pawlow, *The Work of the Digestive Glands,* translated by W. H. Thompson (London: C. G. Griffin, 1902), pp. 49-51, 54, 71.

have here before us [this is a demonstration lecture] a dog . . . [which] possesses an ordinary gastric fistula with metallic cannula [tube], and has had its oesophagus divided as well, so that the mouth is cut off from all communication with the cavity of the stomach. Its stomach has been washed out . . . and . . . not a single drop of fluid escapes from the fistula. I give the dog food. The animal eats greedily, but the whole of the food swallowed comes out again at the oesophageal opening in the neck. After feeding in this way (. . . 'sham feeding') for five minutes, perfectly pure gastric juice makes its appearance at the fistula, the stream steadily becomes greater and greater, and now, five minutes after the commencement of secretion, we have already 20 c.c. of juice. We may continue to feed the dog as long as we wish, the secretion will flow at the same rate for one, two, or more hours. . . . It is obvious that the effect of the feeding is transmitted by nervous channels to the gastric glands.

". . . We will [now] carry our experiment a step farther by dividing the vagi nerves. . . . In the case of this dog, at the time of making the gastric fistula, the right vagus nerve was divided below its recurrent laryngeal and cardiac branches. In this way, only the pulmonary and abdominal branches on the side in question were thrown out of function, the laryngeal and cardiac fibres remained intact. About three hours before the present lecture, I prepared the left vagus free in the neck, passing a loop of thread round the nerve, but not dividing it. I now pull gently on the thread to draw the nerve outwards, and sever it with a sharp snip of the scissors. At present the pulmonary and abdominal vagi on both sides are paralysed, while on the right side the laryngeal and cardiac fibres are intact. . . . The dog . . . shows no indication whatever of a pathological or otherwise uncomfortable condition. . . . We again offer the dog food to eat, which it eats with increasing greed . . . but in sharp contrast to the previous sham feeding, we do not see a single drop of juice flowing from the stomach. We may feed the dog as long as we wish, and repeat our experiment . . . as often as we desire, but never again shall we see a secretion of gastric juice in this animal as the result of sham feeding. . . .

"[In another dog in the same state] the peripheral end of the [left vagus nerve in the neck] had been prepared free, placed on a ligature, and for the time being preserved under the skin. After three to four days the stitches were carefully removed . . . when the nerve lay free before us. In this way we avoided appreciable discomfort to the animal before exciting the nerve. By such precautions we invariably succeeded in obtaining a secretion of juice from the empty stomach when the nerve was subsequently excited by slow induction shocks at intervals of one to two seconds. . . .

"[In still another case] we begin to get ready a meal of flesh and sausage before the animal [with gastric fistula and divided oesophagus] as if we meant to feed it. . . . Precisely five minutes after we begin to tease the animal in this way the first drops of gastric juice appear in the fistula. The secretion grows ever stronger and stronger, till it flows in a considerable stream."

CONSEQUENCES IN THEORY
AND PRACTICE

Apart from his later work on the conditioned reflex (which he discussed in his Nobel lecture, although the Prize had not been awarded with this in mind), the experiments described in the quotation are probably the most famous of the many which Pavlov performed. His great surgical skill contributed to his success, and he is credited with the introduction of aseptic surgery and the "chronic" experiment into physiology. His new experimental procedures included esophagotomy combined with gastric fistula, as well as a new type of stomach pouch designed to preserve blood and nerve supply; he also used new methods of faradization (application of an induced, or faradic, electric current) and was responsible for a number of other innovations or modifications in experimental techniques. His studies of the secretions of the salivary glands, the stomach, the pancreas, and the intestine—indeed, of almost every aspect of digestive secretion—are too far-ranging for brief summation; hence a portion of his work on gastric secretion has been selected as a specimen of his achievement. Professor Babkin summarizes the facts established under ten headings: "(1) It was demonstrated beyond doubt that vagus was the secretory nerve of the gastric glands. (2) It was shown that 'psychic' gastric secretion was a fact of extreme importance. (3) A typical course of gastric secretion in response to different food substances—meat, bread, milk—was established. (4) For the first time it was demonstrated that the peptic power of the gastric juice varied with the nature of the food ingested and the phase of gastric secretion. (5) The constancy of the acidity of the gastric juice was demonstrated. (6) The stimulation of gastric secretion by food introduced directly into the stomach was shown to be due not to the mechanical but to the chemical stimulation of the gastric glands. (7) New secretagogue substances, e.g., water and meat extract, were discovered. (8) The ability of starch to stimulate a greater output of pepsin was shown. (9) The inhibitory effect of fat on gastric secretion was established. (10) The three phases of gastric secretion—the nervous, the pyloric, and the intestinal—were disclosed."

This represents only a part of Pavlov's work on digestion; one therefore feels no surprise at Babkin's further statement that the sum of this work "is the foundation on which modern normal and pathological gastroenterology is based."

Pavlov's discovery of the part played by the vagus nerve was an important contribution to general knowledge of the autonomic control of internal organs and directed further attention to this interesting question. The reflexes described above are unconditioned reflexes. But it is already apparent, in the references to "psychic secretion," that Pavlov was feeling his way toward his concept of the conditioned reflex, initiated by a stimulus inherently meaningless but rendered effective by association. This concept in turn has had widespread influence on physiology, psychology, psychiatry, and even education.

REFERENCES

BABKIN, B. P. *Pavlov: A Biography* (Chicago: University of Chicago Press, 1949).

STAVRAKY, G. W. "Ivan Petrovitch Pavlov," *Archives of Neurology and Psychiatry,* Vol. 33 (May 1935), pp. 1082-1087.

1 9 0 5

ROBERT KOCH

(1843–1910)

"For his investigations and discoveries in regard to tuberculosis."

BIOGRAPHICAL SKETCH

BORN DECEMBER 11, 1843, IN KLAUSTHAL, HANOVER, ROBERT Koch was the son of a mining official and the third of thirteen children. He attended the *Gymnasium* of his native town and at the age of nineteen began his medical studies at Göttingen. Here he was influenced by the teaching of Jacob Henle, who had proposed a theory of contagion in 1840. In 1866, at the age of twenty-three, Koch received the M.D. degree. He then interned at the Hamburg General Hospital and in 1869 commenced practice at Rakwitz, in Posen. The following year he volunteered for medical service in the Franco-Prussian War. He resumed civil practice in 1872 in the town of Bomst (pop. 4000), in Wollstein, Polish Prussia; soon he became district physician, assuming responsibility for a large territory. Despite the heavy pressure of his day-to-day work, he found time for microscopy and conducted original research. His first triumph was his demonstration, in 1876, of the complete life cycle and sporulation of the anthrax bacillus. This historic piece of work was the first demonstration of a specific microorganism as the cause of a definite disease. Koch's ingenious contributions to the technique of bacteriology—isolating, mounting, staining, and photographing bacteria—facilitated his own later

studies. In 1880 he was made a member of the Imperial Board of
Health. This enabled him to give up his country practice and devote
his time to research. The results, which were almost immediate,
were of prime importance. In 1881 he introduced steam sterilization. On March 24, 1882, at a meeting of the Berlin Physiological
Society, he announced his discovery of the bacillus of tuberculosis.
From 1885 to 1891, he was professor of hygiene at the University
of Berlin, where much of his time was given up to teaching; in the
latter year he became the first director of the Institute for Infectious Diseases, turning his full energies to research. In 1883, as
head of the German Cholera Commission, he visited Egypt and
India and discovered the cholera vibrio. Later travels in India, Java,
Africa, and Italy were occasioned by his studies of trypanosomiasis,
malaria, plague, and a variety of other diseases. He and his collaborators were able to show that bubonic plague is transmitted to
human beings by the rat-flea. He came back repeatedly to his labors
on tuberculosis. Koch died at the age of sixty-seven, on May 27,
1910. His body was cremated and the ashes placed in the Berlin
Institute for Infectious Diseases.

DESCRIPTION OF THE PRIZE-WINNING WORK *

"[Jean Antoine] Villemin's discovery that tuberculosis is trans-
missible to animals [1865] has found varied confirmation, as is
well known, but also apparently well-founded opposition, so that,
up to a few years ago, it remained undecided whether or not tuberculosis is an infectious disease. [It was commonly blamed on nutritional disturbances.] Since then, however . . . inoculations into
the anterior chamber of the eye . . . and in addition, inhalation
experiments . . . have proven the transmissibility of tuberculosis
beyond a doubt. . . .

"Attempts have been made repeatedly to investigate the nature
of tuberculosis thoroughly, but up to now [1882] they have been

---

* From *Berliner klinische Wochenschrift*, Vol. 19 (1882), pp. 221-230; reprinted
in *Medical Classics* (Baltimore: Williams & Wilkins, 1938), Vol. 11, pp. 821-
852 (translation on pp. 853-880). The translation given here is modified slightly
from that of Dr. W. de Rouville in *Medical Classics*.

fruitless. The staining methods so frequently used with success for the demonstration of pathogenic microorganisms have left this disease in the lurch, and the attempts made to isolate and cultivate the virus of tuberculosis up to the present cannot be regarded as successful. . . .

"In my investigations of tuberculosis, I at first followed the known methods without obtaining any explanation as to the true nature of the disease. However, several opportune observations caused me to abandon these methods and to adopt others which finally led me to positive results. . . .

"The material to be examined is prepared in the usual manner for examining for pathogenic bacteria, and either spread on the cover slip, dried, and heated or cut into sections after fixation in alcohol. The cover slips or sections are placed in a staining solution of the following constitution: 200 c.c. of distilled water are mixed with 1 c.c. of a concentrated alcoholic solution of methylene blue, shaken up, and then 0.2 c.c. of a 10 percent solution of potassium hydroxide is added with repeated shaking. This mixture must show no precipitate after standing for several days. The materials to be stained remain in this solution for 20 to 24 hours. By heating the solution to 40° C in a water bath this time can be shortened to $\frac{1}{2}$ to 1 hour. Following this the cover slips are covered with a concentrated aqueous solution of vesuvin, which is filtered each time before using, and after 1 to 2 minutes rinsed with distilled water. When the cover slips come from the methylene blue, the attached layer appears dark blue and is markedly overstained. During the treatment with vesuvin this blue color is lost and it appears stained a faint brown. Under the microscope all the constituents of animal tissue, that is, the cell nuclei and their products of disintegration, appear brown, while the tubercle bacilli, on the other hand, stain a beautiful blue. Moreover, all other bacteria which I have investigated to date, with the exception of the lepra bacilli [discovered by Hansen in 1875], take on a brown color with this staining method. The color contrast between the brown stained tissue and the blue tubercle bacilli is so striking that the latter, which are present often only in very small number, are nevertheless to be found and identified with the greatest certainty. . . ."

[Koch indicates the diseased tissue, both human and animal,

examined by him in his search for the bacilli. He studied not only a large number of cases of spontaneous tuberculosis, but also many animals infected by inoculation.]

"On the basis of my numerous observations I state it to be proved that the bacteria designated by me as the tubercle bacilli are present in all cases of tuberculous disease of man and animals, and that they may be differentiated from all other microorganisms by their characteristic properties. It does not necessarily follow from this coincidence of the tuberculous disease and the bacilli that the two phenomena have an original association. . . .

"In order to prove that tuberculosis is a parasitic disease caused by the invasion of the bacilli . . . the bacilli had to be isolated from the body and cultivated in pure culture . . . and, finally, through transfer of the isolated bacilli to animals, the same clinical picture of tuberculosis as is obtained by the injection of naturally developed tuberculosis material had to be produced.

"[The solution of the problem] depends on the use of a solid, transparent culture medium which retains its firm consistency at incubator temperature [a method previously introduced by Koch]. . . .

"Serum of cattle or sheep blood . . . is poured into cotton-stoppered test tubes and daily, for six consecutive days, is heated to a temperature of 58° C for an hour at a time. By this means it is possible to sterilize the serum completely in most instances. . . . Then it is heated to 65° C for several hours. . . .

"On this solidified blood serum, which forms a firm transparent culture medium at incubator temperature, the tuberculous material [excised from diseased organs with disinfected instruments] is placed . . . by means of a just previously flamed platinum wire fused into a glass rod. Naturally the cotton plug is removed for only the shortest possible time. . . .

"The test tubes . . . are placed in the incubator and must remain there constantly at a temperature from 37° to 38° C. . . . The cultures resulting from the growth of tubercle bacilli first appear to the naked eye in the second week after inoculation, usually not until after the tenth day, as very tiny points and dry scales. . . . The markedly slow growth which is attained only at incubator temperature, the peculiarly dry and scale-like condition of these bacillary colonies occur in no other known type of bacteria, so that confusion of the cultures of tubercle bacilli with those of other bacteria is impossible; and after only a small amount of practice nothing is easier to detect at once than accidental contamination of the cultures. . . ."

[The pure cultures thus obtained were used by Koch in a series of animal inoculations, described in detail. The nature of the experiments and the results attained are indicated briefly in Koch's summation.]

"If one looks back over these experiments, it is apparent that a not inconsiderable number of experimental animals that had received the cultures of bacilli in various ways, that is, by simple inoculation into the subcutaneous tissue, through injection into the abdominal cavity, or into the anterior chamber of the eye or directly into the blood stream, had been rendered tuberculous without a single exception; and, indeed, had developed not only a solitary tubercle but an extraordinary number of tubercles proportionate to the large number of infectious germs introduced. In other animals it was possible by the injection of a minimal number of bacilli into the anterior chamber of the eye to produce a tuberculous iritis. . . ."

CONSEQUENCES IN THEORY AND PRACTICE

Tuberculosis is a protean disease, which can affect a number of organs and show a number of different results. Nevertheless some clinicians, notably the great Laënnec, inventor of the stethoscope, had been able to draw upon clinical observations to combine all tubercular processes into a single morbid unity. Later, however, under the influence of Rudolf Virchow, this unity was destroyed and a dualistic conception of tuberculosis grew up on the basis of pathological findings. On March 24, 1882, Koch informed the Berlin Physiological Society that he had discovered the tubercle bacillus. Laënnec's views were thus confirmed and the work of Villemin and other experimenters verified; the dualistic doctrine vanished. Koch could demonstrate tubercle bacilli not only in the lungs but in other infected organs—intestines, bones, kidneys, lymph glands, and skin. A variety of diseases were thus shown to be one and the same. Improvements in staining technique, introduced by Ehrlich and Ziehl, speeded up the detection of the organisms. Soon thousands of examinations were being made and the classification of these tubercular diseases became clear and certain. All were forms of tuberculosis. The clinical aspect of the disease, once complicated, was greatly simplified. "Chronic pneumonia," "apex catarrh," "apex pneumonia," etc., disappeared from the books.

In the tubercle bacillus doctors had a trustworthy diagnostic sign. Found in sputum or urine, it left no doubt of the diagnosis. Furthermore its presence or absence could be used to check on the effectiveness of treatment and on the patient's progress.

Isolation of the exciting cause of tuberculosis made it possible to study the nature and reactions of the responsible organism. All new therapeutic agents must be tried on the bacillus itself, *in vitro* (i.e., in a test tube) first, then *in vivo* (i.e., in the living body). At the present time the clinician has available important drugs for use in the treatment of tuberculosis: the chemotherapeutic substances isoniazid, para-aminosalicylic acid (PAS), and the antibiotic streptomycin (see pp. 298-303).

In 1890 Koch announced that he had found a substance that would check the growth of tubercle bacilli both *in vitro* and *in vivo*. This was tuberculin, a glycerine extract of a pure culture of tubercle bacilli; although it proved disappointing as a remedy, substances not unlike it have since been found of real value in diagnosis. It is also possible that the work on tuberculin, which attracted universal attention, may have served as a step toward the discovery of the antidiphtheria serum.

As shown in the quotation above, the tubercle bacillus is difficult to stain and difficult to cultivate on artificial media. It was Koch's great technical ingenuity that enabled him to devise a staining technique by which he could detect the bacillus and a culture technique by which he could grow it. Also worthy of note are the steps by which he proved it to be the causative factor in the disease. As a pioneer in staining, in the use of solid culture media, in sterilization by steam, and in many lesser technical matters, Koch was the principal founder of modern laboratory bacteriology in all its means and methods. He also imposed upon the growing science certain rigid requirements, known as "Koch's postulates," by which to establish proof of a causative relationship between microbe and disease. Among his own discoveries of this kind, none was more important, or more productive of good results, than his discovery of the tubercle bacillus.

REFERENCES

HEYMANN, B. *Robert Koch*. Leipzig, 1932.
KIRCHNER, M. *Robert Koch*. Vienna, 1924.
LÖBEL, J. *Robert Koch: Geschichte eines Glücklichen*. Zurich, 1935.

1 9 0 6

CAMILLO GOLGI
(1843–1926)

SANTIAGO RAMÓN Y CAJAL
(1852–1934)

"In recognition of their work on the structure of the nervous system."

BIOGRAPHICAL SKETCH

GOLGI

CAMILLO GOLGI WAS BORN IN CORTENO, IN BRESCIA, ITALY, IN 1843, the son of a medical practitioner. He received his medical training at the University of Padua, where he was graduated in 1865. During his postgraduate hospital course he was attracted to the Psychiatric Clinic of Cesare Lombroso, and his first publications were in the field of psychiatry. It was at this time, however, that Virchow's *Cellular Pathology* (1858) was exerting a great influence on medical scientists. Golgi began to work in the Pavian laboratory of Giulio Bizzozero, the histologist, where he conducted his first studies on the lymphatics of the brain and on the nature of the neuroglia. In 1872 circumstances forced him to take a post in the small hospital for incurables at Abbiategrasso, but despite disheartening conditions he carried on his researches and developed his famous silver-impregnation method of staining nervous tissues

32

(1873). He applied this method to the central nervous system, discovering the "Golgi cells" and providing evidence for the neuron theory. Meanwhile he had also done useful work in neuropathology. In 1879 he was appointed professor of anatomy at the University of Siena, but left the following year to return to Pavia as professor of histology and general pathology. He continued to conduct important studies in neuroanatomy, but much of his later work was in pathology. In a series of publications from 1886 to 1893 he established the cycle of development of the parasites of quartan and tertian malaria. He received many honorary degrees as well as other awards and was probably the best-known Italian medical scientist of his time. He died in 1926.

RAMÓN Y CAJAL

SANTIAGO RAMÓN Y CAJAL WAS BORN MAY 1, 1852, IN PETILLA, an isolated village in the Spanish Pyrenees, where his father was "surgeon of the second class." The elder Ramón later extended his studies and in time became professor of anatomy at Zaragoza. The son's unfortunate early schooling, under tyrannical teachers, failed to reveal his gifts. It was followed by apprenticeship, first to a barber, then to a shoemaker. His father then undertook to teach him, particularly in osteology, which revealed the boy's talent as a draftsman. Thereafter he studied medicine at Zaragoza and was graduated in 1873. Then came compulsory service in the Spanish army, chiefly in Cuba, until 1875; during this interval he suffered severely from malaria and dysentery. After taking a medical degree at Madrid, he became a demonstrator and then, in 1877, professor of anatomy at Zaragoza; but he was soon forced to interrupt his work because of pulmonary tuberculosis. He married in 1879 and in 1884 was called to the chair of anatomy at Valencia. For a time he worked at bacteriology and serology, but turned to his proper field, histology, and in 1887 was given a chair in that subject at Barcelona. Learning of the Golgi silver stain from Luis Simarra, a neuropsychiatrist of Madrid, Ramón y Cajal developed an improvement of his own which he began to use in the study of the nervous system. This was the first of his several important innovations in staining technique. In 1889 he demonstrated his work before the German Society of Anatomists, was praised by Kölliker, and was soon acclaimed by German histologists generally. In 1892 he was appointed professor of normal histology and pathologic anatomy at Madrid. International honors now accumulated. There followed many years of intensive labor. By 1923 he had already published 237 scientific papers. He also wrote a large number of books, including not only comprehensive works on the nervous system but popular essays, a treatise on color photography, etc. He died on October 18, 1934, at the age of eighty-two.

DESCRIPTIONS OF THE PRIZE-WINNING WORK

GOLGI *

"I have found two quite different kinds of nerve-endings in the tendons:

"(*a*) The one is represented by peculiar bodies which are quite characteristic in appearance, form, structure, and type of connection with the nerve fibrils, and are unlike any other in the known nervous end-apparatus of our organism; it is very probable, then, that their significance lies in correspondence with the function which muscles and tendons have to perform in common. Since they are at times associated with muscles, at times with tendons, one must, I think, confer on them the name of nervous musculo-tendinous end-organs.

"(*b*) The other type is represented by bodies which likewise have a peculiar and striking appearance, but which, on the whole . . . find their counterparts in other known nervous end-organs of our bodies, which they resemble not only in anatomical structure but probably in function also. I want to remark at once that I here refer to the so-called end-bulbs of the conjunctiva, the glands, etc.

---

* Translated from Camillo Golgi, "Über die Nerven der Sehnen des Menschen und anderer Wirbelthiere und über ein neues nervöses musculo-tendinöses Endorgan," *Untersuchungen über den feineren Bau des centralen und peripherischen Nervensystems* . . . übersetzt von Dr. R. Teuscher (Jena: G. Fischer, 1894), pp. 207-209.

"Just as these two kinds of end-organs are distinguished one from another by form, structure and nerve-fibril connections, so, too, do they differ from one another in their location. The first are always found in deep layers of the tendon origins, at the transition point where muscle becomes tendon; always, too, in relation to the muscular fasciculi. The second, on the contrary, lie as a rule in the superficial layers of the tendons or in the tendinous extensions.

". . . [The] principal anatomical characteristics [of the musculo-tendinous organs] may be summed up briefly as follows:

"In general they are spindle-shaped, and one of their ends is always connected with the fasciculi of the muscle fibers, with the sarcolemma [or sheath] of which their stroma [framework] appears to be in direct union; the other end, occasionally single but usually double, follows the course of the tendon fasciculi and gradually blends with them over a considerable distance.

"Their size varies within fairly wide limits, from 70-80 μ in breadth [μ is short for micron, the millionth of a meter or thousandth of a millimeter] and 300-400 μ in length to 100-120 μ in breadth and over 800 μ in length; the latter, especially if stained with gold, can easily be distinguished and isolated with the help of a simple lens.

"Their outline tends to be very distinct and even appears at times in the form of a slender, glittering border, along which one catches sight of nuclei. . . .

"As far as the structure is concerned, if one disregards the medullated nerve fibers, which penetrate from without in varying number, one must believe them to consist simply of fibrillary connective tissue with nuclei scattered through it. . . .

"The nature of the connection of the little bodies described here with the nerve fibrils is characteristic.

"For the most part there is only one fibril allotted to each of these little bodies, but fairly often two, three, and even four medullated fibrils enter a single one. Entry can take place either at one end, regularly at that which blends with the tendon fasciculi, or also at the side, and indeed precisely at the thickest part of the spindle.

"However large the number of fibrils entering, they proceed to separate, in that they advance to the middle of the body and each fibril of the second or third order, while retaining the character of a medullated fibril, diverges from the others and turns toward the periphery. . . . All this can be perceived with the simplest means of observation. . . . The further, ultimate conduct of the separate fibrils can only be made clear by the gold reaction. With this method one can now make the following observations.

"After the medullated fibrils have changed to nonmedullated, these bifurcating branches diverge helter-skelter and pursue their further course to the periphery of the body. Having reached it, they form at short intervals, by means of still finer and more frequent divisions, numerous circumscribed, longish, reticular plexuses, which lie parallel with the surface. . . ."

RAMÓN Y CAJAL *

"From the sum of my researches springs a general concept which comprehends the following propositions:

"The nerve cells are morphologic units, the neurons, to use the word sanctioned by the authority of Professor Waldeyer. This had already been demonstrated, as regards the dendritic or protoplasmic extensions of the nerve cells, by my illustrious colleague Professor Golgi; but when our researches began there were only conjectures more or less tenable regarding the way in which the ultimate divisions of the axons and nerve collaterals are arranged. Our observations, with Golgi's method, which we applied first in the cerebellum, then in the spinal marrow, the brain, the olfactory bulb, the optic lobe, the retina, etc. of embryos and young animals, revealed, in my opinion, the terminal disposition of the nerve fibers. These, in their ramifications to several junctures, incline constantly toward the neuronal body and toward the protoplasmic expansions, around which arise plexuses, or nerve nests, very close-woven and very rich. The . . . morphologic dispositions, which vary in form according to the nerve centers one studies, attest that the nerve elements have reciprocal relations of *contiguity* and not of *continuity,* and that communications, more or less intimate, are always established not only between the nervous arborizations but between the

---

* Translated from Santiago Ramón y Cajal, "Structure et Connexions des Neurones," *Les Prix Nobel en 1906.*

ramifications of one part and the body and protoplasmic extensions of another part. . . .

"These facts, recognized in all the nerve centers with the aid of two very different methods (Golgi's and Ehrlich's) . . . involve three physiological postulates:

"(1) Since nature, in order to assure and amplify contacts, has created complicated systems of ramifications around the cells (systems which would become incomprehensible by the hypothesis of continuity), it is necessary to admit that the nervous currents are transmitted from one element to another by virtue of a sort of induction, or influence at a distance.

"(2) It is also necessary to suppose that the cellular bodies and the dendritic prolongations, like the axis cylinders, are induction apparatus, since they represent intermediate links between the afferent nerve fibers and the axons mentioned. This is what Bethe, Simarro, Donaggio, we ourselves, etc., have confirmed quite recently, in demonstrating, with the aid of neurofibrillary methods, a perfect structural concordance between the dendrites and the axis-cylinder prolongation.

"(3) Examination of the transmission of nerve impulses in the sense organs, such as the retina, the olfactory bulb, the sensory ganglions and the spinal marrow, etc., show not only that the protoplasmic expansions play a conducting role but also that the movement of the nerve impulse in these prolongations is *toward the cell body*, whereas in the axons it is *away from the cell body*. This principle, called *the dynamic polarization of neurons*, formulated a long time ago by van Gehuchten and us as an induction drawn from numerous morphological facts, is not contrary to the new researches on the constitution of nerve protoplasm. In fact we shall see that the framework of neurofibrils makes up a continuous reticulum from the dendrites and the cell body to the axon and its peripheral termination."

CONSEQUENCES IN THEORY AND PRACTICE

The investigations of Golgi and Ramón y Cajal were to a large extent complementary, although on many points they disagreed.

(Golgi's Nobel lecture was largely a series of qualifications of the neuron theory as set forth above by his Spanish colleague.) Ramón y Cajal began his work on the nervous system using the Golgi stain. Between the two men, they worked out the finer details of the structure of nervous tissue in a thorough and comprehensive manner.

In 1873, using his new method, Golgi gave his description of the two main types of nerve cells, since known as Golgi cells type I and type II, the long and short axon nerve cells respectively. In 1874 he described the large nerve cells of the granular layer of the cerebellum, which are also known by his name. He likewise described the structure of the olfactory bulb. His name is attached to the internal reticular apparatus of cells, the nature and function of which have not been fully determined even yet. In addition to this he discovered the muscle spindles which are described in the quotation above. This passage has been selected as a characteristic and important piece of work, and also because knowledge of the receptor organs in muscle was the starting point for a valuable contribution to neurophysiology made by Sir Charles Sherrington (see below, pp. 160 ff; 166).

The discoveries in normal histology mentioned here are only the best known among a large number. Golgi also contributed to the knowledge of nerve pathology. He was able to show, for example, that the disease called chorea is not due to a mere functional disturbance but is associated with definite lesions in the nervous system. It was Golgi, too, who pointed out the microscopic characteristics which distinguish sarcomas from gliomas, two kinds of brain tumor which previously were often confused; this was of practical importance, for gliomas, although "malignant" from their location, do not metastasize (i.e., establish cellular colonies in other parts), as do the more dangerous sarcomas. Here again, it is possible only to single out one or two among Golgi's major contributions to neuropathology. His work on the structure of the kidney and other organs and his important studies of malaria parasites fall outside the limits of the Nobel citation.

The quotation from Ramón y Cajal has been selected as the latter's attempt at a general summation of an important part of his work. The neuron theory, here presented in a condensed form, was firmly established by his researches. Its importance to subsequent investigators can hardly be assessed in a few words. It underlies the exceedingly important work of Sir Charles Sherrington. It guided the thought of Egas Moniz, who introduced prefrontal leucotomy (see below, pp. 270-276). It is one of the basic theories of modern biological science.

Ramón y Cajal's contributions are also too numerous and too complex for summary treatment. As he himself said, "Unfortunately it is absolutely impossible to condense in a few pages morphological facts the description of which occupies a large number of brochures with hundreds of drawings." It may be mentioned, however, that another Nobel laureate, Robert Bárány (see below, pp. 85-89), in attempting to connect the function of the labyrinth apparatus of the ear with cerebellar function, was initially dependent on the Spanish histologist's account of the nerve connections involved. It is safe to say that there is no neurologist or neuroanatomist of recent times who does not owe him a similar debt.

"Even more lasting than his wealth of recorded observations will be the improved methods of Cajal and his disciples. First, in 1888, he increased the applicability of the Golgi stain. In 1903 he developed his own reduced silver nitrate stain. . . . In 1913 he introduced the gold sublimate stain. . . . His eminent pupils Achucarro and Hortega [introduced] the silver carbonate stains. . . .

"These methods in the hands of Cajal and his students have clarified much of the embryology of each cellular element in the nervous system. Furthermore, the finer details of gliomas revealed by these stains, with the accumulating light from embryology, have given the neurosurgeon useful correlations of structure and biologic characteristics of brain tumors." *

---

* Wilbur Sprong, "Santiago Ramón y Cajal: 1852-1934," *Archives of Neurology and Psychiatry,* Vol. 33 (1935), pp. 156-162.

REFERENCES

GOLGI

CHOROBSKI, JERZY. "Camillo Golgi: 1843-1926," *Archives of Neurology and Psychiatry,* Vol. 33 (1935), pp. 163-170.

DA FANO, C. "Camillo Golgi," *Journal of Pathology and Bacteriology,* Vol. 29 (1926), pp. 500-514.

RAMÓN Y CAJAL

CANNON, DOROTHY F. *Explorer of the Human Brain: The Life of Santiago Ramón y Cajal (1852-1934)* (New York: Schuman, 1949).

RAMÓN Y CAJAL, SANTIAGO. *Recollections of My Life,* translated by E. Horne Craigie and Juan Cano (Philadelphia: American Philosophical Society, 1937), 2 vols.

SPRONG, WILBUR. "Santiago Ramón y Cajal: 1852-1934," *Archives of Neurology and Psychiatry,* Vol. 33 (1935), pp. 156-162.

1 9 0 7
CHARLES LOUIS ALPHONSE LAVERAN
(1845–1922)

"In recognition of his work regarding the role played by protozoa in causing diseases."

BIOGRAPHICAL SKETCH

ALPHONSE LAVERAN WAS BORN IN PARIS ON JUNE 18, 1845. HIS father, a military surgeon, was a professor at the school of Val-de-Grâce. Having completed his preliminary education in Paris, Laveran matriculated as a medical student at Strasbourg, where he was graduated in 1867 with a thesis on regeneration of nerves. In 1874 he, too, joined the staff of the Val-de-Grâce School of Military Medicine. In 1878 he was sent to Algeria, where he remained, in the service of the French army, until 1883. During this period, while at Bône and at Constantine, he carried out his studies of malaria, which led to the discovery of the causative organism, the malarial parasite. In 1884 he was appointed professor of military hygiene and clinical medicine at Val-de-Grâce, where he remained for ten years. For a short time he was engaged in administrative medical and sanitary work at Lille and at Nantes; but with a view to resuming his scientific studies he retired from his administrative position in 1897. He then entered the Pasteur Institute. Here he soon became a professor, and devoted the rest of his life to a continuation of his work in tropical medicine and parasitology. The recipient of many scientific honors, he was one of the founders, and first president, of the Société de Pathologie Exotique. His work was terminated only by his death, which took place in Paris on May 18, 1922.

DESCRIPTION OF THE PRIZE-WINNING WORK*

"On arriving at Bona in 1878 I had the opportunity of making autopsies on subjects who had died from pernicious attacks, and I was struck with the fact that melanaemia [the presence of a black pigment in the blood, causing a brown coloration of certain organs] was a lesion peculiar to and very characteristic of paludism [i.e., malaria, or marsh fever, from the Latin *palus,* marsh]; my attention was naturally directed to this lesion, which I had never met in any other disease. [Although often described in connection with malaria before this time, the color change here mentioned had not generally been considered either as constant, or as peculiar to the disease.]

"Melanaemia is specially very pronounced in individuals who died from acute paludism (pernicious attacks); the colour which it gives to certain organs, particularly to the spleen, the liver, and the grey substance of the brain, is almost always sufficient to show from microscopic examination if death is the result of paludism. . . .

"Some observers have been able to maintain that occasionally no single characteristic alteration was found in individuals who had died of pernicious fever.

"This assertion does not stand a strict examination, and could only be put forward at a time when the importance of melanaemia was not known. It might be affirmed on the contrary, that in these cases there always remain lesions specially pronounced in the spleen and liver. The spleen increases in volume and weight, but the increase is not always considerable. . . . The shape of the organ is modified, the edges are rounded; the spleen tends to take a globular form, which is explained by the softening, the pulpiness of the

---

* From Alphonse Laveran, *Paludism,* translated by J. W. Martin (London: New Sydenham Society, 1893), pp. 5-9.

splenic parenchyma [the specific substance of the spleen, supported and held together by fibrous elements]. It often happens that the mere act of grasping the spleen to pull it out from the abdomen causes rupture of the distended and thin capsule; the fingers sink into splenic pulp.

"The colour is characteristic; instead of the normal red colour the spleen shows in the inner parts, as well as on the surface, a brownish tint which has been compared to chocolate and water.

"If you examine a drop of splenic fluid with the microscope you will find in the midst of the blood, and the elements proper to the spleen which are separated, the existence of pigmented elements in great numbers, and free granules of pigment; the pigmented elements are either leucocytes [white blood cells] loaded with pigment [i.e., "melaniferous," the term used hereafter], or hyaline bodies of irregular shape: one finds in those preparations of the spleen pigmented granules much more numerous than in blood taken from the vessels of other organs. . . .

"[Similar changes are then described as they are seen in liver, kidney, and brain tissue.] The other tissues have a normal tint, but by histological sections it is easy to see that the capillary vessels contain pigmented elements more or less numerous, and that melanaemia is really, as the etymology implies, a general alteration of the blood, which is only more pronounced in the spleen, in the medulla of bones, and the liver than in the other viscera, which is naturally all the more apparent as the tissues are more vascular.

"When one examines a drop of blood taken from the dead body of a palustral subject in the ordinary conditions of autopsy—that is to say, twenty-four hours after death—one sees in the midst of the blood numerous pigmented bodies. Many of these elements are melaniferous leucocytes, the nuclei of which can be coloured and stained with carmine; but besides these leucocytes, hyaline pigmented irregular bodies are seen, which can only be coloured slightly, or not at all, by carmine, and which do not contain any nuclei. These latter elements have great analogy in their dimensions, and often in their shape, with melaniferous leucocytes, and it can easily be understood that they may have been confused with them. If the blood is taken shortly after death the parasitic elements characteristic of paludism can be recognised.

"In 1880, as I was trying to account for the mode of formation of the pigment in the palustral blood, I was led to see that besides melaniferous leucocytes, spherical hyaline corpuscles without nucleus could be seen, and also very characteristic crescent-shaped bodies.

"I had proceeded thus far with my researches, and was still hesitating whether these elements were parasites, when on November 6th, 1880, on examining the pigmented spherical bodies mentioned above, I observed, on the edge of several of these elements, moveable filaments or flagella [literally, "whips"], whose extremely rapid and varied movements left no doubt as to their nature.

"I published in 1881 the observation of the patient in whose blood I saw the flagella for the first time. . . .

"The very fact that I can quote the day on which I observed the flagella for the first time shows how characteristic these elements are. It was natural to suppose that these parasitic elements, for the most part pigmented, were the cause of palustral melanaemia, and also the cause of the phenomena of paludism. Numerous facts soon came to confirm this hypothesis."

CONSEQUENCES IN THEORY AND PRACTICE

The citation for the Nobel Prize in 1907 refers to the sum of Laveran's work "regarding the role played by protozoa in causing diseases." (The protozoa include all the unicellular animal organisms. Literally the word means "first animals.") Since the terms which govern the award require that it be given for recent work, or for work recently seen to be of importance, it is probable that this phrasing was chosen to comply with the rule by including Laveran's later studies; nevertheless it was in fact the reward for his quarter-century-old discovery of the malarial parasite. It is, of course, quite true that this discovery, the first of the kind, stimulated interest in protozoal disease agents, and that although Laveran himself made no other such epochal discoveries he did open the field to other workers and he also made solid contributions of his own toward extending our knowledge of similar organisms. During his years at the Pasteur Institute he collaborated with Professor Mesnil, and together they published an important work on trypanosomes and trypanosomiasis. (G. H. Evans and D. Bruce were chiefly responsible for showing that trypanosomes cause sleeping sickness.) Laveran likewise published the first treatise on leishmaniasis (leishmania are protozoans which cause kala-azar, oriental boil, etc.) and investigated many of the flagellate parasites of man and animals.

Laveran's discovery of the malarial parasite did not receive immediate recognition from all authorities, but his findings were soon confirmed and extended by others, and his own pathological, clinical, geographical, and therapeutic studies all tended to establish the role of the organisms he had discovered, which later came to be known as plasmodia. Their presence in the blood of malaria patients, their disappearance after treatment with quinine, their absence in healthy persons, and their association with the characteristic malaria pigment made it highly probable that they were indeed the long-sought causative organisms of malaria. This could not be readily demonstrated, as in bacterial diseases, according to "Koch's postulates" (see above, p. 28), because in contrast with bacteria the plasmodia could not be cultivated outside the living body. But further evidence, strongly supporting Laveran's view, was provided by another Nobel laureate, Camillo Golgi (see above, pp. 33, 38), who showed that some plasmodia require forty-eight hours to develop to the stage when the red blood cells are broken down and the parasites are released, that others need seventy-two hours, and that these periods correspond exactly to the afebrile intervals of tertian and quartan fever. The different types of plasmodia and the stages in the plasmodial life cycle were worked out by Italian, American, and English scientists. These workers, including the early Nobel laureate Sir Ronald Ross, built upon the foundations laid by Laveran. The practical significance of knowing what the causative organism is (Laveran) and how it spreads (Ross) has been briefly discussed in an earlier section (see above, pp. 13-14).

1 9 0 8

ELIE METCHNIKOFF
(1845–1916)

"In recognition of his work on immunity."
(*The award for 1908 was shared with Paul Ehrlich, see below, pp. 51-56.*)

BIOGRAPHICAL SKETCH

ILIA ILICH MECHNIKOV, BETTER KNOWN AS ELIE METCHNIKOFF, son of an officer of the Imperial Guard, was born in the province of Kharkov, Little Russia, on May 16, 1845. Privately tutored at first, he later entered the *lycée* at Kharkov, where his scientific interests, already formed, were stimulated in the direction of physiology and zoology. He found little to satisfy such interests at the University of Kharkov, but after graduation did independent and original work in Helgoland and at Giessen. He was then given a scholarship by the Russian Ministry of Public Instruction, which enabled him to travel and study abroad. He worked for a time at Naples, in association with the young Kovalevsky, then at Göttingen, where he spent a short interlude with Keferstein and Henle. At Munich his preceptor was von Siebold. In 1867 he returned to Russia to become docent at the new University of Odessa. He soon shifted to St. Petersburg as professor of zoology, but worked at intervals in Messina and elsewhere. In 1886 he became director of the Bacteriological Institute in Odessa, but left in 1887 and went to Paris, where he resided till the end of his life. He carried on his work at the Pasteur Institute, of which he became subdirector. His first paper on phagocytosis was read at a congress in Odessa in 1883; the initial observations and experiments had been made at Messina earlier in the same year.

DESCRIPTION OF THE PRIZE-WINNING WORK*

"Occupied with the origin of the digestive organs in the animal world, we were struck by the fact that certain elements of the organism which do not take any part in the digestion of food are nevertheless capable of engrossing foreign bodies. To us it appeared that the reason for this was that these elements formerly participated in the digestive function. . . .

"Certain lower animals, transparent enough to be observed in the living state, show clearly in their interior a host of little cells provided with mobile extensions. The least lesion of these animals brings an accumulation of these elements right to the spot which has been injured. In the little transparent larvae, one can easily ascertain that the mobile cellules, gathered at the point of injury, often contain the debris of foreign bodies.

"Similar facts, on the one hand tending to confirm our supposition of the origin of the migratory elements, on the other hand suggested the idea that their accumulation in the neighborhood of lesions constitutes a sort of natural defense of the organism. It was necessary to find some method of verifying this hypothesis. Finding myself at this time—more than twenty-five years ago—at Messina, I turned my attention to the floating larvae of starfish. . . . Large enough to undergo some operations, they are, however, sufficiently transparent and can be observed under the microscope in the living state.

"Having introduced pointed splinters into the bodies of these [larvae], I was able next day to see a mass of mobile cellules enclosing the foreign body, forming a thick layer. The analogy of this phenomenon with that which takes place when a man pricks himself with a splinter, bringing on inflammation accompanied by suppuration, is astonishing. Only in the starfish larva, the accumu-

---

* Elie Metchnikoff, "Sur l'état actuel de la question de l'immunité dans les maladies infectieuses," *Les Prix Nobel en 1908.*

lation of mobile cellules around the foreign body takes place without the least concurrence of blood vessels or nervous system, for the simple reason that these animals possess neither the one nor the other. So it is thanks to a sort of spontaneous action that the cellules are gathered round the splinter.

"The experiment which I have just presented to you shows the first step, so to speak, of an inflammation in the animal world. But . . . in men and the higher animals, this phenomenon is almost always the result of the intervention of some pathogenic microbe. . . .

"It was therefore necessary . . . to find some higher animal sufficiently small and transparent to be observed alive by the microscope and . . . to subject to some microbe disease.

"After several attempts in this direction, it became possible to study the progress of an infection among the fresh-water animals commonly known as "water fleas." These little crustaceans are very widespread in all sorts of stagnant waters and are subject to several diseases. One of these is occasioned by a little microbe which has the peculiarity of producing spores in the form of needles. Swallowed by the water flea . . . these spores easily wound the intestinal wall and penetrate into the body cavity. But once they have stolen into the organism, the spores provoke around them an accumulation of mobile cellules which correspond to human white blood corpuscles. A struggle occurs between the two kinds of elements. Sometimes the spore succeeds in germinating. A generation of microbes is then produced which secrete a substance capable of dissolving the mobile cellules; but these instances are rather rare. Much more frequent, on the contrary, are the cases in which the mobile cellules kill and digest the infectious spores, thus assuring the immunity of the organism. . . .

"Having established the basis of the theory of immunity, it was necessary to apply it to higher organisms and to man himself. The conditions here being incomparably more complicated than among the little transparent animals, all sorts of difficulties sprang up on every side. Because of the impossibility of submitting even the smallest vertebrate animal, such as a newborn mouse, to direct microscopic examination, it was necessary to proceed by a more complicated route, combining the results of researches on the blood and on organs removed from the organism, and linking them by thought. Now under these circumstances the door is wide open to all sorts of errors.

"The study of several infectious diseases of man and the higher animals has shown from the first that the facts observed accord well with the theory based on the research on transparent lower animals. In all cases where the organism enjoys an immunity, the introduction of infectious microbes is followed by an accumulation of mobile cellules, white blood corpuscles in particular, which incorporate the microbes and destroy them. The white corpuscles and the other cellules capable of bringing about this result have been designated 'phagocytes'—that is to say, voracious cellules [i.e., eating cells]—and the sum of the function which assures immunity 'phagocytosis.' "

CONSEQUENCES IN THEORY AND PRACTICE

Metchnikoff's theory that bacteria are destroyed by "eating cells," or phagocytes, at first met with strong opposition. The view was then current that resistance to bacterial infection depends upon chemical properties of the blood, and indeed antibodies had already been demonstrated in blood serum. A long controversy ensued, in which, as it now appears, both sides were partly right. In 1903 two British scientists, Almroth Wright and Stewart Douglas, found that the serum of immunized animals contains substances which appear to prepare bacteria for ingestion by the white blood cells; these substances were named "opsonins," from the Greek verb meaning "to prepare food." The opinion then grew up that phagocytosis can take place only when the microbes have first been "buttered," as it were, with specific antibodies. The phagocytes were thus restricted to a secondary role.

In the last 25 years, however, the Metchnikoff theory has been partly rehabilitated, and the functions of antibodies and phagocytes have been distinguished more clearly. Most bacteria that cause acute infections injure the human body only when they are *outside* of cells; the bacteria that cause chronic infections, on the other hand, do damage *within* the cells. The former are readily engulfed and digested, except when they have outer capsules which protect them from phagocytes; the latter, although readily ingested by phagocytes, can go on living inside. Phagocytosis as a defense mechanism is therefore of much greater importance in acute than in chronic diseases. When the bacteria of the acute diseases are well protected by a capsule, this armor may be broken down by the appropriate antibody. But patients treated with "sulfa" drugs and other antibiotics often recover several days before antibodies can be detected in the blood. The drug slows the multiplication of the bacteria, and phagocytes may then destroy them without the aid of antibodies, provided there is a suitable surface upon which to operate. In lung tissue, for example, the white cells pin the bacteria against the walls of the alveoli (air sacs) and then ingest them. The strands of fibrin, which are a common feature of the inflammatory reaction, also provide suitable surfaces for promoting phagocytosis; or the bacteria may sometimes be trapped against the walls of small blood vessels. The proportion of fluid to phagocytic cells during infection limits the efficacy of this process, for phagocytes diluted in fluid are unable to engulf fully encapsulated bacteria. In the peritoneal cavity of the abdomen, and in other "open" sites, phagocytosis is relatively inefficient, since the white cells do not have sufficient contact with one another and with tissue surfaces.

In the intracellular infections, caused by viruses, some bacteria, and certain protozoa, phagocytosis is not of primary importance, because the parasites can survive and even multiply inside the white cells. But in a great many acute infections, caused by extracellular parasites, the invaders may be slowed down by drugs and destroyed by phagocytes before the relatively slow process of the manufacture of antibodies has taken place. Phagocytosis is thus the first line of defense in acute infections.

This summarizes the current view of the importance of Metchnikoff's phagocytes and of the way in which they operate. The activities of the white cells continue to be investigated, however, for there is much which yet remains mysterious about the body's reaction to invading microorganisms.

REFERENCES

METCHNIKOFF, OLGA. *The Life of Elie Metchnikoff, 1845-1916* (London: Constable; Boston and New York: Houghton Mifflin, 1921).

PETRIE, G. F. "The Scientific Work of Elie Metchnikoff," *Nature* (London), Vol. 149 (1942), p. 149.

WOOD, W. BARRY, JR. "White Blood Cells v. Bacteria," *Scientific American,* Vol. 184 (Feb. 1951), pp. 48-52.

PAUL EHRLICH
(1854–1915)

"In recognition of his work on immunity."
(*The award for 1908 was shared with Elie Metchnikoff; see above, pp. 46-51.*)

BIOGRAPHICAL SKETCH

PAUL EHRLICH WAS BORN AT STREHLEN, A SMALL TOWN IN Silesia, in 1854. He received his early education in his native town and at the *Gymnasium* at Breslau. He also spent his first university semester at Breslau, studying scientific subjects, and then proceeded to Strasbourg, where he took up the study of medicine. While still an undergraduate he attracted the attention of Waldeyer by his application of aniline dyes in histology. After graduation he worked for a year in the Pathological Institute under Cohnheim and Heidenhain. In 1877 he was appointed chief assistant in Frerichs's clinic in Berlin. In 1886 he found that he had contracted tuberculosis, apparently as a result of accidental infection in the course of his researches, and was forced to give up his work for a year and a half, which he spent in traveling abroad. Returning to Berlin, he worked for a time in a small private laboratory, then obtained a post in the Institute for Infectious Diseases, which he held for several years. When the new Serum Institute at Steglitz was opened, in 1896, Ehrlich was appointed director. From 1899 until his death in 1915 he was director of the Royal Institute for Experimental Therapy in Frankfurt am Main. He was raised to the dignity of Privy Councilor with the title "Excellenz" in 1911. It is convenient to divide Ehrlich's work, as W. Bulloch does, into three parts: (1) the application of stains to the differentiation of cells and tissues for the purpose of revealing their function (1877-1890); (2) immunity studies (1890-1900); (3) chemotherapeutic discoveries (1907-1915). He was the founder of modern hematology, one of the chief early contributors to immunology, and, by virtue of the discovery of "606," the founder of chemotherapy.

DESCRIPTION OF THE PRIZE-WINNING WORK*

"At the very beginning of my theoretical work on immunity I made it my first task to introduce measures and figures into investigations regarding the relations existing between toxine and antitoxine. From the outset it was clear that the difficulties to be overcome were extremely great. The toxines, i.e., the poisonous products of bacteria, are unknown in a pure condition. So great is their potency, that we are obliged to assume that the strongest solid poisons which are obtained by precipitating toxic bouillon with ammonium sulphate, represent nothing more than indifferent materials, peptones and the like, to which the specific toxine attaches itself in mere traces beyond the reach of weighing. . . .

"Their presence is only betrayed by the proof of their specific toxicity on the organism. For the exact determination, e.g., of the amount of toxine contained in a culture fluid, the essential condition was that the research animals used should exhibit the requisite uniformity in their susceptibility to the poison. Uniformity is not

* From Paul Ehrlich, "On Immunity with Special Reference to Cell Life," *Proceedings of the Royal Society of London*, Vol. 66 (1900), pp. 424-448.

to be observed in the reaction of the animal body to all toxines. Fortunately in the case of one important body of this nature, viz., the diphtheria toxine, the conditions are such that the guinea-pig affords for investigations the degree of accuracy necessary in purely chemical work. For other toxines this accuracy in measuring the toxicity cannot be attained. It was necessary for me to try to eliminate, as far as possible, the varying factor of the animal body, and bring the investigations more nearly into line with the conditions necessary for experiments of a chemical nature. . . . The relations were simplest in the case of red blood corpuscles. On them, outside the body, the action of many blood poisons, and of their antitoxines, can be most accurately studied, e.g., the actions of ricin, eel-serum, snake-poison, tetanus toxine, etc. In an experiment of this kind, in which are employed a series of test-tubes containing definite quantities of suspended blood corpuscles, each test-tube represents as it were a research animal, uniform in any one series, and one that can be reproduced at will. By means of these test-tube experiments, particularly in the case of ricin, I was able, in the first place, to determine that they yielded an exact quantitative representation of the course of the processes in the living body. The demonstration of this fact formed the basis of a more extended application of experiments of this nature. It was shown that the action of toxine and antitoxine took place quantitatively as in the animal body. Further, these experiments yielded a striking series of facts of importance for the theoretical valuation of the reaction between toxine and antitoxine. It was proved in the case of certain toxines—notably tetanus toxine—that the action of antitoxines is accentuated or diminished under the influence of the same factors which bring about similar modifications in chemical processes—warmth accelerates, cold retards the reaction, and this proceeds more rapidly in concentrated than in dilute solutions. . . . Yet again insurmountable obstacles seemed to present themselves. . . .

"When, in the case of diphtheria toxines of different stocks, that quantity of toxine bouillon which is exactly neutralized by a certain definite quantity of diphtheria antitoxine (the official German immunity unit . . .) was determined, so that every trace of toxic action was abolished, the figures obtained were not in accord. Of one toxine bouillon 0.2 c.c., of another 2.5 c.c., were so neutralised by one immunity unit. Such a relation need not have given rise to surprise, because it was well known that the diphtheria bacillus, according to outside circumstances, yields in the bouillon very different quantities of toxine. It was therefore allowable to infer that the different quantities of toxine bouillon, which were saturated by one immunity unit, were exact expressions of the toxicities of the various bouillons, or, to use other words, indifferently whether the bouillon was strongly or feebly toxic, the same multiple of the minimal lethal dose would be constantly neutralised by one immunity unit, so that in every case the law of equivalent proportions would hold good.

"But when looked into more closely, the relations showed themselves to be by no means so simple. In what manner could one obtain a satisfactory estimation of the strength of a toxine? As the constant factor in such an estimation, it was only possible to proceed from a previously determined standard reaction in the case of a definite species of animal, and so we came to regard as the 'toxic unit' that quantity of toxic bouillon which exactly sufficed to kill, in the course of four days, a guinea-pig of 250 grammes weight.

"When we employed this standard unit, or 'simple lethal dose,' to estimate the amount of toxic bouillon neutralised by one 'immunity unit,' the facts which presented themselves were far more surprising than it was possible to have foreseen at the outset. These results were, that of one toxine, perhaps 20, of a second, perhaps 50, and of yet a third, it might be 130 simple lethal doses were saturated by one immunity unit. Since, however, we had previously assumed that the simple lethal dose alone afforded a standard on which reliance could be placed in determining the combining relations of toxine and antitoxine, it appeared from these results that the neutralisation of toxines by antitoxines did not follow the law of equivalent proportions, and, notwithstanding all earlier work in agreement with such a conception of the action, we were obliged to conclude that between toxine and antitoxine a purely chemical affinity did not exist. The seemingly inexplicable contradiction between the results just stated and previous work was very soon explained. When the neutralisation point of toxine and antitoxine was investigated for one and the same sample of poison, the following results were obtained. Immediately on its preparation, fresh from the incubator, it was found that one immunity unit neutralised a c.c. of toxic bouillon, and this quantity represented β simple lethal doses. When the same toxic bouillon was examined after a considerable interval, the remarkable fact was discovered that exactly a c.c. of the toxic bouillon were again neutralised by one immunity unit; but that these a c.c. now represented only β — x simple lethal doses. It therefore followed that the toxic bouillon had retained exactly the same combining affinity but possessed feebler toxicity. From this it was evident that the toxic action on animals and the combining capacity with antitoxine represented two different functions of the toxine, and that the former of these had become weakened, while the latter had remained constant."

CONSEQUENCES IN THEORY AND PRACTICE

This is not the place to discuss the importance of Ehrlich's studies on the staining of bacteria, nor his related studies of animal cells, especially blood cells, nor his work in chemotherapy. Like these studies, his investigations in immunology, for which the Prize was awarded, were of basic importance. By the researches described above he established the principles of the standardization of bacterial toxins and antitoxins. The practical methods still in use are essentially the same as his. The first disease to which this contribution applied was diphtheria: an exact gradation of the efficacy of antidiphtheritic serum was achieved. In this regard the conception outlined in the last paragraph above is a fundamental one—that the lethal action of a toxin and its antitoxin-combining power are two separate functions. In his work with the vegetable poison known as ricin, Ehrlich discovered that a latent period exists between the injection of the stimulating "antigen" and the production, as a protective response, of the specific "antibody." He also studied the serum fluctuations in the course of the development of antibodies, showing that the antibody titer could be increased by repeated injections of toxin in increasing amounts. Thus, the solution of a problem that had troubled von Behring, that of preparing a diphtheria antitoxin of high potency, was essentially found by

Ehrlich. He also investigated the transmission of immunity, which is not truly hereditary, through the placenta and the milk. In the course of this study he was able to distinguish between active immunity, a more or less lasting condition due to the active manufacture of antibodies in response to antigens, and passive immunity, a transient state due to the transmission of antibodies in the ways already mentioned or by the injection of a ready-made antitoxin. When Bordet's work on hemolysis appeared (see below, pp. 91-96) it was taken up, confirmed and extended by Ehrlich and Morgenroth, who introduced the terms "complement" and "amboceptor." Finally, one more contribution to immunology must be mentioned: Ehrlich's discovery that antibodies are associated with the serum globulins.

At a conference held in New York in honor of the centennial of the birth of Ehrlich, Bela Schick stated, "He not only created the groundwork which led to our full understanding of toxin, toxoid, antitoxin, and immunity, but he also showed the way for further study. . . . Ehrlich realized the limitations of antitoxic serotherapy and developed his own original ideas of chemotherapy. If he were alive today, he could enjoy the satisfaction of seeing how correct his prophetic vision was."

REFERENCES

BROWNING, C. H. "Emil Behring and Paul Ehrlich, their Contributions to Science," *Nature* (London), Vol. 175 (1955), pp. 570-575 and 616-619.

BULLOCH, WILLIAM. *The History of Bacteriology* (London: Oxford University Press, 1938).

MARQUARDT, MARTHA. *Paul Ehrlich* (New York: Schuman, 1951).

MINER, R. W., and GRUNBERG, E. (editors). *Paul Ehrlich Centennial.* Annals of the New York Academy of Sciences, Vol. 59, Article 2 (1954), pp. 141-276. Thirteen essays describing Ehrlich's diverse scientific contributions.

MUIR, R. "Paul Ehrlich," *Journal of Pathology and Bacteriology,* Vol. 20 (1915-1916), pp. 350-360.

Paul Ehrlich: Eine Darstellung seines wissenschaftlichen Wirkens (Jena: G. Fisher, 1914). Essays on Ehrlich's achievements in science, by thirty-seven contributors.

1 9 0 9
THEODOR KOCHER
(1841–1917)

"For his work on the physiology, pathology, and surgery of the thyroid gland."

BIOGRAPHICAL SKETCH

THEODOR KOCHER WAS BORN ON AUGUST 25, 1841, IN BERNE, Switzerland. He was educated in his native city, and after his graduation there in 1865 he spent some time in Berlin, London, Paris, and Vienna. In Vienna he was a pupil of Theodor Billroth (1829-1894), the most famous surgeon of his time. Kocher became professor of clinical surgery at the University of Berne in 1872 and for forty-five years was head of the University Surgical Clinic. The first of his contributions to surgery to attract attention was that in which he worked out the method now known by his name for the reduction of a dislocated shoulder. He afterward devised new methods, or modifications of older methods, for operations upon the lungs, the stomach, the gall bladder, the intestine, cranial nerves, hernia, and so on—all this in addition to his famous work on the surgery of the thyroid gland, described below. He also invented many instruments and appliances. "Kocher's forceps" remain in general use. It is an indication of his scientific objectivity that he was always ready to abandon any of his own techniques or gadgets in favor of improvements introduced by other surgeons. Thus it is said that in his later years he performed the Bassini operation for hernia in preference to his own. In his

57

work on the thyroid, Kocher showed himself to be not only surgeon and anatomist but also physiologist and pathologist. He was diligent and original in research, expert in operating, and effective in teaching, although he left no surgical "school" behind him. His clinic was for many years a mecca for visiting surgeons from all parts of the world. "With the death of Kocher," wrote Sir Berkeley Moynihan in the *British Medical Journal* obituary in 1917, "the world loses its greatest surgeon."

DESCRIPTION OF THE PRIZE-WINNING WORK*

"It was due . . . [in part] to strict asepsis that one of the most difficult, before Lister [one of] the most dangerous, operations, the removal of the thyroid gland, so often appearing urgently necessary because of severe respiratory disturbances, could be performed without substantial danger. We ourselves have contributed a series of three hundred and more goiter operations without a death. Important as this result has been for suffering humanity, it has been far surpassed by the knowledge of the vital *physiological* function of the thyroid, growing up afresh on practical and clinical grounds. . . . In the spring of 1883, at the Congress of the German Surgical Society [Gesellschaft für Chirurgie], we announced that some thirty of our first one hundred thyroidectomies, which we could follow up and investigate, presented a quite definite, characteristic disease-picture, which we designated simply with the name *cachexia strumipriva* [literally, a bad condition due to removal of a struma, or goiter]. This appeared in its completely distinct form only in those patients from whom we had removed the whole thyroid gland; with no more than transitory signs, on the other hand, where all goiter tissue had supposedly been removed, but where in point of fact a piece had remained behind, which grew larger.

"Isolated observations on the connection of cretinoid disturbances with changes in the thyroid gland had already been made by early investigators. . . . [Kocher here mentions the observations on sporadic cretinism of Felix Plater (1536-1614), but not those

---

* Translated from Theodor Kocher, "Über Krankheitserscheinungen bei Schilddrüsenerkrankungen geringen Grades," *Les Prix Nobel en 1909*.

of Paracelsus, who linked cretinism and endemic goiter. Also mentioned are T. B. Curling, who in 1850 suggested that cretinism was due to thyroid deficiency, Hilton Fagge, Sir William Gull, W. M. Ord, etc., and his own contemporaries, the Reverdins, who in 1882 published a short notice on the "bizarre" changes displayed by certain patients after thyroid operations. J. L. Reverdin (1842-1908), also a Swiss surgeon, was best known for his plastic operations, particularly skin grafting.]

"At the time (April 1883) when, in Berlin, I described cachexia strumipriva as the *constant* result of total excision, on the ground of numerous observations, and warned against such excision because it always leads to consequences displaying a well-marked cretinoid character, a brilliant discourse was delivered at the same congress by a first-rate surgeon on the advantages and technique of total excision. . . .

"Further corroborative information on the nature and conduct of the new disease soon followed my contribution. On reviewing their operations the Reverdins recognized the relation of cachexia strumipriva to the myxedema of the English [Gull, Ord, etc.]. . . . At a famous meeting of the Clinical Society in London (November 23, 1883) Felix Semon . . . referred to my work and mentioned a confirmatory case, following total excision by Lister; and Ord read a letter I had written to him on the etiology of the disease and the connection of myxedema with cachexia thyreopriva.

"The impulse was thereby given for the splendid investigations of the Clinical Society Committee, which came to the conclusion that myxedema and sporadic cretinism are identical, and probably cachexia strumipriva also, and that close connections exist with endemic cretinism. . . ."

CONSEQUENCES IN THEORY
AND PRACTICE

Myxedema, due to deficiency of thyroid secretion, had been given its name by W. M. Ord, who read Kocher's letter to the Clinical Society. Cretinism, a form of idiocy and dwarfism with the general symptoms of myxedema, is due to congenital atrophy or absence of the thyroid gland and is also called congenital myxedema. Cachexia strumipriva, following total excision of the thyroid, is operative myxedema. As indicated in the text above, it was Kocher's description of the latter condition, together with his perception of its cause and its relation to other forms of thyroid deficiency, which made possible the grouping of all these "entities" under a single head. This clarified not only the terminology of the subject but also the thinking and the therapy of both physicians and surgeons. Moreover, Kocher was able to point out that hypothyroidism can be traced not only to absence of the gland, whether congenital or due to an operation, but also to a goiter which has made the gland stop working. Incomplete and debatable evidence as to the function of the thyroid could now be reviewed and supplemented, and in the years which followed Kocher's first pronouncement on the subject great advances were made. Murray, Gley, and Vassale administered thyroid in various forms to overcome deficiency. Attempts to produce the essential constituent, the hormone, in a pure state were long unsuccessful but resulted in showing that iodine plays an important part. In 1914 E. C. Kendall finally isolated the hormone—or the effective part of it—called thyroxin, which was later synthesized by C. R. Harrington and G. Barger. Meanwhile the nature of hyperfunction or dysfunction of the gland, causing exophthalmic goiter, was elucidated by Victor Horsley and others, providing a sound basis for surgical intervention. Kocher did much to perfect the technique of the operation and performed more than two thousand thyroidectomies with less than 5 percent mortality; this represents the resultant of a reduction of mortality from 18 percent to less than $\frac{1}{2}$ percent, the ultimate rate in his clinic. He was also a pioneer in stressing the importance of blood-picture change and coagulation time as means of early diagnosis and prognosis both in hyperthyroidism and hypothyroidism. Finally, he made extensive and careful studies of malignant tumors of the thyroid gland.

In the days before anesthesia and antisepsis, thyroidectomy was so dangerous that it was performed only in cases with severe suffocative symptoms. The control of bleeding remained a serious problem, and only from 1870, when the hemostatic forceps came into general use, was the operation a practical one. Understanding of thyroid physiology and pathology extended the range of surgical

intervention. Kocher made important contributions to this understanding.

The prophylactic value of small amounts of iodine in the
prevention of goiter has been shown by D. Marine and others.
Thiouracil and related compounds have been introduced for the
medical treatment of thyrotoxicosis (poisoning by an excess of
thyroid secretion). Radioactive iodine has found a similar use. Yet,
whatever the future holds in the prevention and treatment of the
various forms of thyroid disease, surgery is still of predominant
importance today.

1 9 1 0

ALBRECHT KOSSEL

(1853–1927)

"In recognition of the contributions to the chemistry of the cell made through his work on proteins, including the nucleic substances."

BIOGRAPHICAL SKETCH

ALBRECHT KOSSEL, ELDEST SON OF A MERCHANT AND PRUSSIAN consul, was born in Rostock on September 16, 1853. After attending the *Gymnasium* there, he studied medicine at the University of Strasbourg, where he was much influenced by E. F. Hoppe-Seyler (1825-1895), one of the pioneers of modern physiological chemistry; he also attended the University of Rostock. He passed his state examination for practice in 1877 and became doctor of medicine in the following year. After assisting Hoppe-Seyler for a time, he was summoned by E. Du Bois Reymond to the Physiological Institute in Berlin. In 1895 he became professor of physiology and director of the Physiological Institute at Marburg, where he remained until 1901, when he took over the Heidelberg chair made famous by Willy Kühne and Helmholtz. A physiologist by training, Kossel devoted his researches almost entirely to chemical subjects. His early investigations were concerned with the nucleic acids; later he turned his attention to the protamines of fish roe (first investigated by Miescher), which are comparatively simple proteins, and made a special study of their six-carbon cleavage products, containing nitrogen, called "hexone bases." He reached a position of pre-eminence by his substitution of the exact methods of organic chemistry for the less precise means employed by older physiologists. He had a number of distinguished pupils, including the Englishman H. D. Dakin. His son, Walther, became a well-known theoretical physicist. Professor Kossel died in his seventy-fourth year, after a brief illness, on July 5, 1927. At the time of his death he was emeritus professor of physiology at the University of Heidelberg and director of the Heidelberg Institute for Protein Investigation. For more than thirty years he had been editor of the *Zeitschrift für physiologische Chemie,* in which most of his writings appeared.

DESCRIPTION OF THE PRIZE-WINNING WORK*

"The first observations in this field [the chemistry of the cell nucleus] were undertaken on the nuclei of pus cells during the sixties of the last century in Hoppe-Seyler's laboratory. It fell to Miescher, a pupil of Hoppe-Seyler's, to isolate this nucleus, and he found in it a substance very rich in phosphorus, which he designated 'nuclein.' [This substance is now known to have been nucleo-protein. Friedrich Miescher (1844-1895) is regarded as the founder of our knowledge of the chemistry of the cell nucleus.] A suitable object for the continuation of this work presented itself in a structure arising from the transformation of the nucleus and preserving its chemical nature, obviously a fundamental part of the physiological functions also—namely, in the head of the sperma-tozoon. In the course of the next decades evidence accumulated to show that 'nuclein,' or 'nuclein substance,' is actually peculiar to the nucleus. [This view has had to be altered. See the commentary below.] Still other objects were found, which in some way lent themselves to the isolation of the nuclei, e.g., the red blood cor-puscles of birds, the cell body of which is soluble in water. Further-more, the nuclear substance isolated from them could be submitted to chemical investigation in sufficient quantity, and now the char-acteristics of the nuclear substance were further revealed. Micro-chemical work completed the demonstration. At the same time it showed that the nuclein substance appertained to a definite part of the substance of the nucleus, which separates itself in the trans-

---

* Translated from Albrecht Kossel, "Über die chemische Beschaffenheit des Zellkerns," *Les Prix Nobel en 1910.*

formation processes in a very characteristic way, the quantity of which varies in different nuclei, and which has obtained the name 'chromatin' because of its reaction to certain dyestuffs. Only one difficulty presented itself at first for this doctrine. This was the finding of 'nuclein substance' in animal products which contained no nuclei, and indeed in the vitelline discs [yolk] of eggs and the casein of milk. Strange hypotheses had already been advanced in an attempt to make these facts intelligible, when exact chemical investigation brought enlightenment.

"The chemical structure of these nuclein substances exhibits some peculiarities, which are found in many of the organic constituents of protoplasm, especially in those which take a lively part in metabolic processes. It was observed that such combinations readily break down into a definite number of complete atom groups, which have been compared to building blocks. Such 'building blocks,' in large number and variety and apparently combined according to a definite plan, build the molecule of albuminoid or protein material, also that of starch and glycogen. . . .

"The nuclein substances also exhibit a combination of this kind. Chemical analysis showed first of all that the nuclein substances can in many cases be separated into two parts, one of which bears the character of a protein or albuminoid material. This possesses no other atom groups than the usual albuminoid substances. So characteristic is the structure of the other part that it has received the name *nucleic acid*. It fell to me to obtain from it a series of fragments, which may in part be detached from the molecule even by *gentle* chemical procedures and which are characterized by a quite specific group of nitrogen atoms. There are here side by side four nitrogen-containing atom groups: *cytosine, thymine, adenine,* and *guanine.*

"One of these four bodies, guanine, was already known earlier and in different tissues of the animal organism; e.g., it had been discovered by Piccard in the spermatozoa of salmon. . . . The knowledge of their origin from nucleic acid, which was unexpected and was at first assailed by lively opposition, at once made intelligible separate phenomena which had been encountered without explanation; e.g., it had been observed that guanine and its kindred are found in large amounts in the blood in leukemia. Now this

form of disease is distinguished by the fact that unnucleated red
blood corpuscles [adult cells] are replaced by [young] nucleated
forms. But these latter fall prey in large numbers to decomposition,
and accordingly the body fluids are inundated with the disintegration products of the nuclein substances. So, then, the bases named
or their nearest conversion products are to be met with in large
amounts in the body fluids. Also the contradiction previously mentioned, which seemed to lie in the alleged presence of nuclein substance in vitelline elements and in milk, was now solved. An exact
chemical investigation proved that these elements, which because
of their unusual behavior and their phosphorus content had been
proffered earlier as nuclein substances, possessed another kind of
chemical structure. The building blocks rich in nitrogen which I
have just named are altogether absent from them. . . . [Nucleo-
proteins are nevertheless present in eggs, and embryonic tissues are
rich in nucleic acids.]

"Now the more was known of the relation to the nucleus of the
nitrogen-rich substances, the more also must the question arise of
the arrangement of the nitrogen and carbon atoms in their molecule. Two of the four bodies named, adenine and guanine, belong
to a group of chemical compounds which today are usually grouped
together under the names of alloxur or purine derivatives. . . .
Both thymine and cytosine showed a simple composition; analytical
and synthetic research lead to the result . . . which the following
schema express:

[A number of workers, notably Emil Fischer, contributed to the
establishment of these formulae; the mode of writing them has
here been altered slightly to conform to recent usage.]

Cytosine   Thymine   Adenine   Guanine

CONSEQUENCES IN THEORY
AND PRACTICE

The study of the biochemistry of the nucleic acids, in which Miescher, Altmann, and Kossel were among the pioneers, has assumed ever-increasing importance. Knowledge of the presence or absence of these compounds in certain organic substances has been much extended since Kossel's day, so that some of his assertions, quoted above, are now outdated; nucleoprotein is not peculiar to the cell nucleus as was then supposed (and from which the name is derived), but is also found in the cytoplasm. Nucleic acids of the type found in yeast were once thought to be characteristic of animals, as well; but both kinds have been found in plants and animals alike, and the distinction as to source has been shown to be largely false. Two broad groups of nucleic acid are now recognized: ribonucleic acid (RNA; or pentosenucleic acid, PNA) and deoxyribonucleic acid (deoxypentosenucleic acid, DNA). Both contain Kossel's "nitrogen-rich substances," the purine and pyrimidine compounds (nitrogen bases); a five-carbon carbohydrate (pentose) moiety, either ribose or deoxyribose; and phosphoric acid. The study of the composition and structure of nucleic acids has been one of the most active branches of biochemistry during the last two decades, and many investigators have contributed to our present knowledge.

The metabolic activity of the nucleic acids is of great importance. Their rate of renewal in different parts of the body varies with age, with X-irradiation, with various chemical treatments, and with other factors. Questions of growth, of both the normal and pathological function of the organs, and the transmission of hereditary potentialities, are involved in the study of these substances. Thus, the chromosomes consist of DNA, and they direct the formation of RNA which, in turn, participates in the synthesis of the body's proteins. Formation of new protein takes place all the time in the body; during growth, of course, there is a net increase. Many of the proteins are enzymes, the catalysts of chemical change in the body. Cancer specialists are interested in DNA, because changes in its composition or structure in a given tissue may initiate processes leading to the formation of tumors. These changes are now known to be the physical basis of "mutations," and their study is comprised in the bridging discipline called "biochemical genetics." Many important consequences for man have been recognized, as in enzymic defects associated with disease states, "molecular diseases" like sickle-cell anemia, as well as the general problem of damage by radioactive contamination.

The foundations of biochemical genetics were worked out with lower organisms, including bacteria, and these continue to play an important role in the development of the subject. Bacteria are rich in nucleic acids, and some bacteria are hosts to predators known as bacteriophages. These bacterial viruses consist of nucleoprotein, as do the viruses that affect plants and animals, so that the immediate significance of studies of nucleic acids for human disease as well as for economic welfare is clear. A number of theories implicate nucleic acids also in the processes of learning and memory.

The four nitrogenous bases described by Kossel are found in DNA; thymine does not occur in RNA, but the pyrimidine uracil does so in substantial amounts. Small amounts of other bases have been found in nucleic acids. The fundamental structural unit of the nucleic acids is the nucleotide, consisting of one molecule each of a nitrogen base, pentose, and phosphoric acid. The combination of the first two is called a nucleoside. Some nucleotides, nucleoside diphosphates and nucleoside triphosphates function in their own right as cofactors in metabolic oxidation, in transformations among the carbohydrates, and in the synthesis of lipides in the cell. Vitamins like nicotinic acid, riboflavin, and pantothenic acid are active in the cell in the form of nucleotide-like compounds.

Nucleic acids have so fundamental a part in the direction of events in the organism, not only in man but also in the plants, animals and microorganisms that affect his daily life, that medicine must take cognizance of them. As the mystery of chemical events within the cell is gradually penetrated cellular pathology, initiated by Rudolf Virchow a century ago, gives promise of new and greater usefulness to medicine.

REFERENCES

B., G., "Prof. Albrecht Kossel." *Nature* (London), Vol. 120 (1927), p. 233.

DAVIDSON, J. N. *The Biochemistry of the Nucleic Acids* (London: Methuen, and New York: Wiley, 1960), 4th edition.

EDLBACHER, S. "Albrecht Kossel zum Gedächtnis," *Hoppe-Seylers Zeitschrift für physiologische Chemie,* Vol. 177 (1928), pp. 1-14.

RIESSER, O. "Albrecht Kossel," *Deutsche medizinische Wochenschrift,* Vol. 53 (1927), p. 1441.

1 9 1 1
ALLVAR GULLSTRAND
(1862–1930)

"For his work on the dioptrics of the eye."

BIOGRAPHICAL SKETCH

ALLVAR GULLSTRAND WAS BORN AT LANDSKRONA, SWEDEN, on June 5, 1862. He studied at the University of Uppsala, for one year at Vienna, and finally at Stockholm, where in 1888 he passed the examinations for the license to practice medicine. He sustained his thesis for the doctorate in 1890, and was named docent in ophthalmology in 1891. He was later called to the new chair of ophthalmology at Uppsala. In geometric and physiological optics he was self-taught. His thesis of 1890 ("A Contribution to the Theory of Astigmatism") already contained the foundations of his most notable work, elaborated in three subsequent publications (1900, 1906, and 1908). One of his most remarkable contributions to ophthalmology was the discovery of intracapsular accommodation, described below; he also invented a number of important instruments and made useful modifications in the design of others. He died in 1930.

DESCRIPTION OF THE PRIZE-WINNING WORK *

"It is . . . necessary to remember that the lens fibers are attached both anteriorly and posteriorly, describing in their course

* From Allvar Gullstrand, "Mechanism of Accommodation," an appendix to *Helmholtz's Treatise on Physiological Optics,* translated from the third German edition by James P. C. Southall (Rochester, N. Y.: Optical Society of America), Vol. 1, pp. 388-390.

arcs which are convex toward the equator. When the points of attachment of the fibers are separated from one another by the increase of thickness of the lens, the arches must be spread, involving the greatest amount of dislocation of particles in the parts of the fibers farthest from the points of attachment. If the lens were always symmetrical, a centripetal shifting would have to occur at the equator. If the point of maximum centripetal shifting on each lens fiber were determined, and a surface passed through all these points, this surface of maximum accommodative shifting would coincide with the equatorial plane. But since the passive lens is asymmetrical, and the change of shape is particularly marked on the anterior surface, the surface of maximum accommodative shifting must be concave toward the front. This conclusion, drawn entirely from the anatomical structure of the lens with respect to its asymmetrical accommodative change of shape, may also be deduced directly from . . . mathematical analysis. The slight change of form of the posterior surface of the lens demonstrates that the points of attachment of the lens fibers adjacent to this surface must, on the average, be less separated from one another during accommodation than those of the fibers lying on the anterior surface. Since, on the whole, the fibers of the posterior surface have their points of attachment situated more toward the periphery on the anterior surface, and toward the center on the posterior surface, and as these conditions are reversed in the case of the fibers of the anterior surface, the distance of the posterior pole of the lens from the anterior point of attachment of the *Zonula Zinnii* must be relatively less changed during accommodation than the distance of the anterior pole from the posterior point of attachment. As a result, the shifting at the anterior point of attachment must occur in a direction approximately corresponding to a tangent to the surface. Consequently, it follows from the anatomical structure of the lens that *the increase of curvature of the anterior surface of the lens during the accommodative change of form is accompanied by an axipetal shifting of the anterior point of attachment of the zonule.* . . . Mathematical investigation demonstrates the presence of a corresponding shifting in those parts of the largest closed iso-indicial surface that are nearest to the point of attachment.

"As the surface of maximum accommodative shifting contains

cross or slightly oblique sections of the lens fibers, the rapidity of
the centripetal movement of these sections during accommodation
must be greater at a point nearer the axis than in the vicinity of
the equator. . . . It is true, this mechanism might be impeded by
the fact that the fibers lying nearer the axis would be cut obliquely
by the surface of maximum shifting in the passive state and per-
pendicularly during accommodation, provided the centripetal
movement could occur to a sufficient extent. But in order to com-
pensate the suggested difference of centripetal shifting, the oblique
section must make an angle of 60° with the perpendicular section;
and this is manifestly impossible. Another consequence, therefore,
of the anatomical structure of the lens is that the equatorial diam-
eters of the smaller iso-indicial surfaces must be proportionately
more shortened in accommodation than those of the larger. But
according to the mathematical investigation, this is an expression
of an increase of the total index; and hence *the increase in total
index during accommodation,* as proved by physiological-optical
investigations, *may be deduced directly from the anatomical structure of the lens.* The so-called S-shaped curvature of the lens fibers
is inferred from the fact that the projection of such a fiber on the
equatorial plane is not a straight line; and the reason why in this
discussion of the anatomical structure of the lens the possibility of
a change in this curvature has not been mentioned is that the only
thing which could modify it would be radially directed elevations
and depressions. This is a necessity due to the mode of attachment
of the lens fibers in rows, so that any mutual shifting of the individual fibers at these points is impossible. On the other hand, it
follows again from the anatomical arrangement of the lens fibers
that during the accommodative change of form, such elevations and
depressions must either originate in the iso-indicial surfaces or must
be reversed there, if they are already present. Else they would
undergo a reduction of superficial area during accommodation. This
might perhaps be possible if the lens were composed of freely
movable particles, but is actually impossible because the capability
of movement is restricted by the arrangement of the fibers. However, a necessary mathematical consequence of this accommodative
change of the iso-indicial surfaces is the variation of the star-shaped
appearance of a luminous point.

"A slight increase of the index at any given point may result from the interpenetration of individual fibers between others, even though the physical indices of the individual fibers are not altered. This explains why the smaller iso-indicial surface . . . is apparently a little nearer the anterior pole of the lens during accommodation, because the superficial extent of that portion of it which is nearest the axis is augmented by the forward displacement, and this must involve an interpenetration of fibers from the central region.

"Thus, the dioptric investigation of the lens in accommodation has resulted in finding out the accommodative variations that occur in the substance of the lens. At the same time, it appears that these changes, which for convenience may be grouped together under the name of the *intracapsular mechanism of accommodation*, are not only in complete agreement with the anatomical structure of the lens, but also establish and explain the causal connection between this structure and the variation of the total index of the lens as proved by the change of refraction that occurs when the lens is removed or during the process of accommodation."

CONSEQUENCES IN THEORY
AND PRACTICE

For a proper understanding of Gullstrand's contributions to ophthalmology, a thorough knowledge of the anatomy of the eye and of geometric and physiological optics is essential. Certain points, however, may be noted here as of primary importance. The heterogeneous structure of the lens, described in the quotation, had never before been explained on physiological grounds. According to the classical (Helmholtz) theory of accommodation, the action of the ciliary muscle increases the convexity of the lens, especially of the anterior surface, and no function is ascribed to the non-uniformity of the internal parts of the lens structure. Accommodation, representing a gain in the refractive power of the lens, makes it possible to focus on the *punctum proximum,* or "near point," which varies with the amount of accommodation possessed by the eye and is determined clinically by noting the shortest distance at which it is possible to read the smallest test type. Gullstrand was able to show that this gain in refractive power is only about two-thirds dependent on the increase in surface curvature of the lens; the remaining third is due to a rearrangement of internal elements, as set forth above. This means that approximately two thirds of accommodation is "extracapsular," one third "intracapsular."

Gullstrand's investigation of optical reproduction, begun on the level of pure physics and extended to physiological optics, led him to modify, or supplement, the theory of co-linear reproduction, enabling him to give improved explanations of anisotropic coma and monochromatic aberration. In applying his findings to the human eye he contributed also to present knowledge of the structure and function of the cornea.

In practice, Gullstrand invented improved methods for estimating astigmatism and corneal abnormalities and for locating paralyzed muscles. He improved the design for corrective glasses after removal of the cataractous lens. He devised a reflex-free ophthalmoscope. Perhaps the best known and most useful of his inventions is the slit-lamp. It supplies a brilliant light condensed into a beam, which traverses the parts to be examined, the remainder of the eye being in darkness; the illuminated area is then examined with the binocular microscope. The combination of slit-lamp and corneal microscope makes possible the minute examination of changes in the anterior part of the eye. Exact localization in three planes or dimensions is obtainable with this instrument. Thus the examiner can locate the site of a foreign body or determine the depth of an ulcer. Lens opacities can be located and their progress watched. The very earliest signs of serious inflammations may often be seen with the aid of Gullstrand's slit-lamp. Sometimes a differential diagnosis of great importance can be made when ordinary methods of examination leave doubt. The slit-lamp is now considered an indispensable part of the ophthalmologist's apparatus.

1 9 1 2
ALEXIS CARREL
(1873–1944)

"In recognition of his works on vascular suture and the transplantation of blood vessels and organs."

BIOGRAPHICAL SKETCH

ALEXIS CARREL WAS BORN IN LYONS, FRANCE, ON JUNE 28, 1873. He became a bachelor of letters of the University of Lyons in 1889, bachelor of science in 1890, and doctor of medicine in 1900. He interned in a Lyons hospital, then taught anatomy and operative surgery at the university as a prosector. He began his experimental work in surgery in 1902 in Lyons, whence he went to Chicago at the end of 1904. In 1906 he became attached to the Rockefeller Institute for Medical Research in New York, where he conducted most of the experiments for which the Nobel Prize was awarded him. This was the first Nobel Prize in medicine for the United States. He was made a fellow of the Institute in 1909, a member in 1912, and retired in 1939 as member emeritus.

During the First World War, Carrel served as a major in the French army medical corps and helped to develop the well-known Carrel-Dakin antiseptic solution for sterilization of deep wounds. In 1935, with Col. Charles A. Lindbergh, he announced the development of a mechanical "heart," in which the heart, kidney, etc. of an animal could be kept alive for study in glass chambers supplied by circulation of artificial blood.

When the Second World War broke out, Carrel joined a special mission for the French Ministry of Public Health (1939-1940). At the time of his death, which took place in Paris, on November 5, 1944, he was director of the Vichy government's Carrel Foundation for the Study of Human Problems. His writings included the best-selling *Man, the Unknown,* and he was joint author with Georges Dehelly of *Treatment of Infected Wounds* and with Charles Lindbergh of *The Culture of Organs.*

DESCRIPTION OF THE PRIZE-WINNING WORK*

"The idea of replacing diseased organs by sound ones, of putting back an amputated limb or even of grafting a new limb on to a patient who has undergone an amputation, is far from being original. Many surgeons before me have had this idea, but they were prevented from applying it, owing to the lack of a method for re-establishing immediately a normal circulation through the transplanted structures. It was of fundamental importance to first discover a suitable method of uniting the blood vessels of the new organ to those of its host. In 1902, therefore, I began to investigate by what means a vascular anastomosis [union between blood vessels] might be effected without producing either stenosis [narrowing], or thrombosis [plugging by clot formation]. Many surgeons had previously to myself performed vascular anastomosis, but the results were far from satisfactory. I began by using Payr's and Murphy's methods, after which I proceeded to study the principles for a new technique on human cadavers. I next performed some vascular anastomoses on living dogs at the University of Lyons in the laboratory of Prof. Soulier and with the collaboration of Dr. Morel. This study was continued at the University of Chicago in Professor Stewart's laboratory and with the collaboration of Doctor Guthrie. Later, at the Rockefeller Institute for Medical Research, the causes of all possible complications were analysed and greater perfection of methods was obtained. With this modified technique a great many experimental operations were performed

---

* From Alexis Carrel, "Suture of Blood-Vessels and Transplantation of Organs," *Les Prix Nobel en 1912.*

and their clinical and anatomical results were observed during a period of three and four years. . . .

"In operations on blood vessels certain general rules must be followed. These rules have been adopted with the view of eliminating the complications which are especially liable to occur after vascular sutures, namely, stenosis, haemhorrhage and thrombosis. A rigid asepsis is absolutely essential. Sutures of blood-vessels must never be performed in infected wounds. It seems that the degree of asepsis under which general surgical operations can safely be made may be insufficient for the success of a vascular operation. It is possible that a slight non-suppurative infection, which does not prevent the union of tissues 'per primam intentionem' ['by first intent'], may yet be sufficient to cause thrombosis. The obliteration of the vessel also follows injuries to its walls. The arteries and veins can be freely handled with the fingers without being injured, but it is often harmful to use forceps or other instruments. If a forceps be used, it must take between its jaws nothing but the external sheath. When temporary haemostasis [control of bleeding] is obtained by means of forceps or clamps, these instruments must be smooth-jawed and their pressure carefully regulated. The desiccation of the endothelium [lining membrane] may also lead to the formation of a thrombus. Therefore, during the operation the wall of the vessels must be humidified . . . or be covered with vaseline. . . . As perforating stitches are always used, the endothelial layer is necessarily wounded by the needle. These wounds, however, are rendered as harmless as possible by the use of very fine and sharp round needles. Extremely small wounds are made. The threads are sterilized in vaseline and kept heavily coated with it during the suture. . . . The operating-field is circumscribed by a black Japanese silk towel on which the fine threads can easily be seen. . . .

"*The termino-terminal* [end-to-end] *anastomosis* is effected by bringing the extremities of the vessels into contact, no traction being necessary. The ends are united by three retaining stitches located in three equidistant points of their circumference. By traction on the threads the circumference of the artery can be transformed into a triangle, and the perimeter can be dilated at will. Then the edges of each side of the triangle are united by a continuous suture whilst they are under tension. During the suture great care is taken to approximate exactly the surfaces of section of the wall. Before the last stitch is made, the remaining vaseline is removed by pressure from the lumen [cavity] of the vessel. In venous anastomoses the ends of the veins are also united by three retaining stitches. A venous suture, however, requires more stitches than an arterial suture, on account of the thinness of the walls. The union of the extremities is made by eversion of the edges, which are united not by their surface of section, but by their endothelial surfaces. An inversion of the edges would be very dangerous and would provoke the formation of a thrombus."

CONSEQUENCES IN THEORY
AND PRACTICE

Aiming at successful replacement or transplantation of organs, Alexis Carrel perceived that the chief difficulty was the re-establishment of circulation without hemorrhage or thrombosis. He therefore worked out the method described above; then he proceeded to apply it. Using his new techniques he was able to remove entire organs, such as the spleen or kidney, and replace them either in the original location or occasionally, in still more spectacular operations, in different parts of the body, where they functioned fairly well. He was even able to replace an amputated limb.

Before the introduction of citrate to prevent blood from clotting (see below, p. 149), vascular suture was used in blood transfusions, a donor blood vessel being anastomosed to a recipient vessel. This method has since been abandoned, but it is repeatedly necessary, in the surgery of injuries and wounds, to restore the continuity of divided blood vessels. Here the Carrel technique finds application.

Vascular surgery is now an important specialty. As a result of a congenital malformation, the greatest of the arteries, the aorta, may be so constricted at some point that the blood supply to the lower half of the body becomes inadequate. This condition is often overlooked, as the patient may be active for years and experience little or no difficulty; but the average duration of life is only about thirty-five years. In 1944 C. Crafoord, and in 1945 R. E. Gross, performed the first operations for this condition, known as coarctation (narrowing) of the aorta. The local constriction is removed and the Carrel method makes it possible to join together the two ends and thus provide an aortic lumen of adequate size.

Certain other kinds of congenital heart disease may now be remedied by somewhat similar techniques. The "blue baby" operation, introduced in 1944 by A. Blalock and H. G. Taussig, involves a rerouting of congenitally misdirected blood flow, using a piece of vein to form a new link between two arteries. In this way it is possible to direct a larger proportion of the blood through the pulmonary circuit, originally by-passed in part, and so to assure sufficient oxidation of the blood as it circles through the lungs.

The domain of vascular surgery is undergoing remarkable extension. Among the surgical techniques which have made this possible, the suture method devised by Carrel is of basic importance. Present-day surgery allied with a growing knowledge of mechanisms of immunity holds out the promise of successful transplantation of various organs to replace defective or diseased ones. At the present time the kidney has been transplanted from one identical (uni-ovular) twin to the other, but in other cases the individuality of the immune system has hindered the taking of the graft. By suppression of the recipient's immune response through use of x-ray irradiation and large doses of cortisone, some apparently successful transplants of the kidney have been achieved between unrelated persons. Antibiotics protect the patient from infection until his immune response has been permitted to return to normal. Other organs fare better, without requiring the temporary suppression of immunity. Thus, the cornea's lack of blood vessels protects it from blood-borne cells of the recipient that might otherwise cast it off. Bone and artery grafts act primarily as the template for regenerating tissue of the host.

1 9 1 3

CHARLES RICHET

(1850–1935)

"In recognition of his work on anaphylaxis."

BIOGRAPHICAL SKETCH

CHARLES RICHET WAS BORN ON AUGUST 26, 1850, IN PARIS, where his father, Alfred Richet, was professor of clinical surgery in the Faculty of Medicine. He was graduated in medicine in 1876, and then worked under Marey at the Collège de France. In 1887 he was appointed professor of physiology at the University of Paris. An industrious and versatile worker, he did not limit himself to the usual confines of physiology but also published papers on physiological chemistry, experimental pathology and pharmacology, and normal and pathological psychology. He did original work on gastric secretion. He also investigated the relation between respiration and the area of body surface, and carried out extensive research on animal heat. In addition he studied the effect of chloride deprivation on epilepsy, and of a diet of raw meat in the treatment of tuberculosis. Work begun in 1887 led Richet to the concept of immune serum, and in 1890 he performed the first serotherapeutic injection on a human subject. Richet's attempt to follow this clue in his work on tuberculosis was disappointing, but von Behring and Kitasato pursued it with greater success in studies of tetanus and diphtheria. In 1898, with his collaborator, Héricourt, Richet studied the effect of eel serum on dogs, observing that a condition of hypersensitiveness could develop. This was followed by his work with P. Portier in 1902 and his own later independent studies of anaphylaxis, described in part below, for which he received the Nobel Prize. In his later years Richet's inclination toward the study of psychology increased. Side by side with this, he nurtured an interest in clairvoyance, telepathy, and materialization—an interest that he did not find incompatible with rigid mechanistic determinism. He followed the development of aeronautics very closely and actually designed an airplane. He was the author of a number of novels and plays. He was also active in pacifist movements. Richet died of pneumonia on December 4, 1935.

DESCRIPTION OF THE PRIZE-WINNING WORK*

"*Phylaxis,* a word but little used, means, in Greek, protection. And the word *anaphylaxis* will then signify the contrary of protection. Thus, through its Greek etymology, anaphylaxis means a state of the organism in which . . . , in place of being protected, [it] has become more sensitive. [Richet coined the word *anaphylaxis* in 1902.]

"To state the ideas precisely, we are going to examine what takes place in an individual receiving a poison.

"Let us suppose the dose a moderate one, and the individual restored, after some days, to his original state, at least to all appearance. If, then, the same dose of the same poison is injected anew, what is going to happen?

"We can suppose three cases.

"The first, the simplest, is that nothing has been changed in his organism, and that on receiving the same dose as a month ago, exactly the same phenomena will reappear under the same conditions. . . .

"The second possibility is that the organism may have become less sensitive. In other words, a certain state of habituation, or insensibility, has been produced by the preceding intoxication; so that a stronger dose has become necessary, at the second injection,

---

* Translated from Charles Richet, "Conférence Nobel sur l'anaphylaxie," *Les Prix Nobel en 1913.*

to produce the same effect. It is the case of immunity (relative). . . .

"These two cases: unmodified sensitivity or *stability*, diminished sensitivity or *habituation*, had been known for a long time. But I have shown that very frequently, under certain conditions which I have been able to specify, a third modality is seen: it is increased sensitivity, of such a kind that the first injection, in place of protecting the organism, makes it frailer, more susceptible, it is *anaphylaxis*.

"Let me tell you under what circumstances I observed this phenomenon for the first time. I may be permitted to enter into some details on its origin. You will see, as a matter of fact, that it is not at all the result of deep thinking, but of a simple observation, almost accidental; so that I have had no other merit than that of not refusing to see the facts which presented themselves before me, completely evident.

"In equatorial seas one comes across Coelenterates [a sub-kingdom of animals comprising the Actinozoa and Hydrozoa] called Physalia (Portuguese men-of-war). These animals are formed essentially of a sac full of air, which allows them to float like a leather bottle. Associated with this sac is a bucco-anal cavity, furnished with very long tentacles, which hang down in the water. These tentacular filaments, sometimes two or three meters in length, are armed with little "gadgets" which adhere like suckers to objects which they encounter. And in the interior of each of these innumerable suckers there is a sharp little point, which penetrates the foreign body touched. At the same time this point imparts a subtle poison, very active, contained in the tentacles; so that the contact of the Physalia's filament is equivalent to a multiple injection of poison. The moment you touch a Physalia, you feel an intense pain, owing to the penetration of this venomous liquid. . . .

"Now, in the course of a cruise made on the yacht of Prince Albert of Monaco, the Prince advised me, as well as our friends Georges Richard and Paul Portier, to study the poison of these Physaliae. We saw that it dissolves readily in glycerine, and that on injecting this glycerinated liquid one reproduces the symptoms of Physalian poisoning.

"Having returned to France, and no longer being able to obtain

Physaliae, I thought of studying comparatively the tentacles of Actiniae [sea anemones] . . . which can be obtained in abundance; for the Actiniae swarm on the rocks of all the European coasts.

"Now the tentacles of the Actiniae, treated with glycerine, yield their poison to the glycerine, and the extract is toxic. Working with Portier, I then sought to determine the toxic dose. This was difficult enough, because this poison acts slowly, and one must wait three or four days before knowing whether or not one has reached the fatal dose. With the solutions that I was using, a kilo of glycerine to a kilo of tentacles [a kilo, or kilogram, is a little more than two pounds], it required, after filtration, about 0.1 of liquid per kilo of live weight to bring about death.

"But certain dogs escaped, whether because they had received too weak a dose, or from some other cause. And at the end of two, three, or four weeks, as they seemed altogether restored to their normal state, I made use of them for a new experiment.

"Then an unforeseen phenomenon presented itself, which to us appeared extraordinary. If the dog, injected beforehand, received an extremely weak dose, for example 0.005 per kilo, he immediately exhibited dreadful symptoms: vomiting, bloody diarrhea, syncope, loss of consciousness, asphyxia, and death. Repeating on different occasions this fundamental experiment, we were able to establish, in 1902, these three principal facts, which are the very foundation of the story of anaphylaxis: first, an animal injected beforehand is enormously more sensitive than a new animal; second, the symptoms which supervene on the second injection, characterized by a rapid and total depression of the nervous system, have no resemblance to the symptoms produced by the first injection; third, this anaphylactic state requires an interval of three or four weeks to establish itself. It is what is called an incubation period.

"After the initial facts of anaphylaxis had been solidly established, the domain was enormously enlarged at once, thanks to the beautiful experiments of clever investigators.

"In 1903, Arthus, of Lausanne, showed that if a rabbit is given an intravenous injection of serum, this first injection of serum is anaphylactogenic—that is to say that three weeks after the first injection the rabbit has become very sensitive to the second injection. Thus the phenomenon of anaphylaxis was generalized; and instead of its being specific to toxins and toxalbumin it was extended to all proteins, whether toxic on first injection or not. [Arthus observed a local reaction since known as the 'Arthus phenomenon'.]

"Two years later, two American physiologists, Rosenau and Anderson, established in a remarkable memoir that the anaphylactic phenomenon is seen after every injection of serum, even when the quantity injected is minuscule, be it 0.00001 c.c., the tiniest quantity, but sufficient to give an animal anaphylactic sensitivity. They gave examples of anaphylaxis with all the organic liquids: milk, serum, egg, muscular extract. They indicated the specificity of this reaction, and finally they clearly established that of all animals the guinea pig appears to be the most sensitive to the anaphylactic reaction.

"In 1907, I made an experiment which notably clarified the pathogenesis [the mode of origin] of anaphylaxis. In taking the blood of a sensitized animal, and injecting it into a normal animal, the anaphylactic state is developed. Thus the anaphylactogenic poison is a chemical substance contained in the blood.

"Such, as it seems, are the principal phases through which our knowledge has passed."

CONSEQUENCES IN THEORY AND PRACTICE

Richet was not the only investigator to report intensified results from a preliminary conditioning expected to create, if anything, a state of immunity. Thus Edward Jenner had long ago noticed a similar occurrence in performing vaccinations, and von Behring had observed that a second injection of diphtheria toxin seemed at times to have a greater toxic effect than anticipated. But the regularity of the phenomenon was Richet's discovery; he not only observed and named it but clearly expounded as a general principle what had been noted from time to time in the past as an exceptional and bizarre occurrence. Furthermore, he showed that it was not a mere intensification of an ordinary toxic action but was a specific effect with characteristic signs and symptoms.

The term "anaphylaxis" may refer to increased susceptibility to an injection under the conditions described above; more commonly it means the reaction to a foreign substance, usually a protein such as animal serum, following a previous introduction, by injection or otherwise, of the same substance. The effect is the same regardless of what substance is used to cause it, but the conditioning is specific for each substance. Often the preliminary introduction of the substance in question has taken place accidentally or obscurely, or the sensitivity may be inherited; in other cases there is a clear history of the previous introduction. Because spontaneous or hereditary cases occur, and because the history and other indications are often unreliable, test doses are introduced into the skin or the eye before serums are injected. Anaphylactic shock, which is sudden and often fatal, or the slower "serum sickness," may be avoided by the use of a type of serum different from the one previously introduced. The risks connected with serum treatment may also be overcome, as A. Besredka has shown, by desensitization—that is, by beginning with extremely small doses and gradually increasing them.

Antigens causing reactions akin to those of anaphylaxis may gain entrance to the body by ingestion, by inhalation, by injection, from a focus of infection, or from external contacts. Proteins are the commonest, but not the only, antigens. The list includes the pollens, danders and many other air-borne substances of animal and vegetable origin, foods, drugs, therapeutic serums, and bacteria and their products. Diseases of allergy now form an important division of internal medicine. They include not only asthma, hay fever, and serum sickness but also contact dermatitis in a wide variety of forms. This whole domain of medical science and practice finds its starting point in the investigations of Charles Richet.

1 9 1 4
ROBERT BÁRÁNY
(1876–1936)

"For his work on the physiology and pathology of the vestibular apparatus."

BIOGRAPHICAL SKETCH

ROBERT BÁRÁNY, AN AUSTRO-HUNGARIAN, WAS BORN IN Vienna, on April 22, 1876. He was educated chiefly in the city of his birth, and was graduated in medicine in 1900. After two years spent at various German clinics in the study of internal medicine and psychiatry, he returned to Vienna, where he soon restricted his work to otology (the study of diseases of the ear) and related problems as they affect certain parts of the brain. He became famous for his studies of the vestibular apparatus in the ear and of the cerebellum (the "little brain," or that part of the brain behind and beneath the larger cerebrum; see below). In 1913-1914 he was awarded a number of international prizes, culminating in his selection as Nobel laureate. The confusion which accompanied the outbreak of the First World War caused postponement of the 1914 award until 1915. At that time Bárány was a Russian prisoner of war in Siberia. Through the intercession of the Swedish Red Cross, however, he was released, and the award presented to him through diplomatic channels. After 1917 his work was done at Uppsala University. He died in 1936, at the age of sixty.

DESCRIPTION OF THE PRIZE-WINNING
WORK*

"As a young otologist I practiced in the clinic of Privy Councillor
Professor Politzer in Vienna. Among my patients there were many
whose ears I had to flush out. A number of these patients com-
plained of dizziness after the flushing procedure. It naturally occurred to me to examine their eyes, and there I observed marked
nystagmus [involuntary, spasmodic motion of the eyeballs, a jerky
rolling of the eyes]. I made a note of this observation. After a
while, when I had collected about twenty observations, I compared
them and was surprised to find the same observations recorded
every time. Then I recognized that a general law must underlie
these observations. I did not yet know, however, the basis of the
conformity to law. Chance came to my aid. One of the patients
whom I syringed explained to me: 'Doctor, I only get dizzy when
the water is not warm enough. When I flush out my ears for myself
at home and use warm enough water, I don't get dizzy.' Thereupon I called the attendant and instructed her to give me warmer
water for the flushing process. She explained that the water was
warm enough. I retorted that if the patient found the water too
cold, we had to adjust ourselves to the patient. The next time she
put very hot water in the bulb of the syringe. When I syringed the
patient, he cried out: 'But Doctor, the water is much too hot; now
I'm becoming dizzy again.' Hurriedly I observed the patient's eyes,
and noticed that now the nystagmus was exactly opposite in direction to that seen earlier when syringing with water that was too
cold. Then in a flash it became clear to me that naturally the temperature of the water was responsible for the nystagmus. I drew
some conclusions from this at once. If the temperature is to blame,
then, to be sure, water of exactly body temperature must produce
no nystagmus and no dizziness. Experiment confirmed this conclusion. I said further, if it is a matter of water temperature, then
nystagmus must be producible by syringing in normal people, too,

* Translated from "Nobel-Vortrag . . . von Dr. Robert Bárány," *Les Prix Nobel
en 1914-18.*

and not merely in people with suppurations of the ear. This inference also proved to be right.

"On the ground of my previous studies, I did not doubt for a moment that as regards this nystagmus it was a question of a reflex initiated in the semicircular canals. [The three semicircular canals, or ducts, which are membranous, are contained in corresponding bony canals in the internal ear within the skull; the canals lie in planes approximately at right angles to one another. Their function, briefly stated, is to initiate the reflexes which cause us to right ourselves involuntarily by compensatory movements, in response to changes in velocity or direction of motion. These reflexes effect movements of eyes and limbs. There are also reflexes which influence the tone, or steady, continuous action, of the muscles responsible, in their coordination, for posture.] Thence the further conclusion was also obvious that the semicircular canals being destroyed, this reflex must fail to appear. I now sought a case of this kind in the rich material of the Vienna ear clinic. I had soon found a case of severe suppuration of the middle ear, showing no nystagmus reaction on long-continued flushing with quite cold water. I diagnosed destruction of the labyrinth (with respect to the semicircular duct apparatus); in point of fact the operation showed the expected finding. This made clear the significance of the new reaction for the diagnosis of diseases of the inner ear. Yet a series of cases was required for corroboration. This was forthcoming. . . . I had already perceived the significance of the caloric reaction, and yet I did not know how to explain it. I thought it over in vain. Then one day an idea struck me. I remembered the water heater, and my astonishment, as a child, when I found the water just above the fire quite cold, but right at the top the bath-oven was so hot it burned the fingers. The labyrinth now represented in my mind the water heater—i.e., a vessel filled with fluid. The temperature of this fluid is naturally 37° C—the body temperature. I squirt cold water at one side of the vessel. What must happen? What must naturally occur is that the water lying against this wall is cooled down; in this way it acquires a higher specific gravity than the surrounding water and sinks to the bottom of the vessel. On the other hand, water still at body temperature takes its place. If I syringe the ear with hot water, then the motion must be precisely contrary. But the motion of the fluid must be altered if I alter the position of the vessel. And it must be changed to the exact opposite if I turn the vessel through 180°. The test which had to be the crucial experiment for this theory occurred to me at once. If syringing, be it with cold fluid or hot, succeeded in evoking nystagmus precisely opposite in direction for two positions of the head differing by 180°, then the theory must be the right one. I now went to the clinic and undertook the experiment. As it turned out, the anticipated result appeared with the greatest clearness. Two positions of the head, encompassing between them 180°, gave directly opposite nystagmus reactions. . . ."

CONSEQUENCES IN THEORY AND PRACTICE

"Bárány's caloric test," the first result of his study of the vestibular apparatus, consists in irrigating the canal of the external ear with either hot or cold water. This normally causes stimulation of the vestibular apparatus resulting in nystagmus. In vestibular disease, the response fails relatively or entirely. This method for diagnosing disease of the semicircular canals is the most widely used of several "Bárány tests" and has borne his name to clinics and hospitals the world over. But this was not the end of his investigations. Starting from the work of Ramón y Cajal (see above, pp. 33-40), who traced the communications of the vestibular nerve, and from the studies of the Dutch comparative anatomist Louis Bolk, Bárány concluded that influences on the musculature of the whole body which result in disturbances of equilibrium pass from the semicircular ducts by way of the cerebellum. The study of these disturbances, and the belief that there is definite localization in the cerebellum for movement, led him to devise certain tests for the integrity of the control centers, as reflected in movement of the extremities and even of particular joints. A normal subject with his eyes shut will "past point" to the right beyond the spot he attempts to touch, if the right vestibular apparatus has been stimulated with cold water. The direction of "past pointing" is always opposite to the direction of nystagmus. But Bárány found that spontaneous "past pointing" sometimes occurred. If the patient "past pointed" to the right, stimulation of the vestibular apparatus to induce a swing to the left failed to work; it merely caused the patient to point correctly. Bárány assumed that "there are in the cerebellum four centers . . . namely, a center directing to the right, one to the left, one up, and one down. . . . At any time two of these centers work like two reins, between which the arm, for instance, moves. If both of these reins are stretched equally taut, then the arm moves without fail to each point desired. But now I can pull one rein harder than the other. This happens if I stimulate the semicircular duct apparatus." It is obvious that a lesion of some sort, a local sickness in one of these centers, will act like the cutting of a rein. Attempts to "pull" this rein will fail, as in the instance of spontaneous "past pointing" mentioned above. Hence it is possible to use Bárány tests not only for diagnosing certain ailments in the inner ear but also for investigating some of the activities of the cerebellum.

1 9 1 5 – 1 9 1 8

No Award

1 9 1 9
JULES BORDET
(1870–1961)

"For his discoveries in regard to immunity."

BIOGRAPHICAL SKETCH

JULES (JEAN BAPTISTE VINCENT) BORDET, FAMOUS BELGIAN bacteriologist and immunologist, was born on June 13, 1870, at Soignies, Belgium. He studied at the University of Brussels, where he was graduated as doctor of medicine in 1892. In 1894 he went to the Pasteur Institute, Paris, where he was *attaché* or *préparateur* in Metchnikoff's laboratory until 1901, when he founded the Pasteur Institute in Brussels and became its director. In 1907 he was appointed professor of bacteriology at the University of Brussels. His numerous and important contributions to immunology made him widely known. He was elected a foreign member of the Royal Society in 1916. From the considerable range of Bordet's work in serology the contribution quoted below has been selected as of outstanding importance to medicine. His collaborator in this work was Octave Gengou, a fellow Belgian, with whom he later described the whooping-cough bacillus (1906). Bordet died at his home at Ixelles in 1961.

DESCRIPTION OF THE PRIZE-WINNING WORK*

"The serum of numerous animals contains alexin [now generally known as "complement," the name given to it by Ehrlich],

---

* Translated from J. Bordet and O. Gengou, "Sur l'existence de substances sensibilisatrices dans la plupart des sérums antimicrobiens," *Annales de l'Institut Pasteur*, Vol. 15 (1901), pp. 289-302.

that is to say, an ill-defined material, its chemical constitution still unknown, to the presence of which is attributed that property which serums in general possess of exercising a destructive influence on diverse cellules and on certain microbes. The alexin loses its activity when the serum which contains it is heated to 55°. This material is to be met with, in quite comparable amounts, in the serum of normal animals and in that of vaccinated animals: artificial immunization does not modify it appreciably, either in quantity or in character.

"When an animal is vaccinated against the cholera vibrio [bacteria], the organism elaborates a particular substance, the preventive or *sensitizing* material [amboceptor], the presence of which can be detected in the serum and which resists quite elevated temperatures. By itself, it is not at all bactericidal for the vibrio. But it favors considerably, and in a specific way, the destructive action which the alexin can exercise on this microbe. One can also say that the specific vibrio-killing property of cholera serum, although due primarily to alexin . . . , results from the collaboration of two substances, on one hand the alexin, on the other the favoring (sensitizing) material with which only the serum of vaccinated individuals is endowed in large degree. . . . [These ideas were established by Bordet in 1895. He applied them, first, to cholera serum, secondly, to specific hemolytic serums. He supposed the phenomenon to occur more generally, but the method he had used for these instances was not generally applicable. In brief it was this. Cholera vibrios are destroyed (bacteriolysis) to a very marked degree by immune serum from a vaccinated animal, to a very slight degree by normal serum. The power of either serum may be abolished by 55° of heat. But adding to normal, feebly active serum a small amount of preheated immune serum, inactive in itself, results in a strongly bactericidal mixture. Hence, the conclusion, as above, that it contains a "sensitizer" (amboceptor) which adds to the otherwise slight power of the "alexin" (complement) in the normal serum. A similar method applied where hemolysis, rather than bacteriolysis, was the revealing change. But where neither of these changes took place another method was needed.]

"As a preliminary, we must recall to the reader an experiment related a year ago in these *Annales* [Bordet, in May 1900], and of which the following is the principle:

"If one adds to a suitable quantity of the serum of a normal animal, such as the guinea pig (serum recently obtained, unheated, thus containing alexin), some red cells (of a rabbit for example) [which have been] strongly *sensitized* (that is to say, mixed with some hemolytic serum, active vis-à-vis these cells, and which has been heated to 55°), one observes . . . the destruction of the corpuscles. At the end of a certain time some *sensitized* cholera vibrios (added to cholera serum preheated to 55°) are added to the mixture, which is incubated at 37°. One ascertains that the vibrio . . . retains its normal form. Consequently one can affirm that at the moment when the vibrios were introduced, the mixture no longer contained alexin. . . . [This could be reversed—i.e., the "alexin" could be used up by "sensitized" vibrios and would then fail to hemolyze "sensitized" corpuscles.]

"These experiments have established . . . two quite distinct ideas: (1) Corpuscles or microbes, *under the influence of sensitization, acquire the power of absorbing alexin avidly,* and thus of making it disappear from the surrounding liquid. (2) In the same serum, *the same alexin* can provoke either hemolysis or bacteriolysis. . . . [The authors assert as the aim of the present paper to show that] *to denote the existence of a sensitizer in an antimicrobic serum* one can use the property with which this substance is endowed of causing the absorption of the alexin by the microbe which it affects . . .

"[Serum from a horse vaccinated against bacillus pestis, the cause of plague] is heated to 56° for half an hour, at the same time as some serum from a normal horse; this heating renders the alexin inactive. A 24-hour culture of bacillus pestis on gelose [gelatinous part of agar-agar, a solidifying agent used in culture mediums] is diluted in quite a small amount of a physiological solution of NaCl; one thus obtains a very turbid emulsion, rich in microbes. Some serum is also prepared, well cleared of corpuscles by centrifugation, from a normal guinea pig bled the day before. This is the alexic serum [i.e., serum containing alexin, or complement]. The following six mixtures are prepared in test tubes: (*a*) This tube contains: 2/10 c.c. alexic serum; 4/10 c.c. bacillus pestis emulsion; 12/10 c.c. antiplague serum (preheated to 56°). (*b*) [The same as *a* except that] it contains, in place of antiplague horse serum, 12/10 c.c. of normal horse serum (preheated to 56°). (*c*) [The same as *a* but without bacillus pestis emulsion.] (*d*) [The same as *b* but without bacillus pestis. These four mixtures contain the same dose of alexin.] (*e*) Contains 4/10 c.c. plague emulsion; 12/10 c.c. antiplague serum. (*f*) Contains 4/10 c.c. plague emulsion; 12/10 c.c. normal horse serum. These last two tubes are the same, respectively, as *a* and *b,* except that they do not contain alexin.

"One waits about five hours, while the mixtures remain at laboratory temperature (15-20°). Then one introduces into the different tubes, at the same moment, 2/10 c.c. of the following mixture: 2 c.c. of serum (previously heated for half an hour to 55°) from a guinea pig treated in advance with three or four injections of 4-5 c.c. of defibrinated rabbit blood; 20 drops of defibrinated rabbit blood. In other words each tube receives two drops of *very strongly sensitized blood.*

"Here is the result of the experiment: Hemolysis appears very quickly, with very similar rapidity, in the tubes *b, c, d.* After 5-10 minutes these mixtures no longer contain intact corpuscles. In the tube *a,* which contains, besides alexic serum, the bacilli and the antiplague serum, *hemolysis does not occur.* The corpuscles remain intact for days at a time. They also remain intact . . . in the tubes *e* and *f,* which do not contain alexin. Thus we see, first, that the bacillus pestis mixed with normal horse serum does not absorb alexin (or absorbs it only to an insignificant degree); second, that the same bacillus, in the presence of antiplague serum from a vaccinated horse, fixes the alexin with great avidity, and makes it disappear from the surrounding liquid; third, the antiplague serum, without the addition of bacilli, leaves the alexin perfectly free.

"Consequently it is necessary to conclude that the serum of a horse vaccinated against the bacillus pestis contains a *sensitizer which confers on this microbe the power of fixing alexin* [complement]."

CONSEQUENCES IN THEORY
AND PRACTICE

Bordet and Gengou formed an effective team and worked together for years. (The organism called Hemophilus pertussis, the
cause of whooping cough, was originally known as the "Bordet-
Gengou" bacillus, after its discoverers; it was first described by
them in 1906-1907.) But the fundamental work which made possible the discovery set forth in the above quotation had been carried out by Bordet some years earlier. His publication of 1895 had
shown two different substances to be involved in the phenomenon
of bacteriolysis. That the terminology has changed makes little difference. It was Bordet who discovered that two factors, not a single
antibody as previously supposed, are concerned in the lytic (destructive) action. One of these substances is present both in normal
and fresh immune serum and is thermolabile (subject to alteration
or destruction by heat), the other is peculiar to the immune serum
and is thermostable (heat-resistant). He called these, respectively,
"alexine" (from the Greek *alexo,* "I ward off") and "substance
sensibilisatrice." These terms have been replaced by the names
given to the substances by Ehrlich, "complement" and "amboceptor." It was found, chiefly as a result of Bordet's further experiments, that lytic action is not limited to bacteria. Red blood cells
are destroyed by a similar mechanism, hemolysis.

"The possibility of . . . a practical test [using immune serum]
was first made known by R. Pfeiffer (1894), who found that the
bacteriolytic destruction of cholera vibrios in the peritoneum was
so specific that this method could be employed for the differentiation of cholera vibrios from vibrios otherwise indistinguishable.
Bordet (1895) utilized this principle and applied it *in vitro* [in
the test tube] instead of *in vivo* [in the living animal]. . . .

"Of particular medical importance is the so-called complement
fixation test. . . . Gengou (1902) showed . . . that 'sensitizers'
(amboceptors) are developed in the blood-serum of animals which
have been injected with milk, and that such sensitizers are also
capable of fixing complement. . . . [I.e., Gengou further generalized the discovery.]

"These facts were extended by C. Moreschi (1905), who showed that complement fixation occurs in the presence of normal serum mixed with the serum of an animal injected with normal serum, and he demonstrated that extraordinarily small quantities of serum (1/100,000 c.c.) can be detected by this method of diagnosis. M. Neisser and Sachs (1905) recommended the method for the diagnosis of blood in medico-legal work. In 1906 Wassermann, Neisser, and Bruck published their historic account in which they described the discovery of antibodies to syphilis antigen in the serum of syphilitic monkeys. In the same year Wassermann and Plaut (1906), by demonstrating syphilitic antibodies in the cerebrospinal fluids of general paralytics [see below, p. 129], proved this disease to be syphilis, and Wassermann, Neisser, Bruck and Schucht (1906) demonstrated similar antibodies in the blood-serum of syphilitics. Since that time the 'Wassermann reaction' has been practised to an enormous extent in the diagnosis of syphilis and is regarded as a test of deadly accuracy. The complement fixation test has been permanently accepted also in the case of the diagnosis of glanders." *

* William Bulloch, *The History of Bacteriology* (London and New York: Oxford University Press, 1938), pp. 281-283.

1 9 2 0
AUGUST KROGH
(1874–1949)

"For his discovery of the regulation of the motor mechanism of capillaries."

BIOGRAPHICAL SKETCH

AUGUST KROGH WAS BORN AT GRENAA, IN JUTLAND, DENMARK, on November 15, 1874. He studied zoology at the University of Copenhagen, receiving the M.A. degree in 1899. Even before this, beginning in 1897, he had been carrying on research in the physiology laboratory under Christian Bohr, with whom he continued to work for some years. In 1902 he took part in an expedition to Greenland to study arctic animals. Krogh early turned his attention to studies in gaseous pressures, first in natural waters, afterward in animal physiology. His doctoral thesis (1903) dealt with the respiration of frogs. Much of his subsequent work on the pressures of oxygen and carbon dioxide in the blood was carried out in collaboration with his wife, Dr. Marie Krogh. That the affinity of blood for oxygen depends upon carbon dioxide pressure was demonstrated in 1904 by Bohr, Hasselbalch, and Krogh. In 1908 Krogh became associate in animal physiology at the University of Copenhagen, but had no laboratory until 1910 and did not become titular professor until 1916. His investigations, in some of which Lindhard was associated, were concerned chiefly with the physiology of respiration and blood circulation, but covered a wide range of interests.

DESCRIPTION OF THE PRIZE-WINNING
WORK *

"The current view of the capillary circulation, at least until a few years ago, was . . . that blood is flowing continuously through all [capillaries] at rates which are determined by the state of contraction or dilatation of the corresponding arterioles, and that the dilatation of an arteriole will cause a rise of pressure in the corresponding capillaries, which will become passively expanded, to contract again by their own elasticity when the pressure is reduced. . . . An increase in [arterial and arteriolar] current must always be accompanied by a corresponding increase in capillary pressure, and when the requirements are small the quantity of blood in a large number of the capillaries would serve no useful purpose. A much more effective distribution would obviously be obtained if the capillaries themselves were contractile, if in a resting organ only a limited number of capillaries . . . were kept open. . . . This hypothetical conception was to me personally the starting point and guide in the experimental study of capillary contractility. . . .

[Krogh here reviews earlier work on the subject, beginning with S. Stricker (1865) and extending to H. H. Dale and A. N. Richards (1918). Most of this work was based on direct microscopic observations of capillaries. Sources of error inherent in the method were not sufficiently guarded against. V. Ebbecke, however, and at the same time (1917) Cotton, Slade, and Lewis, had published evidence based on the local vasomotor reactions of the skin and internal organs, and Dale and Richards had compared the actions of three "depressor" drugs, leading to the conclusion that two of them, histamine and adrenaline, must produce relaxation of the capillary wall.]

"My own first contribution to the problem . . . was published in Danish in 1918 . . . and appeared in the British *Journal of Physiology* (1919). . . . I found it possible to observe at least the superficial capillaries of muscles both in the frog and in mammals through a binocular microscope. . . . Resting muscles observed

---

* From August Krogh, *The Anatomy and Physiology of Capillaries* (New Haven: Yale University Press, 1922), Silliman Memorial Lectures, Lecture II.

in this way are usually quite pale, and the microscope reveals only a few capillaries at fairly regular intervals. These capillaries are so narrow that red corpuscles can pass through only at a slow rate and with a change of form from the ordinary flat discs to elongated sausages. When the muscle . . . is stimulated to contractions a large number of capillaries become visible and dilated. . . . Since capillaries, even in a group fed by the same arteriole, do not all behave in the same way, the changes obviously cannot be due to arterial pressure changes. . . .

"[Measurements showed the average distance between open capillaries in resting muscle to be much greater than in muscle which had just contracted.] The measurement of distances between open capillaries made upon living specimens could not, of course, be very accurate. . . . I had, therefore, to try and devise a method by which the state of the vessels at any given moment could be studied after fixation. This I succeeded in doing by injecting an India ink solution . . . [made] isotonic with the blood and [freed from] toxic substances. . . . When a suitable quantity of India ink is introduced into the circulation of a living anaesthetized animal it is evenly mixed with the blood, and if the animal is suddenly killed by stopping the circulation a few minutes later, and preparations are made from the muscles and other organs, these show the capillaries which were open at the time.

"On frogs I found by this method that there were large differences between different organs in the number of open capillaries. The skin, liver and brain [organs which are constantly active] were always well injected, with all, or nearly all, capillaries open. The tongue was generally white and nearly bloodless, when not stimulated before being removed. The empty stomach and intestines had only a small number of open capillaries. The injection of muscles was variable, but in most of the resting muscles few capillaries only were open, while muscles which had been [stimulated] before stopping the circulation were almost black from the large number of injected capillaries."

CONSEQUENCES IN THEORY
AND PRACTICE

It was stated above, in the biographical sketch, that a large part of Krogh's work was concerned with the physiology of respiration and circulation. His primary interest appears to have been respiration, and many of his studies of circulatory mechanisms were aimed at finding out how the circulation carries oxygen to the tissues. Some of his earlier studies had dealt with gas exchange in the lungs. When the organism is under stress, breathing quickens and deepens. In determinations of the amount of blood which the heart pumps around the blood-vessel circuit in one minute, Krogh had found that when muscular work is performed there is a marked increase in the blood flow. Thus the extra oxygen taken in is passed along to the tissues. But a problem remained. Under these conditions of stress the oxygen of each cubic centimeter of blood is used up more quickly than when the body is at rest, so that obviously the demand for extra oxygen is not being met solely by the greater cardiac output. In the experiments described in the quotation, Krogh found that there was a great variation in the number of capillaries which might be open at a given moment. The number of patent vessels was directly related to the activity of the tissue at the time, being much larger in active than in resting muscle. Sometimes in resting muscle he could observe that a tiny vessel was so constricted that the oxygen-bearing red corpuscles could not enter it, the plasma alone being allowed to pass. (This he called "plasma skimming.") In active muscle, on the other hand, a larger number of vascular channels were opened, and they were opened more widely, so that as many red corpuscles as possible might carry their oxygen to the tissues. The extra blood supplied by the greater blood flow through the whole body was passed into as many as possible of the small channels where oxygen is given up *in those parts of the body needing it;* elsewhere the capillaries were constricted. Krogh considered that these changes play an important role in the mechanism for the regulation of the oxygen supply to tissues.

The physiology of the capillaries is a subject of great importance to medicine. Studies in normal and disordered blood pressure require minute and accurate knowledge of the behavior of the smaller divisions of the arterial tree. Inflammatory symptoms and allergic reactions of certain kinds depend on capillary changes. The permeability of capillary walls is altered in some hemorrhagic diseases. Accumulations of fluids in dropsical maladies are also determined in this way, and changes in the state of the capillaries explain many of the symptoms of shock. August Krogh has made valuable contributions to this basic knowledge of the anatomy and physiology of the capillaries.

REFERENCES

REHBERG, BRANDT P. "August Krogh, November 15, 1874-September 13, 1949," *Yale Journal of Biology and Medicine*, Vol. 24 (1951), pp. 83-102.

1 9 2 1

No Award

1922

ARCHIBALD VIVIAN HILL

(1886–   )

"For his discovery relating to the production of heat in the muscles."

OTTO MEYERHOF

(1884–1951)

"For his discovery of the fixed relationship between the consumption of oxygen and the metabolism of lactic acid in muscle."

BIOGRAPHICAL SKETCHES

HILL

ARCHIBALD VIVIAN HILL, DISTINGUISHED BIOPHYSICIST, WAS born in England in 1886 and was educated at Blundell's School, Tiverton. He won scholarships to Trinity College, Cambridge, where he studied mathematics. One of his teachers was W. M. Fletcher, who was then associated with F. G. Hopkins in investigating the formation of lactic acid in muscle. Hill apparently turned to physiology on Fletcher's urging, and J. N. Langley suggested that he undertake the work for which he afterward received the Nobel Prize. In 1910-1911 he studied in Germany under Bürker and Paschen. He continued his work at Cambridge until the outbreak of the First World War, in which he served from 1914 to 1919. In 1920 he was appointed to the chair of physiology at Manchester, and from 1923 to 1925 he was Jodrell Professor of Physiology, University College, London. In 1926 came his appointment as Foulerton Research Professor of the Royal Society. As an Independent Conservative he was M.P. for Cambridge University from 1940 to 1945. He was also a member of the War Cabinet Scientific Advisory Committee, as well as of many other scientific and defense committees. From 1935 to 1946 he was Secretary (later Foreign Secretary) of the Royal Society. In 1952-56 he was Secretary-General of the International Council of Scientific Unions.

MEYERHOF

OTTO MEYERHOF, ONE OF THE PIONEERS OF PRESENT-DAY BIO-chemistry, was born in Hanover on April 12, 1884. His family moved to Berlin and he attended the Wilhelms-Gymnasium there, then studied medicine in Freiburg, Berlin, Strasburg, and finally Heidelberg, where he was graduated in 1909, having written a dissertation in psychiatry. He then busied himself chiefly with psychology and philosophy, publishing a book entitled *Contributions to a Psychological Theory of Mental Diseases* and an essay called "Goethe's Methods in Natural Philosophy." Under the influence of Otto Warburg, he transferred his attention to physiology; while in Heidelberg he also worked at physical chemistry. In 1912 he went to Kiel. Lectures delivered in England and the United States appeared as a book, *The Chemical Dynamics of Living Matter,* which helped to make him widely known. Meyerhof occupied a variety of distinguished positions in German science before Germany's scientific and political decline. By 1929 he had become head of the Department of Physiology in the Institute for Medical Research in Heidelberg. Forced to leave Germany in 1938, he continued his work at the Institut de Biologie Physico-Chimique in Paris. After the invasion of France, in 1940, he escaped with his wife to the United States, where he was appointed research professor at the Department of Physiological Chemistry, University of Pennsylvania. Professor Meyerhof died in Philadelphia on October 6, 1951.

DESCRIPTION OF THE PRIZE-WINNING WORK

HILL *

"In the study of thermal changes [in muscle] the most consistent and valuable results have been obtained by utilising the isometric contraction of the sartorius muscle of the frog. [The sartorius is a straplike thigh muscle. "Isometric contraction" refers to the fact that the two ends of the muscle are fixed, so that the effort of contraction does not actually shorten it.] . . . The isometric contraction has the advantage, firstly, that energy is not liberated in it in any other form than heat . . . and secondly, that . . . movements of the instruments are prohibited. . . .

"The fundamental difficulty . . . is the smallness of the changes involved and their rapidity. In the muscle twitch of a frog's sartorius at 20° the rise of temperature is not more than 0.003° C and the time occupied in the earlier phases (as distinguished from the recovery process) is only a few hundredths of a second. The first requisite therefore is a very sensitive thermometric apparatus and great freedom from temperature changes, the second is extreme rapidity and lightness in the recording instruments. . . . [Hill then discusses thermometric apparatus and concludes that a very light, delicate, and sensitive thermopile is the only possibility. A thermopile is a kind of battery, made of alternating pieces of two different metals; heat applied to the junctions, or couples, gives rise to an electric current, the strength of which is measured by a galvanometer; an indirect measure of the heat is thus provided, and very minute temperature changes are detectable. Because of the nature of the apparatus, these readings cannot be accepted at face value, but the factors which distort the results can be eliminated by a control experiment.] Fortunately it is possible to make a direct calibration of the instruments [i.e., to scale them in such a way that results may be read as degrees of temperature] by liberating in the same muscle, in the identical position on the thermopile at the close

---

* From A. V. Hill, "The Mechanism of Muscular Contraction," *Les Prix Nobel en 1923.*

of an experiment, a known amount of heat . . . [first killing the muscle].

"One of my earliest observations on the subject was that the galvanometer deflection persists much longer in a live muscle than in a control experiment. . . . This phenomenon can be due only to a delayed production of heat, and I found that this 'recovery' heat as we called it is appreciable only in oxygen, being abolished by keeping the muscle in nitrogen, or by previous exercise violent enough to use up the oxygen dissolved in the muscle. . . . A rough estimate of the magnitude of the recovery heat production made it approximately equal to the total initial heat. [Hill's later work, with the help of W. Hartree, showed its magnitude to be 1.5 times the total initial heat.] This estimate appeared to answer unequivocally a question long debated, on the fate of lactic acid in the recovery process. Fletcher and Hopkins had found [in 1907] that lactic acid is removed in the presence of oxygen, though the same muscle at the end of the recovery process can liberate during exercise or rigor the same amount of lactic acid as before. Was lactic acid removed by oxidation, or by restoration to the precursor from which it came? Previous experiments of my own had shown that the production of one gramme of lactic acid in rigor leads to the liberation of about 500 calories. . . . Peters had proved that the production of 1 gramme of lactic acid in exercise . . . leads to the liberation of about the same quantity of heat. Hence, if the recovery heat were equal to the initial heat, the oxidative removal of one gramme of lactic acid would lead to the production of about 500 calories, which is less than 1/7th of the heat of oxidation of the acid. The conclusion . . . seemed to me to be inevitable— that the lactic acid is not removed by oxidation. . . .

"The most important point brought out by . . . analysis of the initial heat-production is that relating to the influence, or rather to the absence of influence, of oxygen. . . . No difference whatever can be detected between the curves obtained (a) from a muscle in pure oxygen and (b) from one which has been deprived of oxygen in the most rigorous manner for several hours. The conclusion is important and supplements the observations previously described on the recovery heat-production. Oxygen is not used in the primary break-down at all: it is used simply in the recovery process."

MEYERHOF *

"Let us first of all consider an excised frog's muscle, working
in a maximal supply of oxygen; chemical analysis then reveals only
this, that a definite amount of glycogen disappears from the muscle,
while a quantity of oxygen is taken up and carbonic acid given off
quite adequate for this oxidation. [Glycogen is a compound carbohydrate, 'animal starch,' found in most of the body tissues, especially in the liver and muscles.] But we can analyze the connection
of events more closely if we first let the muscle work under anaerobic conditions [i.e., without oxygen] and then expose it to oxygen.
During the anaerobic phase of work, lactic acid accumulates in the
muscle, approximately in proportion to the work done. Simultaneously a corresponding amount of glycogen disappears. . . . In the
second oxidative phase, on the other hand, the lactic acid which
had been formed disappears, while a quite definite amount of extra
oxygen is taken up, and actually the disappearance of lactic acid
during this period bears an exact proportion to the increased consumption of oxygen. Meantime the oxygen suffices for the oxidation of no more than a fraction of the vanished lactic acid; the rest,
in total fatigue about three quarters of the whole lactic acid, reverts
quantitatively into glycogen. I may say . . . that this ratio of
oxidized lactic acid to the acid which has disappeared is not constant under all conditions."

CONSEQUENCES IN THEORY
AND PRACTICE

The complex of chemical events through which every physiological activity is carried on is a tangled skein to undo, and while
a great deal is known about the body's chemistry, it is generally the
case that each particular process is understood only up to a point; to
push beyond this point is, of course, the object of research, and
explanations which remain true in principle are constantly being
revised in detail. This is what has happened in the case of Meyer-

---

* Translated from Otto Meyerhof, "Die Energieumwandlungen im Muskel,"
Les Prix Nobel en 1923.

hof's discovery. A fundamental point of great importance in muscle physiology was revealed by the work for which he won the Nobel Prize; but the chemistry of muscle is rather more complicated than it appeared at the time, and the work of other chemists, with his own later work, has brought about some revision and extension in the explanations which were given then. Hence the brevity of the quotation above.

Some fifteen years before Hill and Meyerhof delivered their Nobel lectures, W. M. Fletcher and F. G. Hopkins (the latter to become a Nobel laureate in 1929 for his work on vitamins) had shown that lactic acid is an essential part of the muscle machinery. It appears only gradually in a resting muscle, but rapidly during work. It accumulates more and more, until, when it reaches a concentration of a few tenths of one percent, the muscle becomes incapable of further contraction. This lactic acid disappears in the presence of oxygen; the fully recovered muscle is then able to work again and to produce as much lactic acid as before.

These changes of accumulation or removal of the acid could be detected only after evoking a series of responses in the muscle. Each change actually represented a summation of many changes. To study the transformations taking place in a muscle fiber during and immediately after contraction, to study the instantaneous and contemporary events, seemed beyond the reach of chemistry. The only change recorded in this flash-of-lightning way was the contraction itself; but this muscle twitch is merely the final result, the end product of activity. The mechanical record of a unit response told little; the chemical record was apparently not to be had. But the investigation of heat production seemed promising, for heat is associated with the chemical events which cause contraction. In the manner, and with the results, so clearly set forth above, A. V. Hill made use of this approach. It then appeared that the working phase of muscular activity, the actual contraction, is not dependent on oxygen, which is required, rather, for the recovery phase. The oxygen requirement for an exertion may even be met after the event; the body may assume an "oxygen debt," which explains the heavy breathing of an athlete when the race is over. Hill's thermal data had now to be fitted into the larger picture of chemical happenings in muscle.

In 1914 Parnas and Wagner showed that glycogen is the precursor of lactic acid. Meyerhof discovered that the conversion of the one to the other occurs in the course of muscular contraction, so that the disappearance of a certain amount of glycogen is accompanied by the appearance of an equivalent portion of lactic acid. At the same time there is an increase in the phosphoric acid content of the muscle. These changes occur when contraction takes place without a supply of oxygen. However, when the muscle contracts with an adequate oxygen supply, glycogen disappears, carbon dioxide is given off, but now lactic and phosphoric acids do not accumulate.

How are these processes connected with the contraction? The shortening of the muscle—in fact, the contraction of the fibrils of myosin, the chief protein of muscle—depends upon the availability of energy, through the combustion (oxidation) of certain cellular constituents, chief among which are carbohydrates like glycogen and glucose. When oxygen is deficient and oxidation of the foodstuffs cannot occur the energy comes from the breakdown of certain phosphorus-containing compounds, adenosine triphosphate (ATP) and creatine phosphate. During the conversion of glucose to lactic acid small amounts of these compounds are formed and their hydrolysis results in the liberation of inorganic phosphate and simultaneously provides energy needed for muscular contraction. Thus, the two phosphates act as reservoirs for the temporary storage of energy, and these reservoirs are drawn upon when an oxygen lack prevents the muscle from obtaining energy for contraction by oxidation processes. When oxygen is admitted once again a certain proportion of the lactic acid is oxidized to carbon dioxide and water, and the energy derived from this is used to resynthesize glycogen and to restore the stock of "high-energy" phosphate compounds.

This early clarification of the relationship between anaerobic and aerobic processes was important not only for our understanding of the metabolism of muscle, but also for our appreciation of similar or corresponding processes in other tissues and organisms. The formation of lactic acid in the absence of oxygen (anaerobic glycolysis) is perfectly analogous to fermentations catalyzed by yeast (alcoholic fermentation) and microorganisms. Through his classical studies on fermentation, a process that he characterized as "life without oxygen," Pasteur showed that in contrast to aerobic metabolism of yeast, where the amount of nutrients used up is not much greater than the weight of cellular material formed, the amount of sugar decomposed in alcoholic fermentation by yeast is very much larger than the weight of yeast cells formed. This finding had obvious implications for the relative economy of the aerobic and anerobic processes in the life of organisms, but the actual interpretation of the result foundered on some experimental ambiguities and gave rise to controversy over the nature of the "Pasteur reaction." The key point in Pasteur's theory, the lower rate of breakdown of sugar in the presence than in the absence of air, was clearly established by Meyerhof in experiments with yeast in 1925. In this way, fundamental research on lower organisms has elucidated metabolic processes in man. Conversely, we have come to recognize many metabolic pathways that are distributed throughout the animal and plant kingdoms, including some microorganisms. They are testament to the fundamental unity of living things, as established at the biochemical level.

REFERENCE

H.[ILL], A. V. "Otto Fritz Meyerhof," *The Lancet,* October 27, 1951, pp. 790-791.

1 9 2 3

FREDERICK GRANT BANTING
(1891–1941)

JOHN JAMES RICHARD MACLEOD
(1876–1935)

"For their discovery of insulin."

BIOGRAPHICAL SKETCHES

BANTING

FREDERICK G. BANTING WAS BORN ON NOVEMBER 14, 1891, near Alliston, Ontario. He was educated in local schools and then attended the University of Toronto, where he registered as a student of divinity but soon transferred to medicine. He completed his medical studies in 1916 and served overseas as a medical officer from 1917 to 1919. In 1918 he was awarded the Military Cross for heroism under fire. Following a year of the study of orthopedic surgery in Toronto, he commenced practice in London, Ontario, but remained less than a year. Carrying out part-time teaching duties at the University of Western Ontario, he became interested in diabetes. In 1921 he returned to Toronto to undertake research on this problem in Professor Macleod's laboratory, where he was associated with C. H. Best, J. B. Collip, and a number of others.

111

His research and its successful issue are described below. Insulin was isolated in 1921 and the first patients were treated in 1922. In 1923 Banting became professor of medical research. The Banting Institute was opened in 1930 and Banting was knighted in 1934. In later years he was particularly interested in cancer research. In February 1941, while acting as liaison officer between British and North American medical scientists in the Second World War, he was killed in an aircraft disaster in Newfoundland.

MACLEOD

J. J. R. MACLEOD WAS BORN IN CLUNY, PERTHSHIRE, SCOTLAND, on September 6, 1876. He was educated at the Aberdeen Grammar School and the University of Aberdeen, studying medicine at Marischal College. He was graduated in 1898, was awarded the Anderson Research Travelling Fellowship, and studied biochemistry in Leipzig under Siegfried and Burian. In 1900 he became attached to the London Hospital Medical College, as demonstrator in physiology under Leonard Hill. In 1903 he was appointed professor of physiology at the Western Reserve University, Cleveland, Ohio, where he remained for fifteen years; during most of this time he carried on investigations in carbohydrate metabolism. In 1918 he accepted the position of professor of physiology at the University of Toronto, where the work on insulin was performed. In 1928 he returned to Scotland as professor of physiology at the University of Aberdeen. Here he continued his research both within the University and at the Rowett Research Institute. He also served on the Medical Research Council. In his later years Professor Macleod fell victim to a crippling arthritis. His health gradually became worse and he died on March 16, 1935. His scientific, literary, and educational work was very extensive. He was the author of several books, including a well-known text, *Physiology and Biochemistry in Modern Medicine*. He was very successful as a teacher, and some of the most distinguished medical scientists of the present day in the United States and Canada were trained in Macleod's laboratory.

DESCRIPTION OF THE PRIZE-WINNING WORK

BANTING *

"On October 30th, 1920, I was attracted by an article by Moses Barron in which he pointed out the similarity between the degenerative changes in the acinus cells of the pancreas following experimental ligation of the duct, and the changes following blockage of the duct with gall-stones. [Acinus cells secrete a digestive juice and are distinct from hormone-producing cells.] Having read this article the idea presented itself that by ligating the duct and allowing time for the degeneration of the acinus cells, a means might be provided for obtaining an extract of the islet cells free from the destroying influence of trypsin and other pancreatic enzymes. [The islet cells secrete the hormone.]

"On April 14th, 1921, I began working on this idea in the Physiological Laboratory of the University of Toronto. Professor Macleod allotted me Dr. Charles Best as an associate. Our first step was to tie the pancreatic ducts in a number of dogs. At the end of seven weeks these dogs were chloroformed. The pancreas of each dog was removed and all were found to be shrivelled, fibrotic, and about one-third the original size. Histological examination showed that there were no healthy acinus cells. This material was cut into small pieces, ground with sand, extracted with normal saline. This extract was tested on a dog rendered diabetic by the removal of the pancreas. Following the intravenous injection the blood sugars of the depancreatized dogs were reduced to a normal or subnormal level, and the urine became sugar free. There was a marked improvement in the general clinical condition as evidenced by the fact that the animals became stronger and more lively, the broken down wounds healed more kindly, and the life of the animal was undoubtedly prolonged. . . .

"The second type of extract was made from the pancreas of dogs in which acinus cells had been exhausted of trypsin by the long continued injection of secretin. [See above, p. 21.]

---

* From F. G. Banting, "Diabetes and Insulin," Les Prix Nobel en 1924-25.

"The third type of extract used in this series of experiments was made from the pancreas of foetal calves of less than four months development. Laguesse had found that the pancreas of the newborn contained comparatively more islet cells than the pancreas of the adult. Since other glands of internal secretion are known to contain their active principle as soon as they are differentiated in their embryological development, it occurred to me that trypsin might not be present since it is not used till after the birth of the animal. Later I found that Ibrahim had shown that trypsin is not present till seven or eight months of intrauterine development. Foetal extracts could be prepared in a much more concentrated solution than the former two varieties of extract. It produced marked lowering of blood sugar, urine became sugar free and there was marked clinical improvement. Its greatest value however was that the abundance in which it could be obtained enabled us to investigate its chemical extraction.

"Up to this time saline had been used as an extractive. We now found that alcohol slightly acidified extracted the active principle, and by applying this method of extraction to the whole adult beef pancreas active extracts comparatively free from toxic properties were obtained. . . .

"The extracts prepared in this way were tried on depancreatized dogs and in all cases the blood sugar was lowered. . . . Diabetic dogs seldom live more than 12 to 14 days. But with the daily administration of this whole gland extract we were able to keep a depancreatized dog alive and healthy for ten weeks.

"The extract at this time was sufficiently purified to be tested on three cases of diabetes mellitus in the wards of the Toronto General Hospital. There was a marked reduction in blood sugar and the urine was rendered sugar free. . . ."

MACLEOD [*]

"The invariable lowering of the blood sugar which was observed to result from the administration of insulin in animals rendered diabetic by pancreatectomy, raised the question as to

---

[*] From J. J. R. Macleod, "The Physiology of Insulin and Its Source in the Animal Body," *Les Prix Nobel en 1924-25.*

whether such would also occur in those forms of hyperglycaemia which can be induced by other experimental procedures, such as the injection of epinephrin, piqûre or asphyxia. As the first step in the investigation of this question, Collip injected insulin into normal rabbits and found the blood sugar to become lowered, thus furnishing a valuable method for testing the potency of various preparations and, therefore, for affording a basis for their physiological assay. At the same time it was found that neither piqûre, nor epinephrin, nor asphyxia caused any hyperglycaemia in rabbits in which, as a result of injection with insulin, the blood sugar was at a low level to start with.

"Peculiar symptoms (convulsions and coma) were observed in many of the injected animals, and it was soon possible to show that these were related to the lowering of the blood sugar and that they usually supervened when this was about 0.045 per cent. Sometimes the animals recovered spontaneously from these symptoms, but more frequently the coma became so profound, with marked fall of body temperature, that death occurred. That the lowering of blood sugar is closely related to the occurrence of the symptoms, was proved by finding that the subcutaneous injection of a solution of glucose was followed, almost immediately, by complete recovery, even in cases in which death was imminent from deep coma. It has been found, in collaboration with Noble, that glucose is remarkably specific in this regard. . . ."

CONSEQUENCES IN THEORY AND PRACTICE

Long before 1922 the dietary treatment of diabetes had been developed to a high degree of refinement. This treatment, although it helped to minimize symptoms and prolong life, was far from satisfactory, since only the milder cases could be kept under control and even these very often grew worse. Diabetes was then a severe debilitating disease, ultimately fatal in a great majority of cases, usually rapidly fatal in children. Infections of various kinds were very likely to supervene, surgery was most hazardous, and childbearing was dangerous to both mother and child. After the introduction of insulin it became possible to control most cases, and all the incidental dangers were diminished or removed. Life was greatly prolonged and useful activity restored. Unfortunately the diagnosis of the disease and the use of the remedy have not been universal even in the Americas and Europe. Full realization of the benefit of the discovery has therefore never been attained. None the less the transformation in the therapy of diabetes has been as striking as any single advance in modern medicine.

At the time when Banting, Best, Macleod, and Collip were carrying on their research in Toronto, other workers were pursuing the same end in several other centers. After the discovery was announced a further impetus was given to this research and valuable results were achieved in the study of carbohydrate metabolism. On the practical side, H. C. Hagedorn and D. A. Scott were responsible for the production of protamine-zinc insulin, which has a prolonged effect. On the side of "pure" research, B. A. Houssay, in the year after insulin was discovered, began his related studies of the function of the pituitary body (see below, p. 250). These are only two examples of the work which followed the stimulus of the Toronto discovery. A "working cure" for diabetes, a therapy of replacement of the deficient hormone, had been introduced by the Toronto group, and the search for underlying factors in the genesis of the disease had been given not only a new stimulus but a new basis in added knowledge from which to proceed.

In recent years compounds that are much smaller in molecular size and less complex in structure than insulin have become available for use in certain types of diabetes. These drugs are effective by mouth, and have therefore been called "oral insulins." The first one to be studied was related chemically to the sulfa drugs (see p. 215 ff.). During its clinical use as an antibacterial agent, it provoked signs of hypoglycemia in the patients receiving it. This observation by M. Jambon then led to a detailed study of the action of the drug on carbohydrate metabolism by A. Loubatières at the University of Montpelier in France.

The insulin molecule contains four peptide chains consisting of about 100 amino acid units. Frederick Sanger was awarded the Nobel Prize in Chemistry in 1958 for his elucidation of the structure.

REFERENCES

HARRIS, SEALE. *Banting's Miracle* (Philadelphia: Lippincott, 1946).
STEVENSON, LLOYD. *Sir Frederick Banting* (Toronto: Ryerson Press; Springfield, Ill.: Thomas, 2nd ed., 1947).

1924
WILLEM EINTHOVEN
(1860–1927)

"For his discovery of the mechanism of the electro-cardiogram."

BIOGRAPHICAL SKETCH

WILLEM EINTHOVEN WAS BORN ON MAY 21, 1860, IN THE Dutch East Indies, where his father was a practicing physician. When Willem was ten years old his father died; his mother returned to Holland with her six children and settled in Utrecht. In 1878 Einthoven began the study of medicine at the University, where his teachers included the physicist Buys Ballot, the anatomist Koster, and the great physiologist and ophthalmologist F. C. Donders. He became doctor of medicine in 1885 and was called to Leyden in the same year to succeed Heynsius in the chair of physiology; until 1905 his department was also responsible for the teaching of histology. Einthoven approached physiology as a physicist, no doubt partly, at least, as a result of his training in Utrecht; but his knowledge of anatomy, histology, and optics was also of great value to him in his famous work of devising the modern electrocardiograph and interpreting the data obtained by its use. This naturally led him toward pathological physiology and clinical medicine. Einthoven died in 1927.

DESCRIPTION OF THE PRIZE-WINNING
WORK*

"The string galvanometer consists of a delicate thread, conducting electric current, stretched like a string in a magnetic field. As soon as the thread is electrified, it deviates from its equipoise in a direction at right angles to the direction of the magnetic lines of force. The magnitude of the deviation is proportional to the strength of the current flowing through the thread, so that this can be easily and exactly measured. . . . [This instrument, invented by Einthoven, is the essential part of the modern electrocardiograph. The "string" of the latter is a fiber of finely spun silver-coated quartz glass, 0.002 mm. in diameter, or about ¼ of the diameter of a red blood cell; platinum has also been used in place of silvered quartz. A beam of light, directed through holes in the arms of the magnet, throws the shadow of the string on a photographic plate or film, or on sensitive paper, through a series of lenses which magnify the image. This photographic surface, in a camera of special design, moves at an appropriate speed to record the successive positions of the string in its lateral movements, or deflections. The sensitivity of the string is standardized so that a deflection of a certain magnitude represents a certain strength of current. The record is marked out in horizontal lines (to measure the magnitude of deviation, and hence the strength of current) and vertical lines (to indicate the time intervals). Various technical refinements have from time to time been introduced.]

"Just as every muscle in its contraction generates an electric current, so also in the heart there is an evolution of electricity with every systole [contraction]. This was first described by Kölliker and Müller. The English physiologist Augustus D. Waller then showed that differences in potential developed in the heart are conducted to different parts of the body, and that with a sensitive measuring instrument, the capillary electrometer, one is in a position to observe the variations in potential of the human heart. [The capillary electrometer consists of a capillary tube filled with

* Translated from Willem Einthoven, "Das Saitengalvanometer und die Messung der Aktionsströme des Herzens," *Les Prix Nobel en 1924-1925.*

weak acid; a globule of mercury, placed in the center, moves toward the negative pole when an electric current is passed through the tube, and the image of the mercury is projected for photographic record.] One needs only to lead the current from the hands and feet to the measuring instrument in order to see the variations in electric current, which show the same rhythm as the heart action.

"If one records the deviations of the measuring instrument one obtains a curve, which was called the electrocardiogram. But because of the imperfections of the capillary electrometer the curve directly recorded does not portray in an exact manner the actual variations in potential that have occurred. To get an exact picture, one must construct a new curve based on the peculiarities of the instrument used and the data of the recorded curve, work requiring considerable time. This circumstance stood in the way of the practical application of electrocardiography to the investigation of cardiac patients, and general interest in the ECG first developed later, after the string galvanometer made it possible to register the required pattern directly, easily, and quickly, and with satisfactory accuracy. . . ."

CONSEQUENCES IN THEORY AND PRACTICE

Einthoven first constructed a string galvanometer in 1903. From 1906 to 1921 he gradually improved it. It came into fairly general use in hospitals, and the modern electrocardiograph is based on the same principles. By 1906 Einthoven had observed that different types of heart disease show different, and distinctive, tracings on the electrocardiogram. Between 1908 and 1913 he worked on the interpretation of the normal tracing, so as to provide a secure basis for the understanding of deviations from the normal result. His interpretation of each wave and complex in the recorded curve was worked out during this period, and the Prize was actually awarded not for the invention of the string galvanometer, but "for his discovery of the mechanism of the electrocardiogram."

Einthoven's work was confirmed and extended by a number of other scientists, particularly by Thomas Lewis. Analysis of the symptoms of heart disease as seen in the electrocardiogram was developed in detail by a generation of cardiologists who had been provided by Einthoven with a precise tool for their study. This method often makes for quicker and more reliable diagnosis. When recorded serially, electrocardiograms may provide decisive evidence in questionable cases of coronary thrombosis. They aid in localizing the site of the area affected by obstruction of a coronary vessel (the area of "infarction"). In this and other forms of heart disease they establish the nature of the disturbances of the heart's rhythm or mechanism. Often they are of great value in following the course of healing, and so help to determine the nature of treatment.

1 9 2 5

No Award

1926
JOHANNES FIBIGER
(1867–1928)

"For his discovery of the Spiroptera *carcinoma."*

BIOGRAPHICAL SKETCH

JOHANNES ANDREAS GRIB FIBIGER WAS BORN IN SILKEBORG, Denmark, on April 23, 1867. He finished his medical studies in 1890. From 1891 to 1894, after hospital work and some further study with Koch and Behring, he was assistant to C. J. Salmonsen in the bacteriology laboratory of the University of Copenhagen. Then, until 1897, he was associated with the Hospital for Contagious Diseases in Copenhagen, meanwhile (1895) obtaining his doctoral degree with a thesis on the bacteriology of diphtheria. After 1897 he worked at the Institute of Pathological Anatomy of the University and in the army bacteriological laboratory. In 1900 he was named professor of pathological anatomy and head of the Institute. He carried out a large number of official commissions and took part in the direction of numerous institutes and societies. He was co-editor, as well as one of the founders, of *Acta Pathologica et Microbiologica Scandinavica;* he was also co-editor of *Zieglers Beiträge.* Fibiger died on January 30, 1928, in Copenhagen, after a short illness.

DESCRIPTION OF THE PRIZE-WINNING
WORK*

"The researches I am going to communicate started out from some observations I had occasion to make at the end of the year 1907. At the autopsy of three wild rats . . . which originally had served for subcutaneous injections of tubercle bacilli, the stomach showed itself in the three animals to be the site of severe lesions. The stomach was greatly enlarged, heavy, and of firm consistency. The exterior surface was rough, especially at the fundus [the cardiac end of the stomach, where food is received] and divided by means of furrows into slightly elevated parts, gray-yellow in color. After opening it, one found only localized lesions in the fundus, while the pyloric region was normal. The wall of the stomach was greatly thickened at the fundus . . . the mucous membrane arching toward the stomach cavity in the form of folds and of stout, irregular ridges, prolonged in out-juttings, and of papillomatous polyps [see below]. . . .

"Microscope examination ascertained that the enormous thickening of the walls was caused essentially by a very marked epithelial hyperplasia [excessive growth of the surface layer] and by a severe papillomatosis [overgrowth of tiny, nipplelike processes normally present at the surface] and also, but in a less pronounced manner, by acute and chronic inflammatory lesions. . . .

"At the histologic examination one was struck to see that here and there, in a small number of sections, the superficial epithelium contained cavities of different shapes: circular, oval, or cylindrical. Continuing the researches, it was found that in other preparations these cavities were filled by peculiar bodies, not found in the parts of stomachs first examined. . . .

"These bodies had very distinct contours and complicated structure, making the supposition a probable one that this was a matter of the more highly organized animal parasites. . . .

---

* Translated from Johannes Fibiger, "Recherches sur un nématode et sur sa faculté de provoquer des néoformations papillomateuses et carcinomateuses dans l'estomac du rat," *Académie Royale des Sciences et des Lettres de Danemark: Extrait du Bulletin de l'Année 1913, No. 1.*

[In an effort to determine the frequency of this disease, which incidentally had nothing to do with tuberculosis, and also to find new cases for further study, Fibiger examined 1144 rats, with negative results. Back in 1878, M. Galeb had described a nematode, a threadlike worm, as parasitic in rats' stomachs. He had shown that this appeared to be the same nematode already described as early as 1824 as a parasite in a common kind of cockroach, *Periplaneta orientalis*. Feeding nematode-infested cockroaches to rats, Galeb was able to parasitize them. So Fibiger looked for rats and cockroaches together, then examined the stomachs of the rats, but without success. He fed large numbers of cockroaches to rats. No luck.]

"At last, informed that in a locality of the city [Copenhagen] (a great sugar refinery) rats and cockroaches were found en masse, I resolved to examine the rats of this district, too, although the cockroach in question was not the *Periplaneta orientalis* spoken of by M. Galeb, but a different species, the *P. americana*. . . .

"Contrary to all expectation, the result of the examination was positive. . . . [Thus Fibiger's studies could be continued. As it turned out, Galeb's nematode was not the same. Nor, on the other hand, was *P. americana* a necessary part of the story, as Fibiger naturally supposed at first, for the commoner *P. orientalis* would likewise serve his purpose; so that when the sugar refinery burned down, his work was only temporarily interrupted. He had found the required nematode again, and he could show that only a part of its life cycle takes place in the rat, rat-to-rat transmission never occurring. Eggs passed by rats were fed to cockroaches, and the cockroaches were fed to rats. There then appeared to be a proportional relation between the number of parasites and the duration of their life in the stomach, on the one hand, and the degree of anatomic change on the other.]

"In general, the successive development of the anatomical alterations can be represented in the following manner: as the initial phenomenon, simple epithelial hyperplasia, ordinarily followed by acute inflammation. The inflammation ever increasing, the growth of the epithelium in depth, the formation of epithelial papillomata and heterotopia [*heteros*, other + *topos*, place: the presence of these cells in parts where they are normally absent] are added to these phenomena. As the terminal stage: severe papillomatosis, development of large epithelial crypts with the more or less extensive destruction of the stomach wall. As deviations from this course of development: (1) some cases in which the inflammatory processes are little pronounced or totally absent . . . (2) some cases in which the process becomes malignant in the proper sense of the word, by the development of a cancroid having the faculty of producing metastases [new growths in parts of the body remote from the original tumor]."

CONSEQUENCES IN THEORY AND PRACTICE

Fibiger's discovery of *Spiroptera* carcinoma appeared to be a clear confirmation of the view of Rudolf Virchow, the great pioneer of cellular pathology, that cancerous growths are due to chronic irritation. Here was a tiny worm, a nematode, apparently the source of both mechanical and chemical irritation, and it seemed that Fibiger's careful experiments, only partly indicated in the abstract above, had conclusively shown it to be the cause of a particular kind of cancer in rats. Some believed this was due to non-specific irritation; Fibiger thought it due to specific toxins. There was, it is true, some question raised about the real nature of this disease. Parasites of other kinds were known to cause proliferative diseases, but these came to be regarded as noncancerous. The part originally diseased might set up colonies, so to speak, in remote parts of the body; but these were not true "metastases," resulting from the inherent ability of morbidly overactive cells to establish new foci and multiply afresh, for in each of the new locations parasites were found. Like scattered abscesses, these areas represented the migrations of the causative organism. But the metastases seen in Fibiger's disease were true metastases, containing no parasites: the cells themselves had become malignant. There was likewise some dispute over the microscope evidence of the cells (the finer points of the histology have not been given above). But in the course of time it was generally agreed that the tumor was a true malignant, or cancerous, growth. More recently doubts have been raised about the role of the nematodes. It has been suggested that a vitamin deficiency was responsible for Fibiger's results, since A. Y. Fuji-maki was able to produce stomach tumors, some benign and some malignant, by feeding rats on a vitamin-deficient diet. A. Borrel, who anticipated Fibiger in suggesting that parasites might be concerned in causing cancer, continued to maintain his original view that such parasites could only be the carriers of a virus, the real causative agent.

In earlier studies of cancer it had sometimes been found possible to transplant malignant growths to other animals of the same species. But these studies did not show the origin of the tumors, and the earliest stages of their growth could not be followed. It therefore appeared of great importance to have a method at hand for producing a form of cancer experimentally, although this had been done a short time before in the experiments of J. Clunet by X irradiation. Two years after the publication of Fibiger's work, other scientists, perhaps encouraged by his success, were able to produce experimental cancer in rabbits by the use of coal tar. A number of carcinogenic (cancer-causing) substances have since been isolated from coal tar and have been shown to be related chemically to sex hormones, bile acids, and other substances of biological importance.

Fibiger expressed the hope that some forms of human cancer might be shown to be caused by parasites. He did not believe that he had discovered a general principle of broad application, but only that some small part might be found for parasitology in the genesis of human cancer. Even this modest hope was doomed to disappointment. Bilharziasis, a tropical disease caused by a small worm, produces cancers of the bladder or rectum in about 5 per cent of cases; and cancer of the liver is known to follow another kind of infestation. These instances were recognized before the time of Fibiger's work. The vast majority of cancers cannot be explained in this way.

REFERENCES

OBERLING, CHARLES. *The Riddle of Cancer*. Translated by W. H. Woglom. Revised ed. (New Haven: Yale University Press, 1952), pp. 65-74.

1 9 2 7
JULIUS
WAGNER-JAUREGG
(1857–1940)

"For his discovery of the therapeutic value of malaria inoculation in the treatment of dementia paralytica."

BIOGRAPHICAL SKETCH

JULIUS WAGNER-JAUREGG WAS BORN IN WELS, IN UPPER AUS-tria, on March 7, 1857. (The hyphen in "Wagner-Jauregg" takes the place of "von," the distinction of nobility discontinued by the socialist regime after the First World War.) He received the degree of doctor of medicine in 1880 from the University of Vienna, where he began his scientific career in the Department of Experimental Pathology and Internal Medicine. In 1883 he joined the staff of the psychiatric clinic. This was apparently a second choice, forced upon him by circumstances, but he soon became deeply interested in psychiatry and was later renowned not only for his research but also for his activity as a teacher. In a publication of 1887 he proposed to produce febrile diseases deliberately as a treatment for psychiatric patients, using malaria and erysipelas. His preliminary trials did not proceed far. From 1889 to 1893 he was professor of psychiatry and neurology at the University of Graz (Austria). In 1890 Koch introduced tuberculin, and Wagner-Jauregg tried it as a fever-producer on patients at Graz. These experiments were stopped because tuberculin had come to be considered dangerous. At this time he was recalled to Vienna as head of the University Hospital for Nervous and Mental Diseases, and in 1894 he resumed his work with tuberculin. The first malaria inoculations for dementia paralytica were given on June 14, 1917. Wagner-Jauregg published many early contributions on physiology and pharmacology. Later he was interested in forensic psychiatry, in cretinism, myxedema, and the prevention of goiter. He retired from his professorship in 1928, and he died October 1, 1940, in his eighty-fourth year.

DESCRIPTION OF THE PRIZE-WINNING WORK*

"Progressive paralysis [also called paresis, general paralysis of the insane, dementia paralytica] has always been considered an incurable disease, leading in the course of a few years to dementia and death.

"Nevertheless there was on record a series of cases of progressive paralysis which had been cured; cases in which all the symptoms had disappeared so completely as to permit those affected to be independently active for years, in life and employment. And even if such cases were quite extraordinarily rare, there was a comparatively frequent occurrence of remissions of some duration, in which there was a retrogression, greater or less in degree, of symptoms already developed. Thus, in principle at least, progressive paralysis had to be a curable disease. . . .

"The observation was now forthcoming that in the rare cases of healing and in the frequent remissions of progressive paralysis, a febrile infectious malady or a protracted suppuration often preceded the improvement in the state of the disease.

"Therein lay a hint. These cures following febrile infectious diseases, of which I myself had witnessed striking cases, induced me as early as the year 1887 to propose that this natural experiment be imitated by deliberately producing infectious diseases, and at that time I named malaria and erysipelas as suitable diseases. As a particular advantage of malaria, I stressed the fact that it is possible to interrupt the disease at will with quinine, and did not yet suspect

---

* Translated from "Nobel-Vortrag von Julius Wagner-Jauregg," *Les Prix Nobel en 1927.*

at that time to what extent the expectation would be fulfilled through inoculation with malaria.

"Apart from an unsuccessful experiment with erysipelas, I did not proceed as yet to the direct execution of this proposal, and furthermore I would scarcely have had the authority at that time to carry it through.

"Instead, starting in 1890, I attempted to imitate the action of a febrile infectious disease by the use of tuberculin, just introduced by Koch, at first not only in progressive paralysis but also in other mental derangements, and as a matter of fact with favorable results in not a few cases. [This was to some extent a forerunner of the protein therapy which later attained great development.]

"Since there were some cases of progressive paralysis among them, my interest soon concentrated on this disease, for a favorable result could not so easily be considered an accident here as in other psychoses.

"After . . . it had been established that the paralytics treated with tuberculin . . . showed more, and more lasting, remissions than an equal number of untreated paralytics, this treatment was carried out systematically . . . and at the same time an energetic iodine-mercury cure, later combined with injections of salvarsan, was instituted. . . .

"The remissions which were obtained by the mercury-tuberculin treatment did not differ qualitatively from those to be obtained by inoculation with malaria. . . . But the number of relapses was large; the lasting remissions were in the minority.

"I tried to enhance the action of the nonspecific treatment by the use of different vaccines . . . without much effect on the frequency of the discouraging relapses.

"In the course of this therapeutic research, I could repeatedly make the observation that particularly complete and lasting remissions took place in just those cases in which, concurrently with the treatment, some incidental infectious disease occurred, for instance pneumonia [or] an abscess.

"Consequently, in 1917, I set about the execution of the proposal I had made in the year 1887, and inoculated nine cases of progressive paralysis with tertian malaria.

"The result was gratifying beyond expectation: six of these nine cases obtained extensive remissions, and in three of these cases the remission proved lasting, so that this year [1927] I was able to present these cases . . . as having carried on their occupations without interruption for ten years. After the outcome of this first experiment had been followed for two years, I undertook, in the autumn of 1919, to pursue this therapeutic research on a large scale. . . ."

CONSEQUENCES IN THEORY
AND PRACTICE

Wagner-Jauregg appears to have contemplated the use of malaria in treating paretic dementia for many years, and when, in 1917, a patient with tertian malaria appeared in one of his wards he considered this as a sign of fate and proceeded to carry out his plan. The tertian variety of the disease is still preferred, although the quartan type has also had its advocates.

Dementia paralytica, perhaps more commonly known as GPI (general paralysis of the insane), or simply general paresis, is a progressive disease of the brain and meninges (brain coverings) due to syphilis. In adults it is usually a late result of an untreated or inadequately treated antecedent syphilis; a juvenile form (juvenile paresis) usually is due to congenital syphilis. The proper treatment of the early stages of syphilis is the only sure means of prevention. Fever therapy is indicated in all cases of GPI, as well as in *paresis sine parese,* meaning the same disease before paralytic signs have occurred but where the mental symptoms and laboratory indications point to neurosyphilis.

Fever therapy since Wagner-Jauregg has taken various forms, ranging from sodoku (rat-bite fever), killed typhoid bacilli, preparations containing colloidal sulfur, and continuous hot-air and hot-water baths, to diathermy. A variety of nonspecific proteins have been employed. Although fever cabinets are widely used, some psychiatrists consider it doubtful that any other fever-producing agent gives results as good as does the malaria treatment. The mortality from malaria is low and it is claimed that about 30 to 40 percent of those so treated show permanent recovery (more than five years). It is especially during the earliest stage that the involvement of the central nervous system is amenable to treatment; no treatment of any kind is capable of restoring damaged brain tissue. Shortly after the end of the Second World War it was found that syphilis, including general paralysis of the insane, is amenable to treatment with penicillin, although much larger doses must be used than for other infectious diseases responding to the antibiotic. Penicillin is now the drug of choice.

1 9 2 8

CHARLES NICOLLE

(1866–1936)

"For his work on typhus."

BIOGRAPHICAL SKETCH

CHARLES NICOLLE WAS BORN SEPTEMBER 21, 1866, AT ROUEN, where his father practiced medicine. He first attended the *lycée* in his native city, then studied medicine in Paris. In 1893, at the conclusion of his studies, he was named to the faculty of the Medical School in Rouen and appointed physician to the Rouen hospitals. At the instigation of his brother, Maurice Nicolle, a microbiologist, he took the Pasteur Institute course in microbiology in 1892. In 1902 he succeeded Adrien Loir as director of the Pasteur Institute in Tunis. Here he carried out the work on typhus described below, in which he demonstrated the role played by the louse. A later achievement of importance was the distinction he helped to draw, after a visit to Mexico, between classic, louse-borne epidemic typhus and the murine variety, which has its reservoir in rats and is transmitted sporadically to man by the rat flea. (The murine type, under the name of *tabardillo,* has appeared epidemically in Mexico. Nicolle has been credited in France with distinguishing murine from classic typhus. It appears, however, that the most important contributions to the knowledge of murine typhus were made by Maxcy, Dyer, Rumreich, Badger, Mooser, Castaneda, and Zinsser.) In 1932 Nicolle took the place of d'Arsonval in the chair once held by Claude Bernard, Magendie, and Laënnec at the Collège de

France. He carried out extensive work on a variety of infectious diseases. In addition to being known for his studies of typhus he was chiefly distinguished for a number of innovations in technique. He was the founder of the *Archives de l'Institut Pasteur de Tunis*. He wrote not only scientific but literary and philosophic works. He died February 28, 1936.

DESCRIPTION OF THE PRIZE-WINNING WORK *

"The center of my observations was the native hospital of Tunis. When I visited this hospital I often stepped over the bodies of typhus patients who had come to be admitted and had fallen down from exhaustion at the door. Now there was a singular event taking place in this hospital, the significance of which no one had understood, and which impressed me. The typhus patients were lodged at this time in the common medical wards. As far as the doors of these rooms they scattered the contagion. Typhus developed on contact with them in the families where they were received, and the doctors required to visit them became infected on contact. Moreover the contagion struck the personnel of the admitting offices of the hospital, the employees whose duty it was to collect the clothes and linen, and the laundresses who washed them. And for all this, a typhus patient once admitted to the common ward did not contaminate a single one of his ward neighbors, not an attendant, not a doctor.

"This observation was my guide. I asked myself what happened between the hospital door and the sickroom. What happened was this: the typhus patient was relieved of his clothes and linen, and was shaved and washed. The agent of the contagion was therefore something attached to his skin, to his linen, and something of which soap and water rid him. This could only be the louse. . . .

"If it had not been possible to reproduce the malady in animals and consequently to verify the hypothesis, this simple determination would have sufficed to make clear the mode of propagation of

---

* Translated from "Conférence Nobel par Charles Nicolle," *Les Prix Nobel en 1928.*

typhus. Fortunately it was possible to bring experimental proof to bear upon it.

"My first attempts to transmit typhus to laboratory animals, consisting of little monkeys, failed, like similar attempts of my predecessors, and for reasons which it is easy for me to explain to myself today.

"I asked my *maître*, M. Roux, to procure a chimpanzee for me, thinking that an anthropoid might be more sensitive than animals of other kinds. The very day I received it, I inoculated it with the blood of a patient. . . . The chimpanzee showed a fever. With its blood, obtained during this fever, I inoculated a macaque (*M. sinicus*), which also showed a fever. On this macaque I fed lice which I transferred to other macaques. These were infected and later showed themselves to be vaccinated against a trial inoculation. . . . [Monkeys are expensive animals for experiment and Nicolle discovered that guinea pigs, rats, and mice are also susceptible to typhus; most of his later work was done on guinea pigs. He found that lice are incapable of spreading contagion until about a week after taking up blood; he also found that development occurs meanwhile in the digestive tract of the louse, and that the feces become virulent.]

"Typhus is characterized in man by a symptomatic triad: fever, eruption, signs of nervous involvement. In animals, fever is the only sign of infection. . . .

"It sometimes happens, especially when one uses blood, that in a lot of guinea pigs, inoculated with the same dose of the same material, certain ones do not show any fever. At first I attributed this failure to a fault in technique, or else to a greater individual resistance. The repetition of negative results did not permit me to accept these too facile explanations for long. The animals for which the virus is pathogenic present a picture of variable sensitivity, which runs from the very severe, often fatal, typhus of the European adult to the merely thermometric fever of the guinea pig, passing through all the intermediate degrees: typhus of the adult native, benign typhus of the children, still more benign in monkeys. I asked myself if there did not exist, below the already very feeble sensitivity of the guinea pig, a yet slighter degree in which the only sign of infection would be the virulent power of the blood during the period when the more sensitive animals show the characteristic fever. It was indeed so."

CONSEQUENCES IN THEORY AND PRACTICE

Nicolle transformed the fight against typhus into a fight against the louse. For many years the methods of delousing were elaborate, laborious, time-consuming, and not altogether effective. To a large degree they worked; the difficulty was to apply such methods on a broad enough scale. Particularly in winter, when lice are favored by heavy clothing, crowding, and infrequent bathing, it proved impossible to put a quick stop to outbreaks of typhus, at least among civilian populations. In the past ten years, however, such outbreaks have been effectually suppressed on several occasions by the liberal use of DDT (see below, p. 264).

Nicolle also gave a convincing demonstration of what he called "inapparent disease." He showed that there are instances in which no symptoms whatever appear, yet the blood is virulent on inoculation. This fact has been brought forward to explain the mystery of how the contagion survives between epidemics.

It is interesting that Theobald Smith, Patrick Manson, David Bruce, and the members of the Yellow Fever Commission—demonstrators of insect vectors in disease—were not rewarded with the Nobel Prize. Possibly the theoretical aspect of Nicolle's work, together with its importance in combating typhus during the First World War, influenced the decision to honor him with the Prize.

Typhus has been known for centuries as one of the great epidemic diseases. It has been associated with a massing of people in cities, armies, prisons, and ships. Its alternative names—ship fever, jail fever, prison fever, camp fever, hospital fever—are revealing. It has also been known as war fever, since fatal epidemics have attended most of the great wars. To an important degree typhus is a social disease, requiring a lousy population to feed upon. Present ability to cope with it in an emergency depends less upon prophylactic vaccination and modern treatment than upon powerful new insecticides. Nicolle convicted the louse; Paul Müller, of DDT fame, discovered the means to kill it.

1929
CHRISTIAAN EIJKMAN
(1858–1930)

"For his discovery of the antineuritic vitamin."

FREDERICK GOWLAND HOPKINS
(1861–1947)

"For his discovery of the growth-stimulating vitamins."

BIOGRAPHICAL SKETCHES

EIJKMAN

THE SON OF A SCHOOLMASTER, CHRISTIAAN EIJKMAN WAS BORN on August 11, 1858, in Nijberk, a small town on the Zuyder Zee. He began his studies at the University of Amsterdam in 1875 and was for some years assistant to the professor of physiology there. In 1883 he joined the colonial army in the Dutch East Indies but he was invalided home two years later and resumed his laboratory work, this time as a bacteriologist. In 1886 he returned to the Dutch East Indies as a member of the Pekelharing-Winkler Commission to study beri-beri. This group vainly sought a bacterial cause for the disease. When his colleagues returned home, Eijkman remained in Batavia as director of a new laboratory for bacteriology and pathology, taking charge of the medical school for native doctors as well. It was during this period that he carried out the work on beri-beri described below. He later studied "tropical anemia," denying it separate existence as a disease entity. He also challenged the assumption that metabolism varied greatly with climate. Among the more important investigations of his later years were his study of fermentation tests and the demonstration of the presence of the colon bacillus in water (Eijkman's test). Ill once again, Eijkman returned home in 1896 and became professor of hygiene at the University of Utrecht; he held this post until 1928. In 1930 he died.

HOPKINS

FREDERICK GOWLAND HOPKINS WAS BORN JUNE 20, 1861, IN Eastbourne, in Sussex, England, where he spent the first ten years of his life alone with his widowed mother, attending a dames' school from the age of six and playing with his father's microscope from the age of eight or nine. After 1871 they lived in Enfield with his mother's brother, James Gowland. For nearly four years Hopkins attended the City of London School, but despite a good record at first he had ultimately to withdraw because of truancy— "sheer boredom" was his own explanation. He then attended a private school. At seventeen he entered an insurance office, but remained for only six months; he then became an articled pupil to an analytical chemist. Later he attended the Royal School of Mines at South Kensington and worked for a few months as assistant in a private laboratory. A few courses at University College and success in examination for associateship of the Institute of Chemistry brought an invitation from Dr. (later Sir Thomas) Stevenson, Medical Jurist at Guy's Hospital and Home Office expert, to assist in his laboratory. While working there, Hopkins took a degree extramurally from the London University. In 1888 he began to study medicine at Guy's. In 1894 he qualified and obtained the London M.B. He then joined the school staff at Guy's but left in 1898, going to Cambridge at the invitation of Michael Foster to develop teaching and research in physiological chemistry. There he spent the rest of his life, at first with meager facilities, but after 1925 in a well-endowed institute. He was everywhere recognized as *facile princeps* of English biochemistry, which he established almost singlehanded. His honors included knighthood, in 1925; the Copley Medal, in 1926; the Nobel Prize, in 1929; presidency of the Royal Society, in 1931; and the Order of Merit, in 1935. He retired in 1943 and died in 1947. In addition to his dietary studies, his work on glutathione and tissue oxidation, on muscle chemistry, and on uric acid are very well known.

DESCRIPTION OF THE PRIZE-WINNING WORK

EIJKMAN *

"An accident set me on the right road.

"In the chicken-run of the laboratory in Batavia there suddenly broke out a disease which was in many ways strikingly similar to human beri-beri, and hence invited penetrating study. . . . [Eijkman here gives a detailed account of the symptoms shown by the birds: unsteady gait, muscular weakness resulting in falls, collapse, progressive paralysis finally affecting the respiratory muscles, cyanosis, or blueness of comb and skin resulting from insufficient oxygen in the blood, stupor, subnormal temperature, and death.]

"As may already be guessed from the symptoms and the course of the disease, and as microscopic study confirmed, it was a question of a polyneuritis [multiple neuritis affecting the nerves generally and not merely in the local area].

"As regards etiology, our original supposition that, considering the striking epizootic commencement of the disease [epizootic = animal epidemic], we had to do with an infection was not confirmed. Search for infection, using material from sick animals or those that had died of the disease, gave no clear result, while all the hens, including those kept separate as controls, were affected. No specific microbe was found, nor any higher organized parasite.

"Then all at once our opportunity for further researches dis-

---

* Translated from Christiaan Eijkman, "Antineuritisches Vitamin und Beri-beri," *Les Prix Nobel en 1929*.

appeared, as the disease came suddenly to a stop. The sick hens got better and no new cases appeared. Fortunately suspicion was then directed toward food, and indeed rightly, as it presently turned out.

"The laboratory was still temporary, and very meagerly housed in the military hospital, although it was administered under the civil authority. The laboratory attendant, his motive economy, had now, as I first learned later, obtained cooking rice from the hospital kitchen to use as chickenfeed. Then, the cook having been transferred, his successor objected to military rice going to civilian hens. So it happened that the hens were fed with cooking rice only from the 10th of June to the 20th of November. But the epizootic began on the 10th of July and ended in the last days of November.

"Deliberate feeding experimentation was then undertaken, aimed at further proof of the presumable connection between food and sickness. This definitely showed that the polyneuritis had its origin in the cooking-rice feed. The hens were thereby subjected to the disease after 3-4 weeks, or not uncommonly somewhat later, while the controls fed with unhulled rice remained healthy. We also not seldom succeeded in restoring animals already sick by a suitable change in feeding.

"This difference between rice that had been hulled, and likewise polished, and whole rice did not consist in a lessening in the quality of the former through storage, for cooking rice freshly prepared from whole grain could also call forth the disease. It turned out that rice half hulled—i.e., freed only of the thick hull—which spoils much more easily [and] is attacked by mites, molds, etc., proved harmless in feeding experiments. This rice, which is obtained through simple pounding, still has the inner hull, the so-called silver skin [Silberhäutchen] (pericarp), and contains the germ, wholly or in large part. As could then be concluded from many different experiments, the effective antineuritic principle occurs particularly in these parts of rice—and of cereal grains generally. It can easily be extracted with water or strong alcohol and can be dialyzed [i.e., the crystalloid and colloid elements of the extraction can be separated by diffusion through a membrane]. I was able to establish further that it can be used as a remedy either by mouth or by injection."

HOPKINS *

"Early in my career I became convinced that current teaching concerning nutrition was inadequate, and while still a student in hospital in the earlier eighteen nineties I made up my mind that the part played by nutritional errors in the causation of disease was underrated. The current treatment of scurvy and rickets seemed to me to ignore the significance of the old recorded observations. I had then a great ambition to study those diseases from a nutritional standpoint; but fate decreed that I was to lose contact with clinical material. I had to employ myself in the laboratory on more academic lines. I realised, however, as did many others at the last century's close, that for a full understanding of nutrition, no less than for an understanding of so many other aspects of biochemistry, further knowledge of proteins was then a prerequisite; and when I was first called to the University of Cambridge I did my best to contribute to that knowledge.

"As an ultimate outcome of my experiments dealing with the relative metabolic importance of individual amino acids from protein my attention was inevitably turned, without, I think, knowledge, or at any rate without memory, of the earlier work, to the necessity for supplying other factors than the then recognised basal elements of diet if the growth and health of an animal were to be maintained. This indeed must at any time come home to every observer who employs in feeding experiments a synthetic dietary composed of adequately purified materials. . . . A good many investigators using synthetic dietaries have, it is true, from time to time expressed doubts upon the point, but we now know that it was because the constituents they used were not pure and not free from adherent vitamins. In 1906-7 I convinced myself by experiments, carried out . . . upon mice, that those small animals at any rate could not survive upon a mixture of the basal foodstuffs alone. I was especially struck at this time, I remember, by striking differences in the apparent nutritive value of different supplies of casein in my possession. One sample used as a protein supply in a syn-

---

* From F. G. Hopkins, "The Earlier History of Vitamin Research," *Les Prix Nobel en 1929.*

thetic dietary might support moderate growth, while another failed even to maintain the animals. I found that a sample of the former sort, if thoroughly washed with water and alcohol, lost its power and also, if added to the samples originally inadequate, made them to some degree efficient in maintaining growth. I found further at that time (1906-7) that small amounts of a yeast extract were more efficient than the casein extracts. Similar experiences were encountered when otherwise adequate mixtures of amino acids were used to replace intact proteins. By sheer good fortune, as it afterwards turned out, I used butter as a fat supply in these early experiments. Upon the evidence of these earlier results I made a public statement in 1907 which has been often quoted. I cannot, however, justly base any claims for any sort of priority upon it, as my experimental evidence was not given on that occasion. It was indeed not till four years later that I published any experimental data. In explanation of this delay I would ask you to consider the circumstances of the time. The early experiments of Lunin and others had been forgotten by most; the calorimetric studies held the field and tentative suggestions concerning their inadequacy were, I found, received with hesitation among my physiological acquaintances. It seemed that a somewhat rigid proof of the facts would be necessary before publication was desirable. Thus came the great temptation to endeavour to isolate the active substance or substances before publication, and I can claim that throughout the year 1909 I was engaged upon such attempts, though without success. At this time I was using what is now the classic subject for vitamin studies, namely the rat. As I was concerned with the maintenance of growth in the animal, the tests applied to successive products of a fractionation took much longer than those which could be used in studying the cure of polyneuritis in birds by what we have learned to call Vitamin B_1, so the work occupied much time. I may perhaps be allowed to mention what was for me a somewhat unfortunate happening in the beginning of 1910, as it is instructive. A commercial firm had prepared for me a special extract of a very large quantity of yeast made on lines that I had found effective on a small scale. With this I intended to repeat some fractionations which had appeared promising. I thought, however, upon trial that the whole product was inactive and it was thrown away. The real explanation, however, was that instead of using butter, as in earlier experiments, I at this moment determined to use lard, and my supply of this, as I learned to understand much later, was doubtless deficient in Vitamins A and D; I was now giving my animals in the main the B Group alone. If I had then had the acumen to suspect that any of the substances I was seeking might be associated with fat I should have progressed faster. Later in 1910, if I may intrude so personal a matter, I suffered a severe breakdown in health and could do nothing further during the year. On my return to work I felt that the evidence I had by then accumulated would be greatly strengthened by a study of the energy consumption of rats, on the one hand when failing on diets free from the accessory factors (as I had then come to call them), and, on the other hand, when, as the result of the addition of minute quantities of milk, they were growing vigorously. These experiments took a long time, but they showed conclusively, as at that time it seemed necessary to show, that the failure in the former group of animals was not due primarily, or at the outset of the feeding, to any deficiency in the total uptake of food.

"My 1912 paper . . . emphasizes on general lines the indispensable nature of food constituents which were then receiving no serious consideration as physiological necessities."

CONSEQUENCES IN THEORY AND PRACTICE

Eijkman and Hopkins are among the half dozen pioneers in the study of vitamins. Eijkman, however, did not at once appreciate the full significance of his important discovery. He did not visualize beri-beri as a deficiency disease, but thought of it as a sort of poisoning, due to a nutritional error, an excess of carbohydrate in a diet of rice; this he considered was counteracted by a protective element, or neutralizing substance, in the rice bran. In 1901, however, G. Grijns put forward the view that the cortical substance in rice filled a universal need for the protection of health; this view was later adopted by Eijkman and the vital substance was eventually identified as vitamin B_1. Since beri-beri, which is characterized by multiple neuritis, edema, atrophy of muscles, and heart symptoms, often co-exists with other nutritional deficiencies, there has been some debate as to whether or not one specific factor is the sole cause; there is no doubt, however, that persons with beri-beri are greatly benefited by vitamin B_1 therapy. It took a long time before the practical value of Eijkman's observations for combating beri-beri was appreciated, although on this point Eijkman himself had recognized the significance of his findings. The outlook for a case of beri-beri, if diagnosed early and adequately treated, is nowadays very good. Prevention, dependent on a well-balanced diet, is a more difficult matter, since it calls for the education of the ignorant masses of the people in the eastern countries, where the disease is most prevalent, and for the raising of their economic level—two very large orders. It is asserted, however, that prevention of the overmilling of grain would go far to solve the problem.

Although there are other claimants for the honor, it is now widely accepted that F. G. Hopkins was the first to realize the full significance of the facts and to recognize the necessity for "accessory factors" in the diet. The important work which has since been carried out in vitamin research was initiated by his discoveries. Osborne and Mendel, and McCollum and his co-workers, distinguished between "water-soluble" and "fat-soluble" vitamins. It was shown by McCollum and Davis (1913) that the growth-promoting effect of milk demonstrated by Hopkins depended on two factors: fat-soluble vitamin A and water-soluble vitamin B. Vitamin B was later shown by Goldberger to consist of a mixture of several vitamins. One of these, vitamin B_1, protects against beri-beri; another is the pellagra-preventing vitamin.

It is not possible to review the later history of vitamin research in a brief space. Rickets, and also scurvy, were added to the list of diseases proved to result from specific deficiencies; there were soon several others. Many contributions have been made by physiologists, pathologists, and chemists to the increasing knowledge of nutritional deficiencies. Attention has been given not only to the vitamins but to the need for small amounts of other substances, particularly minerals. Study of these various substances, and the vitamins most of all, has greatly increased our knowledge of physiology as well as our clinical knowledge of disease.

In the ten years between 1928 and 1937 eight scientists were awarded Nobel Prizes in chemistry, physiology and medicine for their work on vitamins. Additional prizes went in later years to Dam and Doisy (1943) and to Lipmann (1953) for their discoveries in vitamin science. Lynen (1964) has studied the coenzyme forms of two vitamins. Eijkman and Hopkins were among those who opened the gates of an important field in medicine.

REFERENCE

NEEDHAM, JOSEPH, and BALDWIN, ERNEST (editors). *Hopkins and Biochemistry* (Cambridge: Heffer, 1949).

1930
KARL LANDSTEINER
(1868–1943)

"For his discovery of the human blood groups."

BIOGRAPHICAL SKETCH

KARL LANDSTEINER WAS BORN IN VIENNA, ON JUNE 14, 1868. He entered the University of Vienna in 1885 and was graduated as doctor of medicine in 1891. He received his chemical training in the laboratories of Hantzsch in Zurich, Emil Fischer in Würzburg, and E. Bamberger in Munich. Thereupon he turned to bacteriology and pathology, but his approach to these subjects was derived from his thorough training in the fundamental sciences, especially chemistry. In 1896 he became assistant under Dr. Max von Gruber in the Institute of Hygiene at the University of Vienna. From 1898 to 1908 he was an assistant under Professor A. Weichselbaum at the Pathological Institute. In 1908 he was prosector at the Wilhelminspital, where he then served as pathologist from 1909 to 1919, with the rank of professor. After the First World War he left Vienna and went to Holland, to be pathologist at the R. K. Ziekenhuis, the Hague, from 1919 to 1922. In 1922 he became a member of the Rockefeller Institute for Medical Research, in New York, where he continued to work for more than twenty years. In 1939, having reached the mandatory age for retirement, he was made an emeritus member of the Institute, but continued his research with undiminished vigor. Stricken by heart disease while busy in his laboratory, he died two days later, on June 26, 1943, at che Rockefeller Institute Hospital. He had just completed the preparation of a new edition of his book *The Specificity of Serological Reactions,* which was already a classic. Landsteiner published about 330 papers on his investigations in chemistry, in pathological anatomy, in experimental pathology (infectious diseases), and in serology and immunology. His studies of syphilis and poliomyelitis were particularly important. Probably his most far-reaching work was in immunochemistry, a branch of science which he did much to establish.

DESCRIPTION OF THE PRIZE-WINNING WORK*

"The difficulty of dealing with substances of large, complex molecules accounts for the fact that we are still far from the goal of characterizing and determining the constitution of proteins, which rank as the most important constituents of living beings. So it was not the usual methods of chemistry but the application of serologic tests which led to an important general result in protein chemistry, to the knowledge that the albuminous substances differ in the separate kinds of animals and plants and are characteristic for each kind. The diversity is increased still more in that the different organs also contain particular proteins, and consequently special building materials seem to be necessary for each particular form and function of living organisms, in contrast to artificial machines, which can be produced for greatly varied performance from a limited number of materials.

"The question which was raised by the discovery of the biochemical specificity of kinds, and which formed the basis of the investigations to be discussed, was thereupon formulated with the aim of seeing whether differentiation extends beyond the limits of species, and whether the separate individuals of one kind also exhibit similar, if at the same time slight, differences. In the absence of any observations pointing to a circumstance of this sort, I chose the simplest among the research arrangements which offered, and that material which at first glance lent itself to useful application.

---

* Translated from Karl Landsteiner, "Über individuelle Unterschiede des menschlichen Blutes," *Les Prix Nobel en 1930.*

Accordingly the research which I undertook consisted in letting the blood serum and red blood corpuscles of different people react on one another.

"The result was only in part what was expected. In many tests there was no change to be observed, just as if the blood cells had been mixed with their own serum, but often a phenomenon called agglutination took place, the serum causing the cells of the stranger to form clumps.

"The surprising thing was this, that the agglutination, when present at all, was just as pronounced as those reactions already known, which occur with the interaction of serum and cells from different kinds of animals, while in the other cases there seemed to be no difference in the blood of different people. So first of all there was still the consideration that the required individual physiological differences had not been found, and that the phenomena, when seen, too, in the blood of healthy people, could be caused by illnesses which had been overcome. But it soon became apparent that the reactions conform to a law which is valid for everyone's blood, and that the peculiarities found in separate individuals are just as characteristic as the serologic signs for an animal species. The main point, of course, is that there are four different kinds of human blood [Landsteiner first described three], the so-called blood groups. The number of the groups is due to the fact that in the erythrocytes there exist substances (isoagglutinogens) with two different structures, of which both may be lacking or one or both may be present in a man's erythrocytes. That alone would still not explain the reactions; the effective substances of the sera, the isoagglutinins, must also occur in a definite distribution. This is actually the case, for each serum contains that agglutinin which acts on the agglutinogens that are not present in the cells, a noteworthy fact, the cause of which has not yet been established with certainty. From this arise definite relations among the blood groups. . . ."

CONSEQUENCES IN THEORY
AND PRACTICE

Serum from the blood of an animal was known to be capable of causing flocculation (hemoagglutination) and dissolution (hemolysis) of red blood corpuscles in the blood of another animal of different species. That this might also at times occur in mixing serum from one individual with red blood cells from another individual of the *same* animal species (isoagglutination) was observed in 1900 by Ehrlich and Morgenroth. In the same year (1900), Karl Landsteiner and Samuel Shattock, working independently, reported on the incompatibility of different types of human blood. By 1901 Landsteiner had enough data to distinguish three groups and was able to give a clear account of isoagglutination. In 1902, his associate, A. Sturli, working with A. von Decastello, described the fourth group.

The discovery of the human blood groups had important results in (1) clinical medicine and surgery; (2) forensic (legal) medicine; and (3) anthropology.

Isoagglutinogens of two different structures, A and B, occur in red blood corpuscles, either separately, or together (AB). Both may be absent (the O group). An individual's serum cannot normally agglutinate his own blood corpuscles or those of others who belong to the same blood group. Serum from a member of the O group agglutinates the red cells in all the other groups, but the red cells of O group are not affected by any of the four kinds of serum (A, B, AB, O). Serum from a person belonging to A group agglutinates the cells of B-group blood, but not those of A or AB groups. Conversely, serum from B-group blood agglutinates cells of A group but not those of B or AB groups. This knowledge formed the foundation for the development of blood transfusion. Agote, Jeanbrau, and Lewisohn demonstrated the efficacy of adding sodium citrate to prevent coagulation of collected blood before injection into the recipient, a method which helped to make transfusion more generally available. Transfusions are now used for a wide variety of purposes. Lives are saved daily by this means following hemorrhage from injury, operation, gastric ulcer, ruptured ectopic pregnancy, bleeding after childbirth; in bleeding due to hemorrhagic diseases of the blood; and in cases of severe anemia, leukemia, etc. Carbon monoxide gas has a great affinity for the hemoglobin in the blood; an infusion of fresh blood provides unaltered hemoglobin. Transfusions have proved beneficial in some cases of chronic sepsis, and "immunotransfusions" have been used against scarlet fever, typhoid, and septicemia. Whole blood transfusion is especially effective in cases of traumatic or postoperative shock due to loss of blood in an accident or during an operation.

The inheritance of the ABO blood groups was recognized soon after their discovery, but the correct hypothesis regarding the mode of inheritance was proposed only in 1925 by F. Bernstein. He also showed that A and B are strongly dominant. In cases of disputed paternity this fact may be of great value. Although a man cannot be proved to be the father of a child by means of the respective blood groups, it is often possible to prove that he is *not* the father. At least one court case is recorded in which blood typing established that the plaintiff could not have been the *mother* of the child whose paternity had been in question! The blood-group determination may also be of use when bloodstains are brought as evidence in criminal cases.

In 1927 Landsteiner discovered additional agglutinogens in human blood, two of which, M and N, have been of importance in forensic medicine. In 1940, with A. S. Wiener, he discovered the Rhesus (Rh) factor, one that has since assumed great significance in medicine. Incompatibility with respect to this factor is the cause of a fetal disease, erythroblastosis foetalis, which may result in abortion, miscarriage, or a dangerous illness in the newborn child. Many sub-groups of the major types have been described.

Because the blood groups are unevenly distributed among the world's populations they have been employed by geneticists and anthropologists in classifying human races and in discerning man's place among the primates. Landsteiner showed that the blood of anthropoids is more closely related than that of lower monkeys to human blood, and stated that his results "seem to agree with the theory that man and apes are descendants of a common stock rather than that man evolved from one of the apes." The A and B isoagglutinogens are relatively stable under adverse physical and chemical conditions; they have been identified in mummified tissue by W. C. Boyd and L. G. Boyd (1937), a finding that has made it possible for archeologists to identify the blood groups of peoples who have long passed into history.

REFERENCES

LANDSTEINER, KARL. *Specificity of Serological Reactions* (New York: Dover, 1945). Revised edition.

BOYD, WILLIAM C. *Genetics and the Races of Man* (Boston: Little, Brown and Co., 1956).

1 9 3 1
OTTO WARBURG
(1883–   )

*"For his discovery of the nature and mode of action
of the respiratory enzyme."*

BIOGRAPHICAL SKETCH

OTTO HEINRICH WARBURG WAS BORN IN FREIBURG (BADEN) on
October 8, 1883. His father, Emil Warburg (1846-1931) became
Professor of Physics at the University of Berlin in 1896 and the
youth came under the influence of men like Emil Fischer and van't
Hoff. Warburg obtained his doctorate in 1906 with a dissertation
on polypeptides, dealing with research that he had carried out in
Fischer's laboratory. In 1911 he became doctor of medicine as well;
his thesis was on problems of oxidation. He then carried out his
first research on living organisms at the Zoological Research Station
in Naples; his work there dealt with the metabolic activity of the
sea-urchin's egg. Most of his work since that time, except for a
brief sojourn in the United States, has been at the Max Planck Institute for Cell Physiology (formerly called the Kaiser-Wilhelm
Institute), erected in Berlin-Dahlem in 1930 by the Rockefeller
Foundation. Warburg has made many notable contributions to biochemistry: the introduction of manometry for metabolic studies;
investigations in metabolism of tumors; discovery of important enzymes and their activity; and studies in the mechanism of photosynthesis, to name the most outstanding. On his eightieth birthday
the German Society for Physiological Chemistry established an
"Otto Warburg Medal," the first of which was given to F. Lynen,
winner of the Nobel Prize in 1964.

DESCRIPTION OF THE PRIZE-WINNING
WORK*

"That iron occurs in all cells, that it is vital, and that it is [the oxygen-transporting part of] the oxidation catalyst of cellular respiration was first apprehended in recent times. It is the valence change of an iron compound—the oxygen-transporting respiratory ferment—on which catalytic oxidation in living substance depends. . . .

"In the investigation of the chemical constitution of the oxygen-transporting ferment, analytical chemistry according to the usual methods has been abandoned, since in view of the almost infinitely small concentration . . . and the fragility of the ferment, they appear hopeless. . . . [This opinion determined the adoption of other methods, but Warburg has since concluded that isolation of this substance is not impossible.] One looks for substances which specifically and reversibly stop the operation of the oxygen-transporting ferment—that is to say, the oxidation in living substance. Now it cannot be otherwise than that a substance which inactivates the ferment reacts with [it] chemically, so that conclusions can be drawn about the ferment's chemical nature from the kind of retarding substances and from the circumstances to which the retardation is subject. . . . It is an advantage that by so doing one investigates the ferment under natural conditions, in the intact, breathing cells. . . .

"The blocking of intracellular respiration by hydrocyanic acid . . . takes place through a reaction of the hydrocyanic acid with the iron of the oxygen-transporting ferment. . . . Hydrocyanic acid retards the *reduction* of the ferment iron. . . . [That carbon monoxide also inhibits intracellular respiration was discovered by Warburg in 1926.] In accordance with the carbon monoxide and oxygen pressures a greater or smaller part of the ferment iron is eliminated from catalysis by combination with carbon monoxide.

---

* The first quotation is translated from Otto Warburg, "Das sauerstoffübertragende Ferment der Atmung," *Les Prix Nobel en 1931*. The second consists of excerpts from Otto Warburg, *Heavy Metal Prosthetic Groups and Enzyme Action*, translated by Alexander Lawson (Oxford: Clarendon Press, 1949).

. . . Carbon monoxide bars the *oxidation* of the ferment iron.
. . . [It was well known that CO acts on hemoglobin by expelling
the oxygen from its union with iron. The inference as to the iron
content of the ferment is based on analogies of this kind, and on
the evidence, mentioned below, of its absorption spectrum.]

"If one adds carbon monoxide to the oxygen in which living
cells are breathing, then . . . respiration ceases. If one exposes
[this] to light . . . then respiration is resumed. By exposing living, breathing cells to light, and, alternately, darkening them, one
can cause respiration to appear and disappear. In the dark, the iron
of the oxygen-transporting ferment is bound to carbon monoxide;
in the light, the carbon monoxide is split off from the iron, and
the iron is thereby again free for oxygen-activation. This was discovered in 1926 [by Warburg] with Fritz Kubowitz."

[Best known of the iron pigments in the body is hemoglobin,
consisting of a protein, globin, to which is added an iron compound
called a "heme," or "hematin." Such a non-protein compound attached to a molecule is called a "prosthetic group." Although it was once thought that the body contains no iron apart
from hemoglobin, MacMunn in 1885 asserted, on the basis of
spectroscopic examination, that all animal cells contain heme
compounds. Warburg's discovery of 1926 was an extension of
discoveries made by earlier investigators in the 1890's. The photo-
chemical dissociation of certain iron compounds had been discovered in 1891 by Mond and Langer; a few years later J. S.
Haldane and J. L. Smith had observed that light upsets the equilibrium of hemoglobin, carbon monoxide, and oxygen, in favor of
oxygen. Other biological iron pigments were later found to behave
in this way too, and Warburg found the same result with the
respiratory enzyme. This suggested that the enzyme contained a
prosthetic group with the properties of a heme.]

*   *   *

"Probably all carbon monoxide-iron compounds are light-sensi-
tive. . . . On the other hand, up till now it has not been possible
to decompose by light a carbon monoxide compound in which the
carbon monoxide was joined to any metal other than iron. . . .
[What follows is an account of the action of light on the carbon

monoxide inhibition of respiration in yeast cells.] A 75-watt metal filament lamp is placed under two conical manometric vessels [a manometer is an instrument for indicating the pressure of gases] which are shaken in a thermostat. Each vessel contains 2 c.c. of a dilute yeast suspension. The gas space contains nitrogen and oxygen or carbon monoxide and oxygen. The light is switched on and off for periods of 20 minutes. . . . The light in the nitrogen-oxygen mixture has no effect on the respiration. The respiration inhibited by carbon monoxide, however, increases with the light and decreases in the dark. [The gas pressures in the manometer indicate the respiration taking place; see commentary below.] This means that the carbon monoxide compound of the oxygen-transporting enzyme is decomposed by light. . . . In order to verify the influence of wave-length on the reaction we selected four regions of the spectrum, made their intensities the same and irradiated yeast cells, the respiration of which had been inhibited by carbon monoxide. Thus with light of the same intensity but different wavelength, we found [in the blue part of the spectrum, strong action; in the green and yellow, weak action; in the red, no action]. This is the experiment which gave rise to the method for the determination of the absorption spectrum of the oxygen-transporting enzyme." [The 'ferment bands' were compared with the bands shown by a variety of hemes, and the close coincidence of the values in certain instances confirmed Warburg's view as to the nature of the prosthetic group of the enzyme.]

CONSEQUENCES IN THEORY
AND PRACTICE

Lavoisier believed that oxidation takes place in the lungs. It has long been known, however, that the chemical events summed up in the word "respiration" actually occur in the cells, to which molecular oxygen is transported by the hemoglobin of the red blood corpuscles. In the preface to *Heavy Metal Prosthetic Groups and Enzyme Action,* Warburg writes: "Ever since it has been known that cells respire, the chief problem connected with respiration has been to determine which part of the living matter is auto-oxidizable [i.e., which part undergoes spontaneous oxidation]. If the combustible substances in the cell are not auto-oxidizable, and if the cell material itself is not, with what then does the molecular oxygen, which is absorbed by the respiring cell, react? The answer to the problem lies in the auto-oxidizable ferrous iron complex which is oxidized to ferric iron by molecular oxygen and transformed again to ferrous iron by the reducing action of the cell constituents." This iron complex is the active part of Warburg's *Atmungsferment;* the latter, according to him, is "the enzyme which has contributed more than any other to the explanation of life."

In 1925, D. Keilin confirmed and extended the spectroscopic studies of MacMunn, mentioned above (p. 154). He attributed three of the MacMunn bands to three heme compounds, which he called cytochrome a, cytochrome b, and cytochrome c. The word "cytochrome," which is sometimes used alone to comprehend all three variants, means simply cell pigment. Keilin at first identified cytochrome with Warburg's respiratory ferment, but in 1927 Warburg suggested that the oxygen-transporting ferment oxidizes the cytochrome, which thus forms another stage in the process, a view in which Keilin concurred. Disputes arose, however, first as to whether or not the enzyme is really in part a heme compound, and secondly as to the range of application of Warburg's theory. Warburg himself has discovered that in certain plants the oxygen is transported not by iron but by copper; other heavy metals may at times substitute for iron. He also discovered the first of the "yellow enzymes," which do not contain iron, but he states that "in the aerobic cells . . . the yellow enzymes are intermediate members of the enzyme chain at the head of which stands oxygen-transporting iron."

Warburg has made very important contributions toward understanding the complicated mechanism by which oxidation and reduction, essential to all life, are brought about. The importance to biology and medicine of intracellular chemistry has already been discussed in another connection (see above, p. 66). It may be mentioned in this respect that Warburg has made fundamental contributions through his studies of the abnormal metabolism of tumors; the discovery of yellow (i.e. riboflavin-containing) enzymes; his discovery of the vitamin nicotinamide as a constituent of important coenzymes; and studies on photosynthesis. In addition, he has devised technical methods that are widely used in biochemical and physiological research laboratories: the "tissue slice" method for measuring metabolism in small segments of isolated tissues or cells; manometric methods, earlier used by Sir Joseph Barcroft and J. S. Haldane for analysis of blood gases, which he deftly converted into a flexible and versatile tool for the study of metabolic processes; and optical methods for measurement of the dynamics of enzyme action. Warburg is widely recognized as the world's most outstanding biochemist.

REFERENCES

WARBURG, O. *Heavy Metal Prosthetic Groups and Enzyme Action*, translated by Alexander Lawson (Oxford: Clarendon Press, 1949).
————, ed. *The Metabolism of Tumours*, translated by F. Dickens (New York: R. R. Smith, 1931).

1932
CHARLES SHERRINGTON
(1857–1952)

EDGAR DOUGLAS ADRIAN
(1889–   )

"For their discoveries regarding the function of the neurons."

BIOGRAPHICAL SKETCHES

SHERRINGTON

CHARLES SCOTT SHERRINGTON WAS BORN IN LONDON, ON November 27, 1857. He was educated at Queen Elizabeth's School, Ipswich, matriculating in 1881 at Cambridge, where he was admitted to Gonville and Caius College. There he came under the tutelage of Sir Michael Foster and worked in association with Balfour, Gaskell, Langley, Newell Martin, and Sheridan Lea. He published his first paper on the nervous system in 1884, with Langley. After receiving his degree in medicine (M.B.) from Cambridge in 1885, he went to Spain and Italy to study cholera. He continued his work in pathology at Berlin, first with Virchow but for a longer period with Koch. Returning to London, he was made lecturer in physiology at St. Thomas's Hospital, and in 1891 he was appointed Professor-Superintendent of the Brown Institute for Advanced Physiological and Pathological Research, where he succeeded Sir

Victor Horsley. Between 1885 and 1895 Sherrington made several visits to Strasbourg to study under the physiologist Goltz, whose chief interest lay in the function of the central nervous system. In the latter year Sherrington accepted the chair of physiology in the University of Liverpool, where he remained for eighteen years, until he went to Oxford as Waynflete Professor of Physiology. In 1893 he was elected a Fellow of the Royal Society, of which he became president in 1920. He was knighted in 1922. In 1891 he married Ethel Mary Wright. They had one child, Carr E. R. Sherrington, who became a distinguished railroad economist and author. In addition to his scientific papers, Sherrington wrote on more general topics, including public health and the history of medicine, and published a book of verse. His death occurred on March 4, 1952, in his ninety-fifth year.

ADRIAN

EDGAR DOUGLAS ADRIAN WAS BORN IN LONDON, ON NOVEMBER 30, 1889. He was educated at Westminster School and entered Trinity College, Cambridge, with a science scholarship, in 1908. He studied physiology for Part II of the Natural Sciences Tripos and was awarded a first class in 1911. His first research was done in collaboration with Keith Lucas. It was followed by an investigation of the "all or none" principle in nerves, for which he was elected to a fellowship at Trinity College in 1913. Adrian became the ninth Fellow of Trinity to be awarded a Nobel Prize. He took a medical degree in 1915 and worked at clinical neurology, returning to Cambridge in 1919 to lecture on the nervous system. He was made a fellow of the Royal Society in 1923. Two years later he began investigating the sense organs by electrical methods. In 1929 he was made Foulerton Professor of the Royal Society. Probably his best-known works are *The Basis of Sensation* (1927), *The Mechanism of Nervous Action* (1932), and *The Physical Background of Perception* (1947). He has received many honors, including the rare distinction of the Order of Merit, which was also awarded to Sherrington. Adrian was President of the Royal Society from 1950 to 1955. From 1951 to 1965 he held the post, highly distinguished in British university life, of Master of Trinity College. He was Vice-Chancellor of the University of Cambridge from 1957 to 1959. Adrian was created a Baron in 1955.

DESCRIPTION OF THE PRIZE-WINNING WORK

SHERRINGTON *

"The receptors played upon by the events of the external world supply their 'drive' to the muscles. In reflex action they do so far more simply and for far more simple purposes than when the trains of reaction they set going have to thread the mazes of the higher brain, and, so to say, obtaining mental sanction, issue in acts remoter from the original stimulus. Yet in both cases the muscles lie at the behest of the receptors, as instruments of their hand.

"We should go too far, however, did we infer that the muscles themselves are instruments entirely passive under drive of the receptors acting on them from without. That they are agents not purely passive is shown by their possession of receptors of their own. On their own behalf they send messages into the central exchanges. This must mean they have some voice in their own conditions of service, perhaps ring themselves up and ring themselves off. Let us attempt to penetrate into the significance of this their 'receptivity.'

"It is a receptivity differing obviously from that of other receptors, rightly more commonly chosen to exemplify receptive function, such as retina, ear, tongue, tactile organs, and so on, for in the case of the receptors of muscle, instead of being stimulated directly by agents of the external world, they are stimulated by happenings in the microcosm of the body itself—namely, events in the muscles themselves. In muscular receptivity we see the body itself acting as stimulus to its own receptors. The receptors of muscle have therefore been termed 'proprioceptors.' [This term was coined by Sherrington.]

"Following the functional scheme of all receptors, we may be

---

* From C. S. Sherrington, "Problems of Muscular Receptivity," Linacre Lecture, *Nature* (London), June 21 and 28, 1924. Reprinted in D. Denny-Brown, ed., *Selected Writings of Sir Charles Sherrington* (New York: Paul B. Hoeber, 1940), pp. 385-390.

sure that the central reactions provoked by the receptors of muscle will be divisible into, on the one hand, the purely reflex, and on the other hand, those which subserve mental experience.

"Let us turn to the simpler of these divisions, the purely reflex. For that purpose, appeal can be had to what may with justification be regarded as a partially surviving animal—an animal which, its cerebral hemispheres having been removed, is a wholly inconscient and purely reflex automaton. From it no sight or sound evokes evidence of perception. There is total inability to evoke from it any sign of mentality, of emotion, let alone intelligence. It remains motionless hour after hour; yet if planted upon its feet in the upright position it stands, and statuelike continues to stand.

"Now, standing is a postural act, and one of course of high importance. In maintaining posture the muscles, though they perform no external work, are active with an activity often technically termed 'tonus,' a postural contraction. In this maintenance of the erect posture by the decerebrate animal, we meet a co-ordinated posture involving many separate muscles harmoniously co-ordinated reflexly. For this reflex postural act of standing some stimulus must be at work evoking and maintaining it. We have to ask what that stimulus may be.

"If the afferent nerves that pass from a limb to the spinal centres be severed, the standing posture in that limb is no longer fully executed or maintained. The stimulus exciting the posture in that limb must be something which is applied to the receptors of that limb itself. The skin surface of the limb is rich in receptors, one region especially rich being the sole of the foot. On the receptors of the skin of the sole of the foot the external world may evidently be acting as a stimulus in the form of pressure from the ground upon the skin. To test whether that is the source of the reflex posture, the skin of the foot can be deprived of all its receptors by severing their nerves. This is found to exert no obvious influence upon the posture. Nor does severance of all the receptive nerves from the skin of the whole limb, nor, indeed, from that of all the four limbs. The stimulus producing and maintaining the posture is therefore not pressure of the skin against the ground, nor indeed any cutaneous stimulus whatsoever. On the other hand, if, even without interference with the skin nerves, the receptive nerves of the limb-muscles—the motor nerves, of course, remaining intact—

be severed, the reflex posture disappears at once from the limb. The stimulus which produces and maintains the posture is something which is acting on and exciting the receptive nerves of the muscles of the limb.

"What are the muscles which, by their contraction, execute this postural act? The posture keeps the head and neck from sinking, the trunk straightened and the spine supported, the tail from drooping, the limbs from yielding and folding under the superincumbent weight of the body. In a word, this habitual reflex posture counteracts in the various parts of the body the effect of gravity on them in the erect attitude. Experimental analysis shows that throughout the muscular frame of the animal all those muscles, and only those, are in action, the activity of which counteracts gravity in the erect attitude—for example, in the hind-limb the muscles which extend hip, knee, and ankle. The muscles which execute the reflex we may, in short, term 'antigravity' muscles. Even the jaw is included; the lower jaw, which, but for its postural tonus, would drop, is held lifted against the upper.

"If in the limb the receptive nerve of one of these antigravity muscles be cut, that muscle no longer contributes to the reflex posture. On the other hand, severance of the receptive nerves of all the other muscles does not destroy the postural reflex of the muscle the receptive nerve of which remains intact. The stimulus which is the source of this reflex standing is therefore one acting on the receptors of those limb-muscles which are themselves executants of the posture.

"The excitability of a receptor is selective. That is, construction fits the receptor to respond to stimuli of one particular kind only, the so-called 'adequate' stimulus; thus, the retina to light, a taste papilla to 'sweet,' and so on. Hence Pavlov's term 'analyser' for the receptors, because by them the various complex events which play upon the body and cause reactions of it through the nervous system are to some extent analysed. A wave breaking on the shore excites the retina by its reflected lights, the ear by sound vibrations, and, maybe, the skin by the spray dashed up. The wave as 'object' and stimulus from the external world is thus partially analysed by the receptors.

"Seeing that the receptors of muscle are an appendage of an organ mechanical in function, a near supposition is that their adequate stimulus is of mechanical kind. What is the adequate stimulus at work in these antigravity muscles in their posture of standing?

"A muscle representative of the whole antigravity group is the extensor of the knee. Suppose it isolated from the rest and its freed tendon attached to a stiff spring, and to the spring a light lever so fixed that movement of the lever-point is photographically recorded. If then, by its bony attachments, the muscle be pulled against the spring, we can passively stretch the muscle and record the tensile strain developed in it by the stretch. Let us take the case of the muscle paralysed by severance of all nerves both afferent and efferent which connect it with the nerve-centres. The tension developed in the muscle as it is stretched yields a curve resembling that given by various fibrous and elastic tissues of the body, not unlike that given by a strip of indiarubber. Let us repeat the observation, but with the difference that the muscle retains unimpaired its purely efferent motor nerve. The stretching produces the same tensile curve as before, a curve practically indistinguishable from that of the wholly paralytic muscle. Then let us make the observation, with the further difference that the muscle this time retains not only its motor nerve but its receptive nerve as well. We find the muscle yields now a completely different curve of tensile strain. The tension developed by it is much greater, and its curve under equable progressive increase of the stretch runs, tensions being ordinates, convex instead of concave to the abscissa line. The muscle in response to the stretch now replies not merely by passive strain but also by active contraction of its muscle-fibres. In the muscle with its reflex arc intact, the passive pull provokes a reflex contraction of the muscle."

ADRIAN *

"The sense organs respond to certain changes in their environment by sending messages or signals to the central nervous system. The signals travel rapidly over the long threads of protoplasm

* From E. D. Adrian, "The Activity of the Nerve Fibres," *Les Prix Nobel en 1932.*

which form the sensory nerve fibres, and fresh signals are sent out by the motor fibres to arouse contraction in the appropriate muscles. What kind of signals are these? . . . [This question] would have been answered correctly by most physiologists many years ago, but now it can be answered in much greater detail. It can be answered because of a recent improvement in electrical technique. The nerves do their work economically, without visible change and with the smallest expenditure of energy. The signals which they transmit can only be detected as changes of electrical potential, and these changes are very small and of very brief duration. . . .

"The revolution in technique has come about not from any increase in the sensitivity of galvanometers and electrometers but from the use of [amplifiers like those employed in radio] to amplify potential changes. . . . Many workers have contributed to the introduction of this technique in physiology, notably Forbes of Harvard, Gasser of St. Louis [later of New York, winner of the Nobel Prize with Erlanger in 1944], who was the first to use very high amplification, and Mathews of Cambridge. . . .

"Seven years ago [i.e., in 1925] it became clear to me that a combination of the capillary electrometer * with an amplifier would permit the recording of far smaller potential changes than had been dealt with previously, and might enable us to work on the units of the nerve trunk instead of on the aggregate. . . . The problem was then to limit the activity to only one or two nerve fibres. [The difficulty of interpreting the irregular effects from a whole nerve, due to the fact that impulses in the various nerve fibers do not come simultaneously and can therefore nullify or amplify one another, has been likened by Professor Liljestrand to an attempt to construct the separate conversations by listening to the various wires in a telephone cable simultaneously. It was necessary to try to obtain impulses corresponding to one single conversation or one sending station.] In this I was happy to have the co-operation of Dr. Zotterman of the Caroline Institute. We found that the sterno-cutaneous muscle of the frog could be divided progressively until it contained only one sense organ; this could be stimulated by stretch-

---

* See above, pp. 119-120.

ing the muscle, and we could record the succession of impulses which passed up the single sensory nerve fibre.

". . . [The signals] consist of nerve impulses repeated more or less rapidly. . . . The waves [recording potential changes] are of constant size and duration, but they begin at a frequency of about 10 a second, and as the extension increases, their frequency rises to 50 a second or more. The frequency depends on the extent and on the rapidity of the stretch; it depends, that is to say, on the intensity of excitation in the sense organ, and in this way the impulse message can signal far more than the mere fact that excitation has occurred. [There had previously been 'good reason to believe that the nerve impulse was a brief wave of activity depending in no way on the intensity of the stimulus which set it up.']

"In all the sense organs which give a prolonged discharge under constant stimulation the message in the nerve fibre is composed of a rhythmic series of impulses of varying frequency. . . . With some kinds of sense organ there is a rapid adaptation to the stimulus and the nervous discharge is too brief to show a definite rhythm, though it consists as before of repeated impulses of unvarying size.

"The nerve fibre is clearly a signalling mechanism of limited scope. It can only transmit a succession of brief explosive waves, and the message can only be varied by changes in the frequency and in the total number of these waves. Moreover the frequency depends on the rate of development of the stimulus as well as on its intensity; also the briefer the discharge the less opportunity will there be for signalling by change of frequency. But this limitation is really a small matter, for in the body the nervous units do not act in isolation as they do in our experiments. A sensory stimulus will usually affect a number of receptor organs, and its result will depend on the composite message in many nerve fibres. . . . [It has been shown in specific instances that] the impulses in each nerve fibre increase in frequency [when the stimulus increases] and more fibres come into action. Since rapid potential changes can be made audible as sound waves, a gramophone record will illustrate this, and you will be able to hear the two kinds of gradation, the changes in frequency in each unit and in the number of units in action."

CONSEQUENCES IN THEORY
AND PRACTICE

The contributions of Sir Charles Sherrington to neurophysiology, like the contributions of Ramón y Cajal to neuroanatomy, are so numerous and varied that they are difficult to summarize.* One of Sherrington's earlier achievements was to analyze the distribution of the ventral (motor) nerve roots, recording the muscles activated by each; similarly he mapped out sensory distribution for dorsal roots, with results which have formed the basis of all later work on sensory levels.

Prior to 1894 it was generally assumed that all nerves going to muscle were motor nerves. In that year Sherrington published a paper in which he maintained that one third to one half of the nerve fibers in skeletal muscle nerves are sensory. It was not then established that Golgi's spindles (see above, pp. 34-36) were actually sensory. Sherrington cut ventral nerve roots so as to deprive a particular muscle of motor supply, and found that the spindles remained intact with their myelinated fibers; but interruption of dorsal (sensory) roots at a corresponding level caused these end organs to degenerate and disappear. He found that dorsal root section, unlike the severing of cutaneous nerves, caused an animal to lose awareness of the position of its limbs in space, to lose tendon reflexes (such as the knee jerk) and to become ataxic—i.e., to lose the power of muscular coordination. These experiments laid the foundation of knowledge of the "proprioceptive" system, the mechanism for the sense of position and equilibrium, with the fine adjustment of muscular movements depending on stimuli originating within the organism (Latin *proprius,* one's own). The term is Sherrington's and the whole concept is based largely on his work. These experiments incidentally served to explain ataxia in the clinical condition known as tabes dorsalis, in which sensory pathways at dorsal root level are impaired. In a somewhat similar manner many another Sherrington experiment has explained the find-

---

* These paragraphs about Sherrington are based in part on John F. Fulton, "Sherrington's Impact on Neurophysiology," *British Medical Journal,* Vol. II (1947), pp. 807-810.

ings and guided the thought of the clinical neurologist; his writings have also proved source books for the general physiologist and the psychologist.

Sherrington next studied the reflexes in the spinal and decerebrate state and the reciprocal innervation of antagonistic muscles—i.e., the reflex mechanism which results in the coordinated action of muscles of opposing tendency, such as a flexor and an extensor of the same part. This reflex behavior of antagonistic muscles led to the concept of integration, a theme developed in the Silliman Lectures delivered at Yale in 1904, first published in 1906 under the title *The Integrative Action of the Nervous System* (latest edition, 1947). This is one of the classics of modern physiology, embracing a wide range of work on nervous integration.

Another important contribution was the mapping of the motor areas of the cortex in a more exact manner than had ever been done before. His observations in this field at once accounted for the clinical picture of hemiplegia (paralysis of one side of the body) and for the manner in which recovery takes place. The rigidity (contracture) of hemiplegia was explained by Sherrington's studies of decerebrate rigidity, to be caused by the unantagonized activity of subcortical centers. He then turned to the study of special reflexes, such as the swallowing reflex, and in 1924 discovered the "stretch reflex," which accounts for the constant activity of the antigravity muscles. On the nature of cortical inhibition he published his principal paper in 1925; on the ultimate unit of reflex action, in 1930.

This rapid listing of achievements has taken little account of many observations on the physiological anatomy of the tracts of the spinal cord, of investigations of binocular flicker and sensual fusion, of extensive work on general sensation, and of a host of other special contributions. Sherrington has given to medicine not only a multitude of exact and important observations, but new theoretical concepts of the greatest value and striking advances in laboratory technique, as well as in the teaching and practice of mammalian physiology in general. His work and his ideas have entered into the whole structure of the physiology of the nervous system.

The work of E. D. Adrian built upon and extended Sherrington's researches and demonstrated their value. The latter had shown that stimuli from different points can weaken or reinforce a reflex; he had also determined the effect of repeated stimulations at the same point. A motor neuron receiving impulses from many directions discharges its impulse in one way only, through its axon; of several indications for action, "nociceptive," or pain, reflexes predominate, apparently as a protection for the organism. What is the nature of the nerve impulse in afferent and efferent limbs of a reflex? Adrian and his co-workers answered this question in the manner set forth above, working with the "stretch reflex" originating in a single end organ. By repeated stimulations at the same point Sherrington had demonstrated temporal inhibition and summation. Adrian showed that sense organs can adjust themselves so that a stimulus which produces a rapid succession of impulses when first applied has a weaker effect when sustained. Adrian and Zotterman demonstrated the increase in frequency of the signals sent in to the central exchange as the stretching of a muscle becomes greater; with D. Bronk, Adrian showed that heightened activity in the motor limb of the reflex, or of motor nerves generally, is accompanied by an increase in the number of impulses per second. This analysis of the nerve impulses served to explain earlier results, incomprehensible because of their complexity, by the isolation of functional units; synthesis following analysis put the complex pattern together again. Adrian's work threw much light on the adjustment capacity of the nerve action and the sense organs. His work on the electrophysiology of nerve impulse has been complemented by that of two other Nobel laureates, Erlanger and Gasser (see below, pp. 229-234).

REFERENCE

BRAZIER, MARY A. B. "The Electrical Activity of the Nervous System," *Science,* vol. 146 (1964), pp. 1423-1428.

1 9 3 3
THOMAS HUNT MORGAN
(1866–1945)

"For his discoveries concerning the function of the chromosome in the transmission of heredity,"

BIOGRAPHICAL SKETCH

THOMAS HUNT MORGAN WAS BORN IN 1866 AT LEXINGTON, Kentucky. He attended the University of Kentucky and was graduated in 1886. He then entered the Johns Hopkins University, where he studied morphology with Professor W. K. Brooks and physiology with H. Newell Martin. In 1890 he received the Ph.D. degree and was Bruce Fellow for the following year. In 1891 he was appointed associate professor of biology at Bryn Mawr College, where he remained until 1904; in that year he was named professor of experimental zoology at Columbia University. In 1928 he became head of the Kerckhoff Biological Laboratories of the California Institute of Technology, Pasadena, California. From 1909 on, Morgan attracted to his laboratory a brilliant group of workers, including C. B. Bridges and A. H. Sturtevant, with both of whom he shared the Nobel Prize money, and H. J. Muller, who was later awarded the Prize himself for his discovery of X-ray mutations (see below, pp. 244-249). The result of the combined efforts of Morgan's team was a great extension of the knowledge of genetics. Morgan's work and influence were acknowledged by the award of many honors, including foreign membership in the Royal Society. He died at the age of seventy-nine, on December 4, 1945.

DESCRIPTION OF THE PRIZE-WINNING
WORK*

"Mendel's paper was recovered in 1900. [In 1866 J. G. Mendel published an account of his experiments with garden peas, setting forth "Mendel's laws" of heredity. According to the first of these, two different hereditary characters, after being combined in one generation, will again be segregated in the next—i.e., in the new sex cells. The latter being fused with others, new and independent combinations can be formed; this is Mendel's second law, that of independent assortment. No notice was taken of his paper until 1900.] Four years later Bateson and Punnett reported observations that did not give the numerical results expected for two independent pairs of characters. For instance, when a sweet pea having purple flower-color and long pollen grains is crossed to one with red flowers and round pollen grains, the two types that go in together come out together more frequently than expected for independent assortment of purple-red and round-long. They spoke of these results as due to repulsion between the combinations purple and long and red and round, that came from opposite parents. Today these relations are called linkage. By linkage we mean that when certain characters enter a cross together, they tend to remain together in later generations, or, stated in a negative way, certain pairs of characters do not assort at random.

"It would seem, then, so far as linkage holds, that there are limits to the subdivision of the germinal material. For example in the vinegar fly [also called fruit fly], Drosophila melanogaster, ῑere are known about 400 new mutant types that fall into only four linkage groups.

"One of these groups of characters of Drosophila is said to be sex-linked, because in inheritance the characters show certain relations to sex. There are about 150 of these sex-linked mutant characters. Several of them are modifications of the color of the eye, others relate to its shape or its size, or to the regularity of the distribution of its facets. Other characters involve the body color;

---

* T. H. Morgan, *The Theory of the Gene* (New Haven: Yale University Press, rev. ed., 1928), Silliman Lectures, pp. 10-14, 19-20.

others the shape of the wings, or the distribution of its veins; others the spines and hairs that cover the body.

"A second group of about 120 linked characters includes changes in all parts of the body. None of the effects are identical with those of the first group.

"A third group of about 130 characters also involves all parts of the body. None of these characters are the same, as those of the other two groups.

"There is a small fourth group of only three characters; one involves the size of the eyes, leading in extreme cases to their total absence; one involves the mode of carriage of the wings; and the third relates to the reduction in size of the hairs.

"The method of inheritance of linked characters is given in the following example. A male Drosophila with four linked characters (belonging to the second group), black body color, purple eyes, vestigial wings, and a speck at the base of the wings, is crossed to a wild type female with the corresponding normal characters, that may be called gray body color, red eyes, long wings, and absence of speck. The offspring are wild type. If one of the sons is now crossed to a stock female having the four recessive characters (black, purple, vestigial, speck), the offspring are of two kinds only, half are like one grandparent with the four recessive characters, and the other half are wild type like the other grandparent.

"Two sets of contrasted (or allelomorphic) linked genes went into this cross. When the germ-cells in the male hybrid matured, one of these sets of linked genes went into half of the sperm-cells and the corresponding allelomorphic set into the wild type half of the sperm-cells. This was revealed, as described above, by crossing the hybrid (F_1) [first generation] male to a female pure for the four recessive genes. All of her mature eggs contain one set of four recessive genes. Any egg fertilized by a sperm with one set of the dominant wild type genes should give a wild type fly. Any egg fertilized by a sperm with the four recessive genes (which are the same as those in the female here used) should give a black, purple, vestigial, speck fly. These are two kinds of individuals obtained.

"The members of a linked group may not always be completely linked as in the case just given. In fact, in the F_1 female from the same cross, some of the recessive characters of one series may be interchanged for wild type characters from the other series, but even then, since they remained united more often than they interchange, they are still said to be linked together. This interchange is called crossing-over, which means that, between two corresponding linked series, there may take place an orderly interchange involving great numbers of genes. . . .

"A study of crossing-over [in Drosophila] has shown that all possible percentages of crossing-over occur, up to nearly 50 per cent. If exactly 50 per cent of crossing-over took place, the numerical result would be the same as when free assortment occurs. That is, no linkage would be observed even though the characters involved are in the same linkage group. Their relation as members of the same group could, nevertheless, be shown by their common linkage to some third member of the series. If more than 50 per cent crossing-over should be found, a sort of inverted linkage would appear, since the cross-over combinations would then be more frequent than the grandparental types.

"The fact that crossing-over in the female of Drosophila is always less than 50 per cent, is due to another correlated phenomenon called double crossing-over. By double crossing-over is meant that interchange takes place twice between two pairs of genes involved in the cross. The result is to lower the *observed* cases of crossing-over, since a second crossing-over undoes the effect of a single crossing-over."

CONSEQUENCES IN THEORY AND PRACTICE

Professor Morgan began his career as a zoologist on strictly morphological lines—i.e., as a student of form and structure. He became, however, a distinguished experimentalist, particularly in genetics. Deeply interested in evolution, on which he wrote extensively, he was distrustful of Darwin's theory of natural selection and preferred the mutations theory of De Vries as an explanation of the origin of species. That is to say, he was inclined to think new species the consequence of spontaneous, inheritable changes due to aberrations of the chromosomes, threadlike intracellular structures which had been suggested as the carriers of hereditary characters (genes). This suggestion, made at the beginning of the century by W. Sutton and T. Bovery, seemed to fit the scheme of Mendelian heredity. Prior to cell division each chromosome splits longitudinally into two daughter chromosomes; when cell division actually takes place, one of these becomes part of the structure of each new cell, which is thus endowed with the same combination of chromosomes as the original cell. Maturation division, however, which occurs in mature sex cells, is of a different kind: here the number of chromosomes is reduced by one half. When male and female sex cells come together and fuse, the original chromosome number is again restored, but now one half of each pair is derived from the male, the other half from the female, sex cell. If chromosomes were actually the carriers, as Sutton and Bovery suggested, of the hereditary elements, the genes, here was a mechanism to account for the Mendelian ratios in breeding experiments. But of this there was no proof.

It was about this time that Morgan began to work with Drosophila. The fruit fly of this name had already been shown by Lutz, Payne, and others to be amenable to culture in the laboratory. It is particularly well suited for studies in genetics because it breeds very rapidly (ten days from egg to egg) and because its cell nucleus contains only four chromosomes. Morgan found that Drosophila did not give rise to new species, in accord with the theory of De Vries, but rather provided valuable material for the study of Mendelian segregation.

As indicated in the quotation, Mendel's second law is subject to certain exceptions. These were accounted for by the doctrine of linkage. But linkage is not perfectly constant and factors are sometimes separated which usually occur together. Morgan's explanation was that chromosomes belonging to the same pair may exchange genes immediately before the maturation division. One or more breaks occur in each chromosome and the parts are then reunited crosswise. This is the mechanism of the crossing-over already described. The probability that a break will occur between genes when a chromosome is segmented in this way is increased by the distance separating the positions of two such genes; the more commonly such genes break off, the more commonly the factors they represent will be recombined in offspring.

All this assumes that the genes are arranged in straight lines, and not, for example, in circles. If this assumption is made, there is an exact correlation to be expected between the rate of occurrence of these recombinations and the relative distance between the genes in question in a chromosome. Charts of chromosomes have been established in this way, showing the positions of the genes. (Compare H. J. Muller's explanation of X-ray mutations; see below, pp. 245-247.)

Morgan's school of geneticists has been able to present convincing evidence that the chromosome is actually the carrier of the genes. This evidence is of several kinds. There are four chromosomes in Drosophila; there are also four linkage groups. But perhaps the most conclusive evidence is that which comes from the loss or from the addition of one of the small fourth chromosomes of Drosophila. Genetic indications can in this case be verified directly by the microscope.

The Morgan doctrines which are here sketched in outline were built up by the patient and comprehensive work of many years. They have been confirmed by other scientists in studies of both animals and plants. Their integration with biochemistry has been brought to fruition through the work of Beadle and Tatum (winners, with J. Lederberg, of the Nobel Prize in 1958). In the human being, too, it has been possible to identify linkage groups and, through the work of J. H. Tjio, M. Barr, L. Lejeune, and others, to examine the chromosomes in leucocytes and other types of cell. These cytogenetic studies have revealed another type of chromosomal change besides mutation: an increase or decrease in the number of these nuclear bodies. This comes about through the phenomenon of non-disjunction, i.e. incomplete separation of the chromosomes at maturation division, so that one sex cell has an extra chromosome and another has a corresponding deficiency. When such a sex cell combines in fertilization with a normal cell, the resulting fertilized egg will have an abnormal number of chromosomes. This is the case in several diseases, including Down's disease (mongolism) where there is an extra chromosome. The study of chromosomal changes of both types is part of current cancer research.

Finally, the gene theory, which owes so much to Morgan and his school, has proved to be a concept of great practical importance not only in medicine and theoretical biology, but also in agriculture and stock breeding.

1934
GEORGE HOYT WHIPPLE
(1878–)

GEORGE RICHARDS MINOT
(1885–1950)

WILLIAM PARRY MURPHY
(1892--)

"For their discoveries concerning liver therapy against anemias."

BIOGRAPHICAL SKETCHES

WHIPPLE

GEORGE HOYT WHIPPLE WAS BORN IN ASHLAND, NEW HAMP-shire, on August 28, 1878. He was educated at Andover Academy and Yale University (A.B., 1900) and received his M.D. degree from the Johns Hopkins University in 1905. With the exception of one year (1907-1908) as pathologist at the Ancon Hospital, Panama, Dr. Whipple was at the Johns Hopkins Medical School from 1905 to 1914, as assistant in pathology, instructor, associate, and associate professor. From 1914 to 1921 he was professor of

176

research medicine at the University of California Medical School, and director of the Hooper Foundation for Medical Research, University of California. During the year 1920-1921 he was dean of the University of California Medical School. In 1921 Dr. Whipple became professor of pathology and dean of the School of Medicine and Dentistry of the University of Rochester. Much of his research, from the time when he was a junior in the Johns Hopkins Department of Pathology under Dr. William H. Welch, has dealt with normal and pathological liver function. Dr. Whipple has conducted penetrating studies of the origin, function, and fate of bile pigments and other body pigments in health and disease. He has made contributions of basic importance to our knowledge of the anemias. He has also studied plasma protein regeneration and iron metabolism. He became a Trustee of the Rockefeller Foundation in 1927, a member of the Board of Scientific Directors of the Rockefeller Institute in 1936, and a Trustee of the Institute in 1939. He retired as Professor of Medicine at the University of Rochester in 1955. In 1963 President Kennedy presented him with an award for "distinguished federal civilian service."

MINOT

GEORGE RICHARDS MINOT WAS BORN IN BOSTON, ON DECEMBER 2, 1885. He attended Harvard University, receiving the A.B. in 1908, the M.D. in 1912, and the honorary degree of S.D. in 1928. After serving as medical interne at the Massachusetts General Hospital, he worked at the Johns Hopkins Hospital and Medical School under William S. Thayer and William H. Howell. In 1915 he returned to Boston, being appointed assistant in medicine at the Harvard Medical School and Massachusetts General Hospital. In 1922 he became physician in chief of the Collis P. Huntington Memorial Hospital of Harvard University; later he was appointed also to the staff of the Peter Bent Brigham Hospital. In 1928 he was made professor of medicine at Harvard and director of the Thorndike Memorial Laboratory, as well as visiting physician at Boston City Hospital. Although he published papers on a wide variety of subjects, including cancer, arthritis, and dietary deficiency (e.g., the role of dietary factors in "alcoholic" polyneuritis), his chief interest lay in disorders of the blood and the function and dysfunction of bone marrow. He contributed to knowledge concerning coagulation of the blood, the blood platelets, various hemorrhagic disorders, the blood picture in certain industrial poisonings, leukemia, disorders of the lymphatic tissue and polycythemia, as well as the anemias. His most significant contributions were his studies of the anemias, and especially pernicious anemia.

MURPHY

WILLIAM PARRY MURPHY WAS BORN IN STOUGHTON, WISCONsin, on February 6, 1892. His early education was received in the public schools of Wisconsin and Oregon. He received his A.B. from the University of Oregon in 1914 and then for two years taught physics and mathematics in Oregon high schools. After one year in the University of Oregon Medical School, Portland, and a summer session at the Rush Medical School, Chicago, he entered the Harvard Medical School and received the M.D. degree in 1922 as of 1920. After two years as house officer at the Rhode Island Hospital, he became assistant resident physician at the Peter Bent Brigham Hospital under Prof. Henry A. Christian for eighteen months, then junior associate, and later associate in medicine at the same institution. He was assistant in medicine at Harvard from 1923 to 1928, instructor from 1928 to 1935, and associate from 1935 to 1958, when he retired with the title of Emeritus Professor.

DESCRIPTION OF THE PRIZE-WINNING WORK

WHIPPLE *

"At the University of California (1914), Dr. [C. W.] Hooper and I took up a careful study of bile pigment metabolism by means of bile fistulas in dogs and investigated the effect of diet upon bile pigment output. As these studies were continued . . . it became

---

* From G. H. Whipple, "Hemoglobin Regeneration as Influenced by Diet and Other Factors," Les Prix Nobel en 1934.

apparent that we could not understand completely the story of bile pigment metabolism without more knowledge about the construction of blood hemoglobin in the body. Blood hemoglobin is a most important precursor of bile pigment and it was necessary to understand what factors influenced the building of new hemoglobin in the dog.

"For this reason we produced simple anemia in dogs by means of blood withdrawal and in short experiments followed the curve of hemoglobin regeneration back to normal. These experiments with Dr. Hooper were begun in 1917 and it was found at once that diet had a significant influence on this type of blood regeneration. Because of our interest in liver function and injury we soon began testing *liver* as one of the diet factors and could readily demonstrate that it had a powerful effect upon hemoglobin regeneration [1920]. These short anemia experiments were relatively crude and gave at best qualitative values for the various diet factors.

"After the transfer of the anemia colony of dogs from San Francisco to Rochester, New York (1923), Dr. Frieda Robscheit-Robbins and the writer began to use a different type of anemia. Dogs were bled by aspiration from the jugular vein and gradually reduced from a normal hemoglobin level of 140-150 per cent to about 1/3 normal, or 40-50 per cent, and this anemia level was maintained a constant for indefinite periods by suitable removal of new-formed hemoglobin. The potency of the diet factor was then accurately measured in terms of the grams hemoglobin removed to preserve the constant anemia level. The stimulus presumably was maximal and uniform, and the reaction of a given dog to a diet factor was shown to be uniform when repeated time after time.

"Much effort and time were spent in devising a basal ration adequate for health and maintenance during these long anemia periods lasting throughout the entire life of the dog (5-8 years). . . . [Such a diet] permits of minimal new hemoglobin regeneration and therefore gives a low base-line hemoglobin output from which to measure the increased output due to liver, kidney, gizzard or other favourable diet factor. . . .

"[From the results] it is obvious that liver . . . stands out as the most potent diet factor. . . . Gradually various diet factors were standardized and this information was placed at the disposal of physicians who were concerned with the therapeutic treatment of human anemias. Iron was found to be the most potent inorganic element.

"Pernicious anemia, examined from the point of view of the pathologist, was described in 1921 [publication 1922] as a disease in which all pigment factors were present in the body in large excess but with a scarcity of stroma-building material or an abnormality of stroma-building cells." [The "stroma" is the framework, or structural basis, of an organ, tissue, or cell. In pernicious anemia the factors needed to form blood pigment are present, but the red blood cells, the necessary vehicle, do not form properly.]

MINOT *

"The idea that something in food might be of advantage to patients with pernicious anemia was in my mind in 1912, when I was a house officer at the Massachusetts General Hospital, as is noted in certain case records there. . . .

"The study of the patients' diets was begun in 1915 in an attempt to determine if some sort of dietary deficiency could be found. The similarity of certain symptoms and signs of pernicious anemia to those in pellagra, sprue and beriberi was appreciated, as was the fact that certain sorts of anemia were occasionally associated with a faulty diet. Elders, among others, suggested in 1922 that such a state of affairs existed in pernicious anemia. Furthermore, the almost constant occurrence of achlorhydria [absence of hydrochloric acid in the gastric juice] in pernicious anemia . . . led me to wonder if this disorder of the digestive system had something to do with the condition which might be in the nature of a dietary deficiency disease. Indeed, Fenwick, about 1880, suggested the primary role of the stomach, but it remained for Castle, in 1928, to demonstrate the part this organ plays in the causation of the disease. . . . [W. B. Castle showed that meat digested with normal gastric juice was almost as effective as liver, but found that meat by itself, or when digested with the aid of a synthetic gastric juice, failed to give any good effect. Normal gastric juice seems to

---

* From G. R. Minot, "The Development of Liver Therapy in Pernicious Anemia," *Les Prix Nobel en 1934.*

contain an "intrinsic factor," which together with an "extrinsic factor" in meat forms the active substance causing red blood cells to mature. This active substance, called "erythrocyte maturing factor," or "EMF," is stored, among other places, in the liver. This explanation was not forthcoming until Minot and Murphy had shown the value of liver therapy.]

"Although Pepper in 1875 and Cohnheim in 1876 recognized that the bone marrow was abnormal, there was a prevailing opinion in the early part of this century that abnormal blood-destruction played an important or primary role in the production of the disease. Nevertheless it was believed by many physicians, as I was taught, that the production of blood by the bone marrow was also deeply implicated. . . . [This] led me to believe firmly that something was needed to make the primitive red cells that crowd the bone marrow in relapse grow to normal cells. . . . In 1922 Whipple suggested that in pernicious anemia there might be a scarcity of material from which the stroma of the red blood cells was formed, or that there existed a disease of the stroma-forming cells of the bone marrow. This concept fitted with the idea that there was a deficiency of something in the body, and that dysfunction of pigment metabolism was resultant. . . .

"For centuries the concept that food bore a relationship to anemia had been vaguely expressed in the literature. It had been shown that liver and kidneys, rich in complete proteins, promoted the growth of animals, and that substances in liver could enhance cell-division. It was likewise recognized that liver-feeding could benefit patients with sprue (Manson 1883) and pellagra. These were among the reasons that led to the choice of liver as a substance likely to enhance blood-formation. Of invaluable importance was Whipple's fundamental and classical work on hemoglobin regeneration by means of liver and other foods in anemia due to blood-loss in dogs. . . .

"A few patients were fed relatively small amounts of liver during 1924 and early 1925. Although these patients did better than expected, the results permitted no more than speculations. Then Dr. Murphy joined in the work and we pursued the study of these and subsequent cases. Liver had been fed by Gibson and Howard and other individuals to pernicious anemia patients but without persistence or definite results. It seemed to us that to accomplish our object a large weighed amount of liver should be fed daily with regularity. Likewise to determine the effect it was considered essential that data should be obtained in a large number of cases to be appropriately compared with controls. By May, 1926, we had fed liver intensively and daily to 45 patients. In many of these patients symptomatic improvement was obvious within about a week. Soon they craved food and color appeared in their faces. Tongue and digestive symptoms rapidly lessened. Within about 60 days the red blood cell counts had risen on the average from low levels to approximately normal. . . . An objective measure of the effects upon blood-production was the chief basis of our conclusions that by feeding liver significant improvement had been obtained. I refer especially to counts of new adult and young blood cells (reticulocytes) appearing, as Peabody's studies demonstrated later, as a result of the maturation of the immature cells crowding the bone marrow.

"The next step naturally was to attempt to determine the nature of the constituent in liver responsible for the effects and to learn if an extract for therapeutic use could be obtained. Dr. Edwin J. Cohn, . . . of the Harvard Medical School, soon made a potent extract suitable for oral use. . . . It remained for Gänsslen in Germany to produce the first practical extract for parenteral [injection] therapy."

MURPHY *

"Since the earliest use of liver in the treatment of pernicious anemia . . . new fields of observation have been made available both in the clinic and in the laboratory. We have been allowed the thrill of watching the patient through a few days of depression following the institution of liver therapy until remission occurs with its often sudden and almost unbelievable sense of well-being simultaneously with the maximum increase of the reticulocytes or new red blood cells. Then we have followed this remission through to completion, until the blood becomes normal. . . . Perhaps even more dramatic has been the improvement in the disturbances of locomotion resulting from nerve damage. . . .

---

* From W. P. Murphy, "Pernicious Anemia," *Les Prix Nobel en 1934*.

"Observation of the patients at intervals in the office or hospital blood clinic and attention to the important details of treatment have made it possible for us to maintain our patients in a state of economic efficiency and with reasonably good health. Forty-two of the forty-five patients originally treated and discussed in our first paper [Minot and Murphy] in 1926 have been kept under observation. Of this number thirty-one, or approximately three fourths, are living and well [1934] after almost ten years of treatment. Eleven have died from various causes other than pernicious anemia."

CONSEQUENCES IN THEORY AND PRACTICE

The practical results of liver therapy in the treatment of pernicious anemia have already been indicated in quotations from the Nobel lectures of Dr. Minot and Dr. Murphy. Another agent subsequently introduced for the same purpose was a preparation of the stomach wall of the hog—desiccated, defatted and powdered. Its effect is similar to that of liver. These organ extracts have now been joined by vitamin B_{12} in the treatment of the disease. This vitamin is formed by molds of the Streptomyces group and by other types; the molds are grown industrially in large fermentation tanks under precisely controlled conditions. The broth is extracted and treated to obtain the pure vitamin.

Pernicious anemia patients have enough vitamin B_{12} in their diet, but they are unable to absorb the supply normally. Their gastric juice is deficient in a substance that combines with the vitamin to facilitate its absorption from the intestinal tract. Hog stomach powder contains this substance; the injectable liver extracts contain the combination. Injected vitamin B_{12} becomes readily available to the red-cell-forming organs, thus avoiding the need for intrinsic factor. Another vitamin, folic acid, originally isolated from green leaves and from liver, has a certain curative value in that it brings about the production of mature red blood cells; it is not satisfactory in the treatment of pernicious anemia because it does not stop the changes in the nervous system that often accompany the disease. Its main use is in the treatment of certain related anemias.

Here is an insidious, chronic, debilitating disease, ultimately fatal before the introduction of liver therapy, but now controllable. Neither liver nor vitamin B_{12} "cures" the basic defect; they simply permit the patient to avoid its consequences as long as he continues the treatment.

The initial effects of therapy are remarkable. Within a few days the number of reticulocytes (immature blood corpuscles) goes up, showing that the bone marrow, where the cells are formed, is increasingly active. The number of normal cells in the blood gradually increases, and the abnormal ones begin to disappear. Concurrently the patient feels better, looks better, and becomes stronger.

The two great innovations in the treatment of non-infectious disease during the first quarter of the present century were insulin for diabetes and liver for pernicious anemia. Both discoveries stimulated further research. Knowledge of the effect of liver gave a new direction to the study of hematopoiesis (the formation of blood) under both normal and pathological conditions. The search for the chemical nature of the active component of liver extract was, however, unsuccessful until the late nineteen forties, when studies of the nutritional requirements of microorganisms showed that the extract could substitute for a new bacterial vitamin. Man's place as the sole "test organism" available to measure the activity of liver extract was now rapidly filled by the Lactobacillus. The use of this organism soon led to the purification of the vitamin, and the complete elucidation of its chemical structure in 1955. Dorothy Crowfoot Hodgkin, Nobel Prize winner in Chemistry, 1964, played a key role in the determination of structure, using the x-ray diffraction technique.

REFERENCE

CORNER, GEORGE W. *George Hoyt Whipple and his Friends,* .the life-story of a Nobel prize pathologist. (Philadelphia: Lippincott, 1963).

1935
HANS SPEMANN
(1869–1941)

"For his discovery of the organizer effect in embryonic development."

BIOGRAPHICAL SKETCH

HANS SPEMANN WAS BORN ON JUNE 27, 1869, IN STUTTGART, Germany, where he attended the humanistic Eberhard-Ludwig *Gymnasium*. After leaving school he spent a few years in his father's business and in the performance of his military service before beginning the study of medicine at the Universities of Heidelberg, Munich, and Würzburg. At Heidelberg he worked with the anatomist Carl Gegenbaur; at Munich, with August Pauly. He was graduated in 1895 in zoology, botany, and physics, under Theodor Bovery, Julius Sachs, and Wilhelm Röntgen, respectively. The years 1894-1908 were spent in the Zoological Institute at Würzburg. In the latter year he accepted the chair of zoology and comparative anatomy at Rostock. In 1914 he became director of the Kaiser Wilhelm Institute for Biology in Berlin-Dahlem. Finally, in 1919, he was called to the professorship at Freiburg-im-Breisgau, which he held until his retirement in 1935, the year in which he was awarded the Nobel Prize. He died at the end of 1941, in his seventy-third year.

DESCRIPTION OF THE PRIZE-WINNING WORK*

"[My experiments] were all carried out on young amphibian embryos, mostly on those of the ordinary . . . *Triton teaeniatus* [species of newt]. In order to make the experiments understandable to nonspecialists, too, it becomes necessary first of all to picture the highlights of the normal development of these eggs.

"The development begins, in direct response to fertilization, with long-continued cell division . . . known as the segmentation process. Through the formation of a hollow space inside—the segmentation cavity—there arises the germinal vesicle or blastula. Its lower, vegetative half, the thick floor of the germinal vesicle, is composed of large, yolk-rich cells, whereas the upper, animal half, the thin roof, is composed of numerous small cells, poor in yolk substance. The junction between them is formed by the marginal zone, a ring of cells of medium size.

"There now sets in a very complicated process, in many respects mysterious, the so-called gastrulation. Its final result is that the whole material of the marginal zone and the vegetative half of the embryo are doubled into the interior, and are thus covered by the animal material. It is along the line of invagination, at the primitive orifice or blastopore, that the outer germinal layer, the ectoderm, changes to the two layers brought into the interior, the mesoderm, (originating in the marginal zone) and the entoderm (corresponding to the yolk-rich vegetative half of the embryo). . . .

"The anlage of the central nervous system [i.e., the primordial part in the embryo from which the adult structure is formed] arises in the ectoderm of the back . . . as a thickened, shield-shaped plate, broader in its anterior than in its posterior half. It is the medullary plate, the edges of which are thrust up into ridges, the medullary ridges. By the drawing together of the ridges, the plate is closed to form a tube, the medullary tube. This detaches itself from the epidermis and sinks deeper. Its thick anterior end, arising from the broad anterior part of the medullary plate, becomes the

---

* Translated from "Nobel-Vortrag von Hans Spemann," *Les Prix Nobel en 1935.*

brain; its thin posterior half the spinal cord. [Spemann then describes briefly the fate of the mesoderm, which forms the anlage of the vertebral column, etc., and the entoderm, which forms a groove, changing into the intestinal tube.]

"All these events . . . are essentially dependent not on a new formation of embryonic substance but on rearrangement of that already present. It is therefore to some extent possible . . . to mark out a topography of the later anlages of the organs in the blastula or early gastrula.

"In considering such a topographical map, the question recurs whether an actual difference in these parts corresponds to this pattern of presumptive anlages in the gastrula at the beginning; whether they are already more or less firmly ordained for their later fate, predestined [*determiniert*], or whether they are still indifferent and their destiny is first stamped upon them later.

"The first answer to this question was given by isolation experiments. That is to say, if one undertakes a division through the middle, not between the first two segmentation cells, but later, even in the stage of the blastula or the quite young gastrula, twins can still be produced by this means. This becomes especially clear if the division be made in such a way that the ventral half of the embryo is cut off from the dorsal. Then the latter also develops into an embryo of smaller size [but] of normal proportions. Here the new partition of materials is quite plain. The dorsal half, according to the topographical map, possesses almost all the material for the medullary plate, therefore much too much for a half-size embryo; on the other hand it lacks the whole presumptive epidermis. This latter must be made good from the material of the former.

"But now if presumptive medullary plate and presumptive epidermis can substitute for each other, then also they must allow themselves to be interchanged, one for the other, without prejudice to further normal development. Embryonal transplantation must thus in this early stage have another result than in the later stages. . . .

"The success of the new experiments rests on these ideas, and on the development of a method making it possible to manage the extraordinarily fragile young embryos and to operate on them.

"The first experiment now consists in the interchange of a piece of presumptive epidermis and medullary plate between two embryos of the same age, in the beginning of gastrulation. Healing results so smoothly, and the further development goes on so normally, that the margins disappear without a trace, if the implant is not kept visible for a time by natural pigmentation or artificial vital staining. In this case it appears, as expected, that the pieces can interchange mutually, so that presumptive epidermis can become medullary plate, presumptive medullary plate epidermis.

"But from this follows not only the profound indifference of the cells in this early stage of development; rather, the result permits the much more important conclusion that in the new location influences of some sort must govern, which coerce the foreign piece to its fate. . ."

CONSEQUENCES IN THEORY AND PRACTICE

"In order [as Spemann wrote] to make the experiments understandable to nonspecialists," he felt it necessary to devote a large part of his Nobel lecture "to picture the highlights of the normal development of these eggs." The quotation given above terminates with the first indication of the general principle which was Spemann's chief contribution.

Spemann's most important forerunners were Roux and Driesch. W. Roux had obtained half-formations, etc. by destroying some of the cleavage cells in the frog's egg. His experiments led him to the view that up to a certain point something within each part of the embryo determines its fate; thereafter the general requirements of the organism and the need for certain cells determine their appearance and growth.

To illustrate the inductive effect which one embryonal area can exert on another, Spemann performed experiments on the developing eye. The retina grows out from the brain as a vesicle, later changed into a cuplike structure; the lens of the eye, on the other hand, is derived from the near-by epidermis. Spemann showed that the eyeball is able to bring about the formation of a lens from distant epidermis which does not normally develop in this way, in an area having nothing to do, under ordinary circumstances, with lens production. The covering epidermis then begins to clear, as in the formation of the transparent cornea, despite its "foreign," noncorneal location.

Then came the experiments in division of the embryo described in the quotation above, and the transplants of pieces of presumptive medullary plate, showing how rearranged cells develop according to their new local environment. Spemann was also able to show that if a piece of the dorsal blastopore lip is implanted in another embryo, in an area of presumptive skin, the development of a second embryo is thereby induced. This upper blastopore lip he later showed to be the source of influences which determine the fate and cause the structural and functional differentiation of various parts, the medullary plate in particular; he therefore called the upper blastopore lip an "organization center." Other, secondary organization centers were also demonstrated, of which the eyecup may be considered one.

"[Spemann's] great achievement was to bring into fruitful coordination the two, in themselves inconclusive, lines of attack which had been opened up in the casual investigation of development. On one hand, the studies of Roux and Driesch on the developmental potentialities of the first-formed blastomeres of the egg, although they tackled the major problems of the formation of the animal as a whole, seemed to lead only to a sterile paradox. On the other hand, Roux's notion of dependent differentiation appeared to suggest a plausible causal mechanism for development, but the one known example of it, and that a somewhat doubtful one, was concerned with the development of a single organ, the lens of the eye. Spemann entered both these fields, with his famous constriction experiments on the early cleavage states of Triton, and his early grafting experiments on the optic rudiments of the same form. By 1918 he was able to bring forward his concept of the organization-centre' and demonstrate that the morphogenesis of the embryo, in its main outlines as well as in its details, is the result of the interactions between different regions of tissue. For the next fourteen years, Spemann was the leader of a school, which rapidly filled in the outlines of what had come to be called 'embryonic induction.' . . . In 1932 he participated in the next major step forward, the beginning of the physico-chemical investigation of the process.

"Although his work was one of the most important influences in the final discredit of vitalism, Spemann was never one of those who hoped that the discovery of the organizer would rapidly enable us to reduce the problem of biological form to a few simple chemical statements. His attitude was, in fact, much more a biological than a physico-chemical one. The extreme caution with which he formed his conclusions, joined with intense concentration on a narrow field favourable for an attack on fundamental problems, enabled him to lay a foundation on which the science of experi-

Spemann's findings have been confirmed in other species, notably in the chick embryo, through the work of C. H. Waddington. Waddington, along with Joseph Needham and Jean Brachet, studied the chemistry of embryonic development, with particular regard to the nature of the "organizer substances," the chemicals that direct the processes of differentiation. Some quite ordinary substances, unknown however as constituents of the animal body and probably not occurring there, can bring about embryonic changes. One of these substances is methylene blue. Deficiency of certain vitamins can also distort fetal development, but this has been demonstrated thus far only experimentally in animals. The problem of the effect of chemicals upon embryonic development has been pointed up in recent years by the discovery that the sedative drug thalidomide, widely used in Germany and some other countries, sometimes caused serious disturbances of fetal development, such as phocomelia ("flipper-limb") when it was taken by pregnant women. Further studies in chemical morphogenesis may throw new light on the development of embryonic abnormalities in man, where the causes are at present unknown.

REFERENCE

WADDINGTON, C. H. *The Nature of Life* (London: Allen and Unwin, 1961).

---

* Quoted from the obituary by C. H. Waddington in *Nature* (London), Vol. 149 (1942), p. 296.

1 9 3 6
HENRY DALE
(1875–   )

OTTO LOEWI
(1873–1961)

*"For their discoveries relating to the chemical
transmission of nerve impulses."*

BIOGRAPHICAL SKETCHES

DALE

HENRY HALLETT DALE WAS BORN IN LONDON, ON JUNE 9,
1875. From Leys School, Cambridge, he proceeded to Trinity College, Cambridge, in 1894. This step in his education, like every
subsequent stage, was marked by the winning of a scholarship. He
was graduated through the Natural Science Tripos, Part II (Physiology and Zoology.) From 1898-1900 he worked in physiology at
Cambridge under J. N. Langley. In the latter year he turned to
clinical work at St. Bartholomew's Hospital. Cambridge granted
him the B.Ch. in 1903 and the M.D. in 1909. For a time he worked
in University College, London, with E. H. Starling; here he first
met Otto Loewi. There followed four months with Paul Ehrlich

at Frankfort on the Main. Dale then returned for a brief period to University College, but soon entered the Wellcome Physiological Research Laboratories as pharmacologist (1904). From 1906 to 1914 he was director of the Laboratories. It was during this period that he undertook the work on the pharmacology of ergot which led to his later studies on tyramine, histamine, and acetylcholine. In 1914 he was elected Fellow of the Royal Society and in the same year was appointed director of the Department of Biochemistry and Physiology in the newly constituted National Institute for Medical Research. In 1928 he became director of the Institute. Dale has been President of the Royal Society of Medicine (from 1948 to 1950), and Chairman of the Wellcome Trust from 1938 to 1960. In 1950 he was President of the British Council. He is internationally known through his researches, which have won him many honors, his activities on many official commissions, and through his students in many parts of the world.

LOEWI

OTTO LOEWI WAS BORN IN FRANKFORT ON THE MAIN, ON JUNE 3, 1873. He studied in the *Gymnasium* there until 1891, when he undertook the study of medicine at Strasbourg. Later he took a part of his course in Munich but returned to Strasbourg for the degree Dr. med., which was granted in 1896. In 1896-1897 he studied chemistry in Frankfort with Martin Freund, then physiological chemistry with Franz Hofmeister in Strasbourg. In 1897-1898 he was assistant to Karl von Noordens in the City Hospital in Frankfort. He was then appointed assistant at the Pharmacological Institute directed by Hans Horst Meyer in Marburg, and became Privatdozent in 1900. He worked for some months in 1901-1902 with E. H. Starling in London, but remained at Marburg until 1905, when he moved with Meyer to Vienna. For nearly thirty years (1909-1938) he was Professor of Pharmacology in Graz. Obliged to leave when Austria was nazified, he spent some time at Oxford and at Brussels. From 1940 until his death on December 25, 1961, he was research professor at the College of Medicine of New York University.

DESCRIPTION OF THE PRIZE-WINNING WORK

DALE *

"My chemical collaborator [in 1914], Dr. Ewins, had isolated the substance responsible for a characteristic activity which I had detected in certain ergot extracts, and it had proved to be acetylcholine, the very intense activity of which had been observed by Reid Hunt already in 1906. Since we had found this substance in nature, and it was no longer a synthetic curiosity, it seemed to me of interest to explore its activity in greater detail. I was thus able to describe it as having two apparently distinct types of action. Through what I termed its 'muscarine' action, it reproduced at the periphery all the effects of parasympathetic nerves, with a fidelity which, as I indicated, was comparable to that with which adrenaline had been shown, some ten years earlier, to reproduce those of true sympathetic nerves. All these peripheral muscarine actions, these parasympathomimetic effects of acetylcholine, were very readily abolished by atropine. When they were thus suppressed, another type of action was revealed, which I termed the 'nicotine' action, because it closely resembled the action of that alkaloid in its intense stimulant effect on all autonomic ganglion cells, and, as later appeared, on voluntary muscle fibres. . . .

"Effects of acetylcholine, directly analogous to those which Loewi discovered in relation to the heart vagus, were covered by what I had termed the 'muscarine' action of acetylcholine, and were all very readily suppressed by atropine. But there remained, as yet without any corresponding physiological significance, the other type of action of acetylcholine, so similar in distribution to that of nicotine, which had come to my notice nearly twenty years earlier. . . .

"Although from the time when it first became clear that Loewi's Vagusstoff [see pp. 197-198] was acetylcholine, I had begun to consider the possible significance of its 'nicotine' actions, it was long before the possibility of its intervention as transmitter at

---

* H. H. Dale, "Some Recent Extensions of the Chemical Transmission of the Effects of Nerve Impulses," *Les Prix Nobel en 1936.*

ganglionic synapses, or at voluntary motor nerve endings, seemed to be accessible to investigation. Experiments on the ganglion came first in order. Chang and Gaddum had found, confirming an earlier observation by Witanowski, that sympathetic ganglia were rich in acetylcholine. Feldberg . . . had observed . . . that the effects of splanchnic [visceral] nerve stimulation are transmitted to the cells of the suprarenal medulla by the release of acetylcholine in that tissue. Now these medullary cells are morphological analogues of sympathetic ganglion cells, and Feldberg, continuing this study in my laboratory, found that this stimulating action of acetylcholine on the suprarenal medulla belonged to the 'nicotine' side of its actions. Clearly we had to extend these observations to the ganglion; and a method of perfusing the superior cervical ganglion of the cat, then recently described by Kibjakow, made the experiment possible. Feldberg and Gaddum . . . found that, when eserine [see below, p. 197] was added to the fluid perfusing the ganglion, stimulation of the preganglionic fibres regularly caused the appearance of acetylcholine in the venous effluent. It could be identified by its characteristic instability, and by the fact that its activity matched the same known concentration of acetylcholine in a series of different physiological tests, covering both 'muscarine' and 'nicotine' actions. It appeared in the venous fluid in relatively high concentrations, so strong indeed, that reinjection of the fluid into the arterial side of the perfusion caused, on occasion, a direct stimulation of the ganglion-cells. It was clear that, if the liberation took place actually at the synapses, the acetylcholine liberated by each preganglionic impulse, in small dose, indeed, but in much higher concentration than that in which it reached the venous effluent, *must.* act as a stimulus to the corresponding ganglion cells. Feldberg and Vartiainen then showed that it was, in fact, only the arrival of preganglionic impulses at synapses which caused the acetylcholine to appear. They showed, further, that the ganglion cells might be paralysed by nicotine or curarine [the active principle of the arrow-poison, curare], so that they would no longer respond to preganglionic stimulation or to the injection of acetylcholine, but that such treatment did not, in the least, diminish the output of acetylcholine caused by the arrival of preganglionic impulses at the synapses. There was, in this respect, a complete analogy with the paralysing effect of atropine on the action of the heart vagus, which, as Loewi and Navratil had shown many years before, stops the action of acetylcholine on the heart, but does not affect its liberation by the vagus impulses.

"The difficulty facing us in the case of the voluntary muscle was largely a quantitative one. In a sympathetic ganglion, the synaptic junctions, at which the acetylcholine is released . .'. , form a large part of the small amount of tissue perfused. In a voluntary muscle the bulk of tissue, supplied by a rich network of capillary blood vessels, is enormous in relation to the motor nerve endings, of which only one is present in each muscle fibre. The volume of perfusion fluid necessary to maintain functional activity is, therefore, very large in relation to the amount of acetylcholine which the scattered motor nerve endings can be expected to yield when impulses reach them. With the skilled and patient cooperation of Dr. Feldberg and Miss Vogt, however, it was possible to overcome these difficulties, and to demonstrate that, when only the voluntary motor fibres to a muscle are stimulated, to the complete exclusion of the autonomic and sensory components of the mixed nerve, acetylcholine passes into the Locke's solution [chlorides of sodium, calcium, and potassium, with sodium bicarbonate, dextrose, and distilled water], containing a small proportion of eserine, with which the muscle is perfused. If, by calculation, we estimate the amount of acetylcholine thus obtained from the effect of a single motor impulse arriving at a single nerve ending, the quantity is of the same order as that similarly estimated for a single preganglionic impulse and a single ganglion cell. . . . We found that, if the muscle was denervated . . . , direct stimulation, although evoking vigorous contractions, produced no trace of acetylcholine. If, on the other hand, the muscle was completely paralysed to the effects of nerve impulses by curarine, stimulation of its motor nerve fibres caused the usual output of acetylcholine, although the muscle remained completely passive. Again there is a complete analogy with Loewi's observations on the heart vagus and atropine. . . ."

LOEWI *

"Natural or artificial stimulation of nerves induces in them an occurrence known as progressive excitation, which leads to a response in the organ activated by the nerves concerned.

"Up to the year 1921 it was unknown how excitation of a nerve influences its responsive organ to function—in other words, in what way the impulse of the nerve is transferred from the nerve ending to the responsive organ. For the most part it was supposed that there was a direct encroachment of the wave of excitation of the nerve fiber on the organ of response. But as a matter of fact, there were also those who had already formed the opinion that the transference takes place by chemical means, and had communicated [the results of their] researches. Thus W. H. Howell had formed the view on the ground of his own research that vagus stimulation liberates potassium in the heart, and that this occasions the result of stimulation. . . . [The vagus nerve has an inhibitory influence on the heart. In 1908, Howell, with W. W. Duke, reported an increase in the concentration of potassium in the fluid perfusing an isolated mammalian heart during vagal stimulation. Howell's work in this connection dates from 1906. Loewi also mentions the name of W. M. Bayliss, who had written in his famous textbook of physiology (ed. 1902, p. 344) that "the nerve may act by the production of the same chemical substance which excites directly, or the chemical excitant may act on the same terminal mechanism as the excitatory process in the nerve fibre does."]

"Although these data were known to me, I was first made aware a year after my discovery that earlier—i.e., in 1904—[T. R.] Elliott, at the conclusion of a short note, had already intimated the possibility that stimulation of sympathetic nerves works through the liberation of adrenalin, and that [W. E.] Dixon had already [1907], in a place difficult of access, brought out researches aimed at elucidation of the question whether a substance is set free on

---

* Translated from Otto Loewi, "Die chemische Übertragung der Nerven-wirkung," *Les Prix Nobel en 1936*.

stimulating the vagus which induces the result. [Emil Du Bois-Reymond (1818-1896) hinted a similar explanation. It appears that none of these suggestions was supported by satisfactory proof.] "In the year 1921 I succeeded for the first time in furnishing to this end the proof capable of only one interpretation, [by showing] that through stimulation of the nerves of a frog's heart [suspended in a glass vessel containing saline] substances are set free, part of which enter the perfusion fluid of the heart, and being transferred with this to [another] test heart, here work exactly like the stimulation of the corresponding nerves. It was thereby proved that the nerves do not act directly on the heart, but that the immediate result of nerve stimulation is the freeing of chemical substances, and that these first act directly in bringing about the functional change in the heart which is characteristic of nerve action. . . .

[The autonomic, or involuntary, nervous system, controlling those functions that are largely independent of the will and of direct outside influences, has two divisions, called the sympathetic and the parasympathetic. The vagus nerve contains parasympathetic fibers; Loewi and his co-workers investigated the nature of the substance, which he called "Vagusstoff," released by their stimulation.] "We were able to establish that its action is suspended by atropine, and [in any case] disappears very quickly. In the search for a substance sharing both these peculiarities, I found that out of the series of known vagomimetic substances [i.e., chemicals with the physiological effects of "Vagusstoff"], muscarine, pilocarpine, choline, and acetylcholine, this held true only for the latter. It could then be directly established further, that the rapid cessation of the action of Vagusstoff and acetylcholine depends on the decomposition of these substances through the action of an esterase in the heart, already duly postulated by Dale. [An esterase is an enzyme, or ferment, which acts specifically on a certain ester; acetylcholine is numbered chemically among the esters.] I was able to show further that the action of this esterase is specifically retarded by minimal concentrations of eserine. [Eserine is a vegetable substance derived from the Calabar bean of western Africa; chemically it is an alkaloid and is known also as physostigmine. By showing that the breakdown of his "Vagusstoff" could be prevented in this way, Loewi made it relatively easy to enhance its effect and to detect its presence.} . . .

"Not only as regards its reaction with atropine and its destructibility by esterase, but also in respect of all other attributes, Vagusstoff behaves identically with acetylcholine. When, over and above this, acetylcholine could be directly demonstrated in the organs by Dale and Dudley, no doubt remained that Vagusstoff is acetylcholine."

CONSEQUENCES IN THEORY AND PRACTICE

For well over a century the study of the electric changes during nerve activity was the sole path toward knowledge of the mechanism of nervous function. Sherrington and Adrian, Erlanger and Gasser, Eccles, Hodgkin and Huxley—all Nobel laureates—are known in science as electrophysiologists. But all cells, including nerve cells, require energy for their activity; in a living cell chemical reactions are the source of energy; the nerve cell can convert the chemical to electrical energy, i.e. to the nerve impulse. The latter triggers the release of a specific chemical substance from the nerve endings which, diffusing the short distance to the next nerve cell or muscle, evokes electrical change there and characteristic activity of that cell. T. R. Elliott had suggested in 1904 that the then recently discovered adrenaline may be liberated when sympathetic nerves to an organ are stimulated, but correct appreciation of the role of chemical transmitters in nervous processes came only with Loewi's experiments in the early 1920's.

In 1926 A. V. Hill and his associates were able to measure the heat production of the resting nerve and the increased heat production following stimulation (p. 105 ff.). This biophysical approach pointed to chemical changes from which the thermal change resulted. Gerard and Meyerhof, and at the same time (1927) Fenn, confirmed this by measurement of the extra oxygen uptake. The researches initiated by Dale and Loewi clarified another physicochemical relationship in the activity of nerves.

Loewi's work was limited to the autonomic nervous system. Dale and his associates, following the lead of Kibjakow, tried to extend this concept, suggesting that acetylcholine might transmit impulses across ganglionic synapses and at neuromuscular junctions. (It may be noted that an important part of Nobel Prize scientific study has centered in the nerve-muscle relationship.) The evidence, of which only an early indication is given in the excerpt from Sir Henry Dale's lecture, was chiefly based on (1) liberation of acetylcholine after stimulation of preganglionic fibers on motor nerves; (2) stimulation of the sympathetic ganglion and the striated muscle by injection of small amounts of acetylcholine; and (3) "potentiation" of the effects of nerve stimulation by the use of eserine. Dale and his group worked out ingenious techniques and contributed very extensively to the piling up of the evidence.

There were two principal difficulties. Neurons and striated muscle fibers act with lightning speed. Any chemical reaction involved must occur with the same speed. The question was whether or not the rate of acetylcholine metabolism was high enough to fit the timetable of the nervous mechanism. Detailed studies of enzyme chemistry indicate now that this is not an obstacle. The second question was whether the modes of conduction along nerve fibers and across synapses are fundamentally different. According to D. Nachmansohn, they are not; and he and his colleagues have provided a considerable volume of data pointing to the importance of acetylcholine in the transmission of the nerve impulse along the nerve. The hypothesis fails to explain many problems of neurophysiology and physiologists and pharmacologists do not accept the view that acetylcholine plays a key role in transmission of the impulse along the nerve. However, the function of acetylcholine and of the enzymes forming it and hydrolyzing it in nerves other than cholinergic ones remains to be explained.

Discoveries of this kind are contributions to basic knowledge. One should hardly expect any immediate practical results. (William Harvey's discovery of the circulation of the blood, announced in 1628, had little effect on practice for many years, yet this discovery is the foundation of all modern medicine.) In the case of Dale and Loewi, however, a sort of "premium" in the way of practical consequences was not long in appearing. The eserine which played so large a part in their experiments is also known as physostigmine. To put it briefly, this substance inhibits the esterase which destroys acetylcholine, and therefore it "potentiates" the acetylcholine action. A disease called myasthenia gravis is known as a chronic and progressive muscular weakness, usually beginning in the face and throat. Recognizing certain similarities in this to the action of the drug curare, Mary Broadfoot Walker suggested the use of physostigmine in 1934 as a new treatment aimed at overcoming the "curare-like" features of the disease. Together with prostigmine, which is closely similar in action and which was introduced for the same purpose by L. Remen in 1932, physostigmine continues to hold a place in the management of myasthenia gravis.

Other cholinesterase inhibitors have been found among organic esters of phosphoric acid. One of these, known as DFP (di-isopropylfluorophosphate) is used by local application in glaucoma to bring about a prolonged decrease in the intra-ocular pressure. But it has too many side effects to permit its use in myasthenia gravis. Many other chemicals of this series are commonly used as economic poisons in the control of insect predators in agriculture. Others are stockpiled for military purposes to be used as "nerve gases."

The theory of chemical transmission at nerve endings has had practical consequences in respect to the sympathetic nerves as well. The transmitter released by these is now known to be noradrenaline (arterenol), and not adrenaline (epinephrine), as previously thought. Drugs like reserpine, guanethidine, and alpha-methyldopa deplete the stores of this substance at nerve endings; in fact, they are thought to reduce blood pressure in hypertensive patients by this very mechanism: they eliminate the chemical mediator that would otherwise be available to cause constriction of the blood vessels and cause high blood pressure. Still other new drugs inhibit enzymes that normally catalyze the oxidation of substances like noradrenaline and adrenaline and, therefore, terminate their well known biological actions. Some of these drugs are used in the treatment of mental depressions, but much remains to be learned about the nervous mechanisms upon which they operate.

1 9 3 7
ALBERT VON SZENT-GYÖRGYI
(1893–   )

"For his discoveries in connection with the biological combustion processes, with especial reference to vitamin C and the catalysis of fumaric acid."

BIOGRAPHICAL SKETCH

ALBERT VON SZENT-GYÖRGYI [APPROXIMATE PRONUNCIATION, Saint Georgie] was born in Budapest, on September 16, 1893. Receiving his preliminary education in Budapest, he also studied medicine there, beginning in 1911. The professor of anatomy was Szent-Györgyi's uncle, in whose laboratory he began to do research as a first-year student; thereafter he published a series of histological studies. His education was interrupted by the First World War, in which he served on the Russian and Italian fronts. Having been wounded, he returned to the university and completed his course in 1917 He then went to Pozsony as assistant to the pharmacologist G. Mansfeld. Next he studied electrophysiology for a short time with A. von Tschermak in Prague. He also worked with L. Michaelis in Berlin. He spent two years in Hamburg in the study of physical chemistry, and two years in Leyden, Holland, as assistant in the Pharmacological Institute. After this he was assistant to H. J. Hamburger in the Physiological Institute of Groningen, Holland, where he discovered "hexuronic acid" in the adrenal cortex. At this time he was teaching biochemistry as *Privatdozent*. In 1927 he went to Cambridge as a Rockefeller Fellow. The following year he was in Rochester, Minnesota, at the Mayo Foundation, with E. C. Kendall. In 1929 he was back at Cambridge. Finally, in 1930, he returned to Hungary, as professor of medical chemistry at the University of Szeged. It was here that he and Svirbely identified hexuronic acid with vitamin C. Szent-Györgyi's researches led him to the discovery of a new catalyst, cytoflave, which was soon identified with vitamin B_2, or riboflavin, the vitamin that Warburg and Christian had recognized as part of their yellow oxidative enzyme.

During the Second World War Szent-Györgyi was at one point in danger of arrest on Hitler's orders; he was hidden in the Swedish legation in Budapest for a time and was then smuggled out and taken toward the Soviet lines. After the end of the war he took up his work in Hungary once again, but eventually left for Switzerland, and then the United States. For many years he has been director of a new Institute for Muscle Research at the famous Marine Biological Station at Woods Hole, Massachusetts.

A brilliant and original investigator, Szent-Györgyi has trained many enthusiastic pupils in biochemistry. He is an able writer and the author of a number of books.

DESCRIPTION OF THE PRIZE-WINNING WORK *

"I was led into the field of oxidations . . . by a false assumption. I was interested in the function of the adrenal cortex. If the function of this organ is suppressed, life, too, is suppressed (Addison's disease). But before life is extinguished, there appears in man a brown pigmentation, similar to that of certain fruits: apples, pears, bananas, etc., which, in withering, likewise assume a brown color. Through the investigations of the great Russian botanist, Palladin, it was known that this brown coloring of plants is connected with the damaged oxidation mechanism. Since I myself was convinced (and am still convinced) that in the basic functions, as represented, too, by oxidation, there exist no differences in principle between animal and plant, I undertook the study of the oxidation system of potatoes, browning of the plants depending on

* Translated from "Nobel-Vortrag von Albert Szent-Györgyi," *Les Prix Nobel en 1937.*

its damage. I did this in the hope of finding through these studies the key to the understanding of adrenal function.

"It was already known that those plants which turn brown as the result of damage—about half of all plants—contain a polyphenol, . . . besides this a ferment, the polyphenoloxidase, which, with the help of oxygen, oxidizes the polyphenol. There was a complicated interpretation of the working mechanism of this oxidase. It fell to me to show that it is simply a question of the oxidase, along with oxygen, oxidizing the polyphenol to quinone [compound which results when two opposite hydrogen atoms are replaced by oxygen]. In the intact plant the quinone is again reduced by the hydrogen mobilized from foodstuff. The phenol thus works as a hydrogen-transporter between oxygen and H-donator, and we are here confronted . . . with a system of successive hydrogen combustion. . . . In the damaged plant the reduction of the quinone cannot keep pace with the mounting oxidation of the phenol, and the quinones remain unreduced and form pigments.

"But the system gave me no information about adrenal function. So I turned to the plants which do not assume a brown color on withering, and which therefore must contain an oxidation system differently organized. As regards these plants, this much was known, that they contain a very active peroxidase. This peroxidase has the power to activate peroxide. In the presence of this ferment, peroxide is able to oxidize various aromatic substances to colored pigments. Without peroxidase this reaction does not take place. If, for example, benzidine is added to a peroxide in the presence of peroxidase, a deep blue color appears at once, produced by the oxidation of the benzidine. Without peroxidase this reaction, which also serves as a test for the ferment, does not occur.

"But when, in this reaction, I substituted for a purified peroxidase simply the juice squeezed from these plants, and added benzidine and peroxide, then the blue pigment appeared, but only after a slight delay of about a second. The analysis of this retardation showed that it was occasioned by the presence of a strong reducing substance, which again reduced the oxidized benzidine, until it was itself exhausted.

"It was a moment of great excitement, when, in my little cellar room in Groningen, I found that the adrenal cortex contains an analogous reducing substance in relatively large amount.

"My means and my chemical knowledge were both inadequate to investigate this substance more closely. But thanks to the invitation of F. G. Hopkins and the help of the Rockefeller Foundation I was able ten years ago [i.e., in 1927] to transfer my laboratory to Cambridge, where for the first time I could devote myself to chemistry in earnest. Soon I was successful in isolating this fragile substance from adrenal glands and various plants and showing that it corresponded to the formula $C_6H_8O_6$ and was related to the carbohydrates. This latter circumstance induced me to turn to Prof. W. N. Haworth, who at once perceived the chemical interest of the substance and asked me for a larger amount for constitutional analysis. But unfortunately it turned out that adrenal glands were the only material suitable for large-scale preparation. All my efforts to find suitable vegetable material for a starting point remained ineffectual, and adrenal glands in large quantity were not available in England.

"Professor Krogh tried to help me by generously sending me adrenal glands by air from Copenhagen. But unfortunately the substance was spoiled in transit. The Mayo Foundation and Professor Kendall now came to my aid in a magnificent way and made it possible for me, regardless of expense, to work on the material from the great American slaughterhouses. The result of a year's work was 25 g. of a crystalline substance which received the name 'hexuronic acid.' This quantity of the substance I divided with Professor Haworth. He undertook to investigate the exact structural formula. I used the other half of my preparation to obtain a closer insight into the function of the substance. [It] could not take the place of the adrenal glands, but it overcame the pigmentation of Addison's disease to the point of disappearance.

"Unfortunately the amount of the substance proved insufficient for ascertaining the chemical constitution. The preparation could not be repeated for lack of means, and no cheaper material was found permitting extraction of the acid in larger amount.

"From the beginning I suspected the substance to be identical with vitamin C [discovered in 1907 by A. Holst and T. Frölich].

But my wandering life was unsuited for vitamin research, in which, also, I had no experience. In the year 1930, however, I gave up my nomad life, in that I settled down in my fatherland, at the University of Szeged. Also fortune soon sent me an excellent young American co-worker, J. L. Svirbely, who had experience with vitamin research. . . . In the autumn of 1931 our first investigations were concluded and showed clearly that hexuronic acid has an antiscorbutic effect [preventing and counteracting scurvy] and that the antiscorbutic activity of the juices of plants corresponds with their hexuronic acid content. . . . [Szent-Györgyi here mentions related work of Tillman, King, and Waugh.]

"All at once the hexuronic acid that had been so long disregarded pressed into the foreground, and there was urgent need of larger amounts of this substance, in order on the one hand to continue the analysis of its constitution, and on the other to make sure of its vitamin nature. But we used the last remnant of our substance in our vitamin researches; it was impossible for us to undertake its preparation from adrenal glands; and, as I mentioned, every other material was inadequate for large-scale work.

"My city, Szeged, is the center of the Hungarian paprika industry. As this fruit is not transportable in good condition, I had had no earlier opportunity to test it. One evening the sight of this wholesome fruit inspired me with a last hope, and the same night investigation showed that this fruit offers an incredibly rich source of hexuronic acid, which Haworth and I rechristened ascorbic acid. Taking advantage of the last of the paprika season, which was nearing its end, it was possible, through the support given on a generous scale by the American Josiah Macy Jr. Foundation, to prepare more than half a kilogram, in the following year more than 3 kilograms, of crystalline ascorbic acid. I divided this substance among all the investigators who wished to work on it. I also had the privilege of furnishing both my fellow laureates, P. Karrer and W. N. Haworth, with plentiful material, and making possible their analysis of its constitution. I myself, together with Varga, prepared the mono-acetone derivative of ascorbic acid, forming splendid crystals, from which, after repeated recrystallizations, ascorbic acid, undiminished in activity, may again be split off. This was the first proof that ascorbic acid is identical with vitamin C and that the activity of the substance is not dependent on impurities. . . .

"To return to the oxidation processes, I now attempted further analysis of the respiratory system of plants in which ascorbic acid and peroxidase play important roles. I had already found out, while in Rochester, that the peroxidase plants contain a ferment which reversibly oxidizes ascorbic acid, with two valences, in the presence of oxygen. Further analysis showed that here there was a respiratory system in which hydrogen is oxidized step by step. I should like to sum up briefly the result of this research carried out with St. Huszák.

"The ascorbic acid oxidase, with oxygen, reversibly oxidizes the acid to dehydroascorbic acid. The oxygen thereby combines with two labile H-atoms of the acid to form hydrogen peroxide. This peroxide reacts with peroxidase and oxidizes a second molecule of ascorbic acid. Both those molecules of dehydroascorbic acid, possibly by the mediation of SH-groups, now take up hydrogen again from foodstuffs.

"But the peroxidase does not oxidize the ascorbic acid directly. I succeeded in showing that between the two still another substance is inserted, which belongs to the large group of yellow, vegetable, water-soluble phenol-benzol-γ-pyran-dyestuffs (flavone, flavonole, flavanone). The peroxidase here oxidizes the phenol group to quinone, which then oxidizes the ascorbic acid directly by accepting both its H-atoms."

CONSEQUENCES IN THEORY
AND PRACTICE

Many scientists have contributed to our present knowledge of the chemical events known in sum as "respiration." The contributions of Warburg and Keilin have been discussed above (see pp. 152-157). The cytochrome-cytochrome oxidase system (what Szent-Györgyi calls the WK, or Warburg-Keilin, system) is not a very powerful oxidizing agent and could not bring about the breakdown of foodstuff molecules without the assistance of other catalysts. H.

Wieland's role in this area was to show that the foodstuffs, or their metabolic derivatives, are activated by enzymes called dehydrogenases. These make the molecule give up its hydrogen more readily, and the hydrogen is "transported" by other cellular catalysts to the cytochrome system, where it is made to combine with oxygen to form water. The relative importance of oxygen-activation and hydrogen-activation in cellular catalysis was the subject of an historic debate in biochemistry for many years. Szent-Györgyi ended the controversy by showing that both processes are involved in respiration. He eliminated the activation of oxygen by poisoning minced tissue with cyanide; but he also added the dye methylene blue to "accept" hydrogen of the substrate in place of the usual oxygen acceptor. The action of the dehydrogenases led to the reduction (hydrogenation) of the methylene blue and, consequently, to loss of its color. The reduced dye oxidizes spontaneously, however, in the presence of oxygen, and so the process of dehydrogenation can be repeated in a manner that simulates normal cellular respiration.

Szent-Györgyi also took note of the various plant acids that were known to be readily metabolized in cells of many kinds. He was especially fascinated by the dehydrogenases acting upon succinic and citric acids, considering these enzymes to be particularly important in the economy of the cell because they were so closely associated with its structural elements (now known to be the mitochondria). He reasoned that if they were truly of great importance in respiration, then this should stop when their action is inhibited. He found a useful tool to study this in malonic acid, a chemical that J. H. Quastel had shown to inhibit the dehydrogenation of succinic acid. Malonic acid stopped respiration in tissues that ordinarily oxidize succinic acid; because succinic acid is found in tissues only in minute amounts, this effect of malonic acid indicated to Szent-Györgyi that succinic acid and fumaric acid formed from it must have some very special, catalytic role to play in the cellular economy. This work, in fact, laid the foundation for the eventual elucidation of the "citric acid cycle," described by H. A. Krebs (p. 304 ff.).

The nutritional basis of scurvy had long gone unrecognized in medicine. However, in 1907 two Norwegian scientists Holst and Frölich showed that typical scurvy can be produced in guinea pigs by feeding them special (deficient) diets, and that it can be cured by appropriate supplements. The application of this knowledge to human scurvy and to Barlow's disease (the infantile form) followed soon after. Szent-Györgyi's work on "hexuronic acid" led him to believe it to be identical with vitamin C, a fact demonstrated by J. Svirbely in his laboratory in Szeged. The way was opened for clarifying the chemical nature and composition of the substance. Within two years of this work vitamin C was synthesized. It is now manufactured on an industrial scale. The result may be considered a by-product of basic research which had as its chief, although not its most directly useful, consequence added understanding of the catalysts of respiration.

REFERENCE

Szent-Györgyi, Albert. "Lost in the Twentieth Century," *Annual Review of Biochemistry*, vol. 32 (1963), pp. 1-14. This is an autobiographical article.

1 9 3 8

CORNEILLE HEYMANS

(1892–   )

"For his discovery of the role played by the sinus and aortic mechanisms in the regulation of respiration."

BIOGRAPHICAL SKETCH

CORNEILLE JEAN FRANÇOIS HEYMANS WAS BORN AT GHENT, Belgium, on March 18, 1892. He is the son of Dr. J. F. Heymans, at one time professor of pharmacology and rector of the University of Ghent, as well as the founder of the J. F. Heymans Institute of Pharmacology, Pharmacodynamics and Toxicology at the same university. Heymans' father was his first and principal teacher and it was with him that the original experiments, leading to the award of the Nobel Prize, were begun. Corneille Heymans was educated in Ghent, studied later in the laboratories of E. Gley in Paris, N. M. Arthus in Lausanne, H. H. Meyer in Vienna and E. H. Starling in London. In 1927-1928 he worked in the United States. In 1922 he began to teach the course in pharmacodynamics at Ghent, and in 1930 he succeeded his father, retaining this position until his retirement. He is one of the best known of Belgium's biological-medical research investigators. Heymans was awarded the Nobel Prize at an academic ceremony in Ghent on January 16, 1940, by the Swedish Minister to Belgium.

DESCRIPTION OF THE PRIZE-WINNING
WORK*

"It has long been known that . . . elevation of arterial pressure inhibits respiration; sudden and severe hypertension can even provoke [cessation of breathing]. It is equally well known that hypotension [low blood pressure] leads to [abnormally deep and rapid breathing]. These interactions . . . have generally been attributed to a direct action . . . on the activity of the respiratory center [the part of the brain which controls respiratory movements].

[Experiments to test this theory and to reveal the actual mechanism of these events were begun in 1924 by J. F. and C. Heymans, using crossed circulation in dogs. Two dogs, A and B, are anesthetized. The head of dog B is separated from its body, except for the vagus-aortic nerves, connecting with the respiratory center; these are left intact. Life is maintained in the body section by artificial respiration; circulation in the body continues. The isolated head is then linked to the body circulation of the other dog, A, by attaching from the latter the principal arteries for blood supply to the head, the two common carotids; these are anastomosed—i.e., joined end to end—with the corresponding parts of the nearly severed head of B. In the same way the external jugular veins of the two dogs are anastomosed. The severed head is thus completely isolated from its own body as regards circulation, but is connected by the aortic nerves. The effects which this head shows from whatever is done to its own body are mediated by the nerves; whatever is done to the body of the other dog can influence it only through the blood stream. Breathing movements due to the activity of the respiratory center may be seen in the head. A method is thus available for showing whether high and low pressure affect this center directly or by means of a nervous reflex.]

"We observed right away that arterial hypotension limited solely to the body circulation of the dog B brings about a stimulation of the activity of the respiratory center of the perfused head of B;

---

* Translated and paraphrased from Corneille Heymans, "Sur le rôle des presso —et des chimio—récepteurs vasculaires dans la régulation de la respiration," *Les Prix Nobel en 1940-44.*

augmentation of the arterial pressure in the trunk B, on the contrary, causes an inhibition of the activity of [this] respiratory center. . . . When one injects a hypertensive dose of adrenaline into the trunk B, one observes a total inhibition of the respiratory movements of the isolated and perfused head of B. . . ."

[This showed (1) that the effects once thought due to direct action of the blood pressure on the respiratory center are really brought about by a nervous reflex; and (2) that the path of this reflex lies through the aortic nerves. But what sense organ responds to the changes in pressure and starts the reflex? The carotid sinus (a slight enlargement of the common carotid artery at the point where it divides into the external and internal carotids) had previously been shown to play an important role in the regulation of heart rate and arterial blood pressure. Heymans was able to show that respiratory reflexes, as described in the quotation above, can also originate there. There exist in the wall of the sinus sensory organs which are called presso-receptors, because they are sensitive to pressure changes. Cross-circulation experiments of a rather different kind from those detailed above helped to show how they work. The sinus of one dog, B, was isolated from the general circulation and perfused with the blood of another animal, A, while the nerve supply of the sinus was left intact. With sinus B isolated, the arterial pressure of dog A was raised, whereupon that of dog B fell. Conversely, a reduction in blood pressure of dog A caused a rise in the blood pressure of dog B. Obviously the effect of a change in blood pressure upon these presso-receptors is to initiate reflexes which tend to reverse the pressure change. The effects of pressure on respiration are also mediated through reflexes beginning in presso-receptors.

[Close to the carotid sinus is a small structure looking like a gland, called the carotid body, or *glomus caroticum*. Heymans and his associates found this to be chemo-receptive, responding to changes in the chemical composition of the blood as the presso-receptors answer to changes in blood pressure. Variations in oxygen and carbon dioxide affect breathing by this means, although the increased respiration caused by an accumulation of carbon dioxide is partly the result of direct stimulation of the respiratory center. The aortic body (*glomus aorticum*) at the base of the aorta is also chemo-receptive. It was found that certain drugs which stimulate respiration act directly on the respiratory center, but that others work only through the carotid and aortic bodies; still others have both a direct and a reflex action. Most of this information was worked out over a period of many years, with the help of many co-workers; it was accomplished in large part by means of ingenious isolation and cross-circulation experiments such as those described above.]

CONSEQUENCES IN THEORY
AND PRACTICE

In an earlier section (see above, pp. 166-168) some account was given of the work of Sir Charles Sherrington on the integrative action of the nervous system. Sherrington revealed the role of the muscle spindle in initiating reflexes which have to do with posture. Other receptors were also studied by him as the initiators of special reflex action. It was the important contribution of Professor Heymans and his co-workers to show the part played by the sinus and aortic mechanisms in the regulation of respiration and blood pressure. The carotid sinus was demonstrated to be presso-receptive, the carotid and aortic bodies to be chemo-receptive. A later Nobel laureate, W. R. Hess (see below, pp. 266-270) has contributed to the proof that central control of blood pressure lies in groups of cells in the medulla and diencephalon; the peripheral mechanism is the set of reflexes described by Heymans. Hormonal factors, relating especially to the adrenal gland, are also involved. The heart, the kidneys, and the vascular system in general are primarily or secondarily concerned. Clinicians and laboratory scientists are therefore advancing from many directions in their assault on the still unsolved problems of blood-pressure abnormality. It is obvious that the Heymans contribution forms an essential part of the basic knowledge required.

There are, however, more immediate applications of this knowledge. The carotid sinus has nervous connections with the vagus. Among other effects which the latter nerve produces is inhibition of heart action. The sinus is also connected with the cervical sympathetic and the medulla. Now occasionally the sinus becomes hypersensitive and the consequence is a distinctive set of symptoms.

Patients have been observed who suffer from spontaneous attacks of dizziness, weakness, and unconsciousness, with or without convulsions, in whom mechanical stimulation over the division of one or the other carotid artery—i.e., pressure on the carotid sinus— will at once induce an attack. Three forms of this disturbance appear, corresponding to the threefold nervous communication mentioned above. In some cases cardiac inhibition, due to a vagal reflex, is marked; this can be abolished by the use of atropine. In others, vasodilatation, with a consequent fall in arterial blood pressure, is observed; this lowering of pressure and the symptoms which attend it can be prevented by ephedrine. The third, or cerebral variety, is associated with convulsions. Apparently it is best treated by denervation of the sinus—i.e., by cutting the nerve connections involved. Patients with spontaneous epileptic seizures induced by slight pressure on an irritable sinus have been relieved by this operation. Stripping of the nerve plexus from the carotid artery at the bifurcation (division into two parts) may affect a cure, or may give only temporary relief; division of the carotid sinus nerve is considered to give the best results.

It has long been known that pressure exerted on the carotid sinus area will often slow the heart and put a stop to attacks of the disturbance called "auricular paroxysmal tachycardia," a very rapid heartbeat which occurs in sudden paroxysms. This is a dangerous procedure which may stop the heart altogether. It should be performed only by a physician familiar with the proper technique and equipped with the drugs to meet an emergency. The effect was formerly attributed to pressure on the vagus; it is now known to be due to carotid sinus pressure.

1 9 3 9
GERHARD DOMAGK
(1895–1964)

"For his discovery of the antibacterial effects of prontosil."

BIOGRAPHICAL SKETCH

GERHARD DOMAGK WAS BORN ON OCTOBER 30, 1895, IN LAGOW, Brunswick, Germany. He had just entered the University of Kiel when the First World War broke out, and in October 1914, he volunteered for the army, in which he served four years. At first he was in a grenadier regiment, but after being wounded in 1915 he was transferred to the medical corps for the remainder of the war. Returning to Kiel, he was graduated in medicine in 1921. In 1924 Domagk became *Privatdozent* at the University of Griefswald. The following year he received an appointment in the Pathological Institute at Münster, where in 1928 he became Extraordinary Professor of General Pathology and Pathological Anatomy. He then accepted a position with the I. G. Farbenindustrie and became director of the Laboratory for Experimental Pathology and Bacteriology at Wuppertal-Elberfeld. In a preconceived and systematic program, combining a search for new dyes with a search for new drugs, the I. G. Farbenindustrie postulated the preparation of a substance later to be called "prontosil" as early as 1920, but apparently nothing further was done about it until 1932. The synthesis of azo compounds had been entrusted to Drs. Fritz Mietzsch and Joseph Klarer, and it was one of Domagk's duties to test the chemotherapeutic effects of the substances pro-

214

duced. It was in this way that the extraordinary powers of the sulfonamide drugs were first revealed in the trials of prontosil.

When notified in October 1939 that he had won the Nobel Prize, Domagk sent a letter of thanks to the rector of the Caroline Institute, but toward the end of November a second letter reached Stockholm in which Domagk declined the prize in accordance with Nazi law. In the interval he had been arrested by the Gestapo. The second letter was prepared by the Ministry of Education and Domagk signed it under duress. The year of grace permitted by the Nobel regulations had long expired, and the prize money had reverted to Nobel Foundation funds, before Domagk was able to speak freely. In 1947 he visited Stockholm, delivered his Nobel lecture, and received the gold medal and diploma; but it was then too late for the award of the prize money. In his later years Domagk went on to study anti-tubercular drugs; he also engaged in cancer research. He died on April 24, 1964.

DESCRIPTION OF THE PRIZE-WINNING WORK *

"Up to the present time [1935] it has been the general opinion that only protozoal infections were susceptible to chemotherapy. In the sphere of the protozoal infections we possess remedies which are operative against the cause—e.g., against trypanosome infections [sleeping sickness], suramin; against kala-azar, neostibosan; against malaria, plasmochin and atabrin; against spirochete infections, especially syphilis, salvarsan and its modifications.

"Chemotherapeutic agents operative to any extent against infections with cocci have been unknown up to the present. . . . [Cocci are bacteria of spherical shape, including the gonococci, which produce gonorrhea, the meningococci, of a kind of meningitis, the pneumococci, of pneumonia, and the staphylococci and streptococci, which cause a wide variety of infections. Domagk next reviews earlier attempts to find effective drugs for such diseases. These

---

* Translated from Gerhard Domagk, "Ein Beitrag zur Chemotherapie der bakteriellen Infektionen," *Deutsche medizinische Wochenschrift*, Vol. 61 (1935), pp. 250-253.

efforts had centered chiefly on a number of compounds of the metals, particularly gold. All had proved failures for one reason or another, many of the substances being too toxic for use.]

"Because of the disadvantages described, we turned our particular attention toward chemical compounds of other types, on a purely organic, metal-free basis, which in experiments with mice gave perceptible indication of being effective against streptococcal sepsis. Among azo and acridine compounds * we had become acquainted with a series of substances which showed a relatively good effect against streptococci in disinfection research *in vitro* [i.e., in the test tube]. But this effect, in part even an excellent one *in vitro,* was almost always completely lost on the injection of these substances into the animal body. . . . [Here follows an account of this research. One of the substances tested was an azo compound called chrysoidine. It was the addition to this compound (itself ineffective against streptococci) of a sulfonamide group (SO_2NH_2) which produced prontosil.]

"In the course of our investigations, however, we later hit upon a group of very innocuous azo compounds, which, to be sure, showed no substantial disinfective value against streptococci *in vitro,* but now in experiments with mice gave a clear and perceptible effect. To this group belongs *prontosil,* synthesized in 1932 by Mietzsch and Klarer. With prontosil we were able to establish the best chemotherapeutic effects observed at any time in *streptococcal infections in animal research.* It is the hydrochloride of 4'-sulfonamide-2, 4-diaminoazobenzene. . . .

"The harmlessness of the preparation is shown by the toxicological data. . . . [Large amounts, at least 500 mg. per kilo of body weight, were tolerated by mice and rabbits; larger doses were vomited. Similar data are given regarding subcutaneous and intravenous injections. So far as these tests showed, the drug appeared to be nontoxic.]

"Prontosil is . . . an extraordinarily inert compound pharmacologically . . . [i.e., it appeared to have little or no effect on the various functions of the healthy animal body].

---

* Azo compound: an organic substance with two nitrogen atoms interposed between hydrocarbon groups (R), as in R'·N:N-R". Acridine is a substance obtained from coal tar, and is the parent substance of certain synthetic dyes and drugs.

"*Chemotherapeutically, prontosil shows an elective effect in streptococcal sepsis in the mouse* [i.e., it appears to act specifically on streptococci, as if by choice]. . . . All the animals alike were infected with 0.3 c.c. of a 24-hour streptococcal bouillon culture. Of the untreated control animals, none lived after 48 hours, so that no [further] comparisons could be made. . . . When the organs of untreated control animals are investigated, typical signs of severe general infection are found in the liver, spleen, kidneys, heart, and numerous other organs. . . .

"In the animals successfully treated with prontosil all these pathological tissue changes are lacking, when treatment is started promptly with adequate doses. In other cases one hinders the further extension of tissue damage already existing. . . .

"It is worth notice . . . that in research *in vitro*, [prontosil] shows no particular effect against either streptococci or staphylococci. *It works like a true chemotherapeutic agent only in the living organism.* . . ."

CONSEQUENCES IN THEORY AND PRACTICE

Accompanying this first report were three microphotographs of the blood of infected mice. The first, picturing blood from an untreated animal, showed innumerable cocci; the second, taken 24 hours after subcutaneous injection of prontosil, revealed active phagocytosis (the eating up of bacteria by white cells); and the third, taken 48 hours after the injection, displayed a later stage of the same healing process, with no free cocci whatever! These pictures demonstrated how prontosil "works like a true chemotherapeutic agent in the living organism," although not in the test tube.

The original protocol on the value of prontosil in the control of experimental streptococcal infections in mice is dated December 20, 1932. Experimental work on animals was continued. Meanwhile Domagk's young daughter developed a serious streptococcal infection following a needle prick. Ordinary treatment failed to check the spread of the infection. Domagk treated her with large doses of prontosil. She recovered.

Long before Domagk's original paper was published, reports

appeared in the German medical literature. The drug was distributed for clinical trial early in 1933, and on May 17 Foerster read the first report before the Düsseldorf Dermatological Society. In 1936 an outbreak of puerperal sepsis (child-bed fever) threatened the lives of thirty-eight mothers in a London hospital. Prontosil saved thirty-five of them. The drug had well proved its efficacy.

Because chrysoidine was powerless to check streptococci and because the only difference between chrysoidine and prontosil consisted of the sulfonamide group of the latter, it appeared that this group must endow the molecule with its chemotherapeutic properties. Furthermore, prontosil was active in vivo, but not in vitro, and this suggested that the body converts it into something else that is the actual antibacterial substance. Indeed, a group of investigators in France, the Tréfouëls (husband and wife), Nitti and Bovet, revealed that prontosil is metabolized in vivo to sulfanilamide, a sulfonamido-containing compound that had been prepared in 1908 by P. Gelmo in Vienna. As a result of the French researches, sulfanilamide was introduced for clinical trial; it was soon evaluated by Perrin Long and L. Colebrook in the United States. Since that time many new sulfonamides, or "sulfa drugs," have appeared, with special advantages claimed for each, either in reduced toxicity or in the type of organism affected. Because of Gelmo's early published synthesis, the development of the sulfonamides was unhindered by patent restrictions.

"In 1935," writes Professor Spink,* "there was no specific therapy for hemolytic streptococcic infections. Every clinician feared streptococcic bacteremia [the presence of living bacteria in the circulating blood], with its mortality rate approximating 75 per cent. Only a rare patient recovered from streptococcic meningitis. In midwinter, hospital beds were occupied with cases of erysipelas and mastoiditis, all caused by hemolytic streptococci. Sulfanilamide took the sting out of these debilitating and fatal streptococcic diseases. [The operation for mastoiditis has almost become a thing of the past since the advent of sulfatherapy.] The mortality rate of untreated pneumococcic meningitis was 100 per cent, but patients recovered following the use of sulfapyridine. Chronic cases of

* Wesley W. Spink, "Present Status of Sulfonamide Therapy," *The Merck Report*, Apr. 1951, pp. 17-19.

gonorrhea clogged up the out-patient services of hospitals, and its devastating complication, gonococcal arthritis, was the frequent cause of prolonged hospitalization. The sulfonamides soon offered a more hopeful outlook for these individuals. The sulfonamides proved to be highly effective in meningococcic bacteremia and meningitis. A new chapter, and a dramatic one, had been written in the therapy of human disease."

There were certain drawbacks. The "sulfa drugs" often provoked serious side effects, especially kidney failure. Many patients showed hypersensitivity to the drugs after one or more courses of treatment, in the form of skin eruptions and fever. Secondly, strains of bacteria, notably gonococci, soon appeared which were resistant to the sulfonamides. Thirdly, the sulfonamides had a relatively narrow range of activity; many of the causative agents of infectious disease were not susceptible to their action.

Although antibiotics such as penicillin, chloramphenicol and tetracycline now occupy a more prominent place in the treatment of infectious diseases because of their lower toxicity, greater efficiency and wider range, the sulfonamides continue to be widely used. Ease of administration and low cost contribute to their enduring popularity. The ever-present possibility of developing resistance to the antibiotics or of evoking a sensitization reaction to, say, penicillin, has been a negative factor in promoting the use of sulfonamides where an equal choice could otherwise be made. There are a number of diseases in which they have been given simultaneously with an antibiotic, although it is considered difficult to assess the merit of this practice. These drugs not only find a wide application in the treatment of disease but have also been used successfully in the prevention of such diseases as epidemic meningococcic meningitis.

The sulfonamides revolutionized the management of a considerable number of important infectious diseases. The knowledge acquired through the study of these drugs in laboratory and clinic has been put to further use in more recent work on the antibiotics.

REFERENCES

LONG, PERRIN H. "Award of the Nobel Prize in Physiology and Medicine to Dr. Gerhard Domagk," *Scientific Monthly,* Vol. 50 (1940), pp. 83-84.

ANONYMOUS. "Gerhard Domagk: Obituary," *The Lancet,* vol. 1 (May 2, 1964), p. 992.

1 9 4 0 – 1 9 4 2

No Award

1 9 4 3
HENRIK DAM
(1895–   )

"For his discovery of vitamin K."

EDWARD A. DOISY
(1893–   )

"For his discovery of the chemical nature of vitamin K."

BIOGRAPHICAL SKETCHES

DAM

(CARL PETER) HENRIK DAM WAS BORN IN COPENHAGEN, ON February 21, 1895. He was graduated in chemistry from the Polytechnic Institute there in 1920, and was awarded the degree Sc. Dr. in biochemistry by the University of Copenhagen in 1934. Meanwhile he had studied microchemistry with F. Pregl in Graz, Austria, in 1925, and metabolism of sterols in Rudolph Schoenheimer's laboratory in Freiburg, Germany, as a Rockefeller Fellow, in 1932-1933. He also worked with P. Karrer, in Zürich, in 1935 and later. Dam was appointed instructor in chemistry at the School of Agriculture and Veterinary Medicine in Copenhagen in 1920; instructor in biochemistry at the Physiological Laboratory, University of Copenhagen, in 1923; and assistant professor at the Institute of

Biochemistry of the same institution in 1928. He served as associate professor at the University from 1929 to 1941, and lectured in the United States and Canada in 1940-1941. This tour was planned before Denmark was occupied by German troops (April 1940). Dr. Dam carried out research in Woods Hole Marine Biological Laboratories in 1941; at the University of Rochester, New York, 1942-1945, as a senior research associate; and at the Rockefeller Institute for Medical Research, 1945, as an associate member. Despite his absence from Denmark he had meanwhile been appointed professor of biochemistry at the Polytechnic Institute, Copenhagen. His many papers, some published jointly and others alone, deal mainly with the biochemistry of sterols, fats, and the vitamins K and E.

From 1956 until 1963 Professor Dam was Director of the Biochemical Division of the Danish Fat Research Institute. He is a member of the Royal Danish Academy of Sciences and Letters, and has received many other honors.

DOISY

EDWARD A. DOISY WAS BORN IN HUME, ILLINOIS, ON NOVEMBER 13, 1893. From the University of Illinois he received his A.B. in 1914 and his M.S. in 1916; he was awarded a Harvard Ph.D. in 1920 and has since been granted honorary degrees by several universities, in addition to a large number of medals and prizes. He was assistant in biochemistry, Harvard Medical School, 1915-1917. From 1917 to 1919 he served in the U. S. Army. He then became, successively, instructor, associate, and associate professor in biochemistry, Washington University School of Medicine, 1919-1923; was appointed professor of biochemistry at the St. Louis University School of Medicine, in 1923; and was appointed director of the Department of Biochemistry, St. Mary's Hospital, in 1924. Dr. Doisy has been active in professional associations and has served on the League of Nations Committee on the Standardization of the Sex Hormones. His publications have dealt with various aspects of metabolism; insulin; blood buffers; isolation and chemical characterization of theilin, theelol, and dihydrotheelin; ovarian hormones and estrogenic substances; gonadotropic and thyrotropic principles, as well as various other aspects of endocrinology; isolation of vitamins K_1 and K_2; determination of constitution and synthesis of vitamin K_1; and antibiotic compounds.

DESCRIPTION OF THE PRIZE-WINNING WORK

DAM *

"The discovery of vitamin K arose from some studies on the cholesterol metabolism of chicks carried out during the years 1928-30 in the biochemical institute of the University of Copenhagen. [Cholesterol, which chemists classify as an alcohol, is found in bile, brain, blood cells, egg yolk, etc., and in varying amounts in animal tissues. It belongs among the sterols, solid alcohols closely related to steroids; the latter include a number of important hormones. Another sterol is ergosterol, which, when irradiated, forms vitamin D_2.] It was then already known that rats, mice and dogs can synthesize cholesterol but some experiments had been published which seemed to show that chicks could not thrive on a diet from which the sterols had been removed by extraction. When these experiments were published . . . in 1914, the role of fat-soluble vitamins was not very well recognized, and I therefore found it interesting to repeat them using artificial, practically sterolfree diets to which vitamins A and D were added in the form of sterol-free concentrates made from cod-liver oil, or of small amounts of cod-liver oil of known cholesterol content. Chicks were reared on such diets for different lengths of time from the day of hatching and the amount of cholesterol in their excretions and their body was determined and compared with the cholesterol content in newly hatched chicks from the same litter. It was thereby found that a considerable part of the cholesterol which the newly hatched chick has taken over from the egg yolk disappears during the first 2 or 3 weeks, whereafter cholesterol is formed in increasing amount as the body weight increases. Chicks therefore are able to synthesize cholesterol, just as well as are rats, mice and dogs, and they are also able to break it down.

---

* From Henrik Dam, "The Discovery of Vitamin K, Its Biological Functions and Therapeutical Applications," *Les Prix Nobel en 1946*, pp. 205-220.

"More interesting than this finding was, however, an unexpected symptom which showed up in some of the chicks which were kept on the diet for more than 2 or 3 weeks. They got hemorrhages under the skin, in muscles or other organs, and blood occasionally taken out for examination showed delayed coagulation.

"The lack or low content of cholesterol in the diet could not be the cause of the hemorrhages, since the experiments showed that chicks can synthesize cholesterol. Further, the hemorrhages also appeared in chicks which received a daily supplement of cholesterol.

"The low amount of fat in the diet would, apparently, also be ruled out as a cause of the symptom since it was found that linseed oil and triolein could not prevent its appearance. . . . Other authors had already reported that chicks do not require vitamin C, and daily ingestion of lemon juice . . . also proved to be ineffective. . . . [When] pure vitamin C became available . . . I could easily show that . . . injections of ascorbic acid failed to prevent the disease. . . .

"The salt mixture could be varied considerably without influence on the disease, and wheat germ oil was without protective effect, whereas a high content of cereals and seeds in the diet prevented the symptom. It was therefore safe to announce that the new experimental disease was due to the lack of a hitherto unrecognized factor in the diet. This was done in 1934.

"Then a number of animal organs and plant material were examined for their ability to protect against the disease and it was found that green leaves and hog liver were among the most potent sources. It was also found that the factor was fat-soluble, and in 1935 it was characterized as a new fat-soluble vitamin and given the designation vitamin K. The letter K was the first one in the alphabet which had not, with more or less justification, been used to designate other vitamins, and it also happened to be the first letter in the word "koagulation" according to the Scandinavian and German spelling. . . .

"The hemorrhages in vitamin K deficiency develop in this way, that minute vascular lesions caused by minor mechanical trauma are not closed by rapid clotting, as is the case in normal animals. This causes oozing of blood from the impaired region.

"According to the accepted theory the process of blood coagulation may be separated into two stages.

"(1) Prothrombin + Thromboplastin + Ca → Thrombin

"(2) Fibrinogen + Thrombin → Fibrin . . .

"It is easy to show that it is *prothrombin* and no other component which is lacking when vitamin K has been withdrawn from the diet. . . .

"Vitamin K from green plants is called K_1. Chemically it differs slightly from vitamin K formed by putrefaction, which is called K_2 [discovered by Almquist and Stokstad, University of California].

. . . The preparation of pure vitamin K from green leaves was first reported by Dam, Karrer and co-workers, 1939. . . . The elucidation of its composition was accomplished by Doisy and co-workers, and by Fieser and co-workers. Doisy and co-workers also prepared pure vitamin K_2 from putrefied fishmeal [and established its chemical difference from K_1.] . . .

"Andrus, Lord and Moore, 1939, excised the liver in normal dogs and studied the prothrombin level with and without ingestion of vitamin K and bile salts. They found that the blood prothrombin decreased in both instances, indicating that the liver is necessary for the action of vitamin K. Several other observations also show that the liver is the organ concerned with prothrombin formation."

DOISY

[Doisy and his co-workers in the St. Louis University School of Medicine isolated vitamin K_1 from alfalfa (*Journal of Biological Chemistry*, Vol. 130 [1939], pp. 219-234). Partition among various solvents and crystallization from solvents proved unsuccessful, and the large amount of impurities in crude preparations made low-pressure distillations difficult and impractical; at the same time the inactivity of the vitamin toward many chemical reagents and its instability toward others eliminated chemical reactions as a means of isolation. After extraction, therefore, repeated adsorptions were used to obtain the vitamin. In a similar manner vitamin K_2 was isolated from purified fish meal (*Journal of Biological Chemistry*, Vol. 131 [1939], pp. 327-344). The constitution of vitamin K_1 was worked out and its synthesis accomplished by the same group in

St. Louis. Almost simultaneously three other groups, Almquist and Klose, Fieser *et al.*, and Karrer *et al.*, reached the same goal. Doisy and his co-workers summarized their findings on vitamin K_1 as follows.*]

"Vitamin K_1 was found to be a 2, 3-disubstituted α-naphthoquinone having an unsaturated side chain. By oxidation of the vitamin with chromic acid phthalic acid was formed,' which demonstrated that the benzenoid ring of the vitamin carries no side chain. A second acid isolated from the oxidation products was identified as 2-methyl-1, 4-naphthoquinone-3-acetic acid, which showed that the quinone nucleus has a methyl group at the 2 position and that the side chain in the 3 position has an ethylenic linkage between the 2nd and 3rd carbon atoms from the quinone ring. These conclusions were confirmed by the products obtained by degradation of the diacetyl dihydro derivative of the vitamin. Oxidation with chromic acid formed the diacetyl dihydro derivative of the quinone acid, and a ketone $C_{18}H_{36}O$. This ketone was also formed by ozonolysis of the diacetyl dihydro vitamin and was identified as 2, 6, 10-trimethylpentadecanone-14 which proved the arrangement of the remaining carbon atoms of the unsaturated side chain.

"The constitution of vitamin K_1 as 2-methyl-3-phytyl-1, 4-naphthoquinone was confirmed by synthesis. Phytyl bromide was condensed with the monosodium salt of 2-methyl-1, 4-naphthohydroquinone, the vitamin being isolated in the pure condition as the diacetyl dihydro derivative. The synthetic compound was degraded by the same procedure as that used for the natural vitamin derivative and shown to give the same degradation products."

CONSEQUENCES IN THEORY AND PRACTICE

The first hemorrhagic disease in man to be recognized as due to a deficiency of vitamin K was the bleeding which accompanies obstructive jaundice. Bile is important for the proper absorption of vitamin K from the intestine,† and when the bile duct is blocked

---

* *Journal of Biological Chemistry*, Vol. 131 (1939), p. 369.
† Vitamin K is insoluble in water and its absorption and transportation depend on the presence of desoxycholic acid.

by gallstones or tumor a bleeding tendency is one of the consequences. This formerly constituted a real danger in operations for the relief of obstruction. But in 1938 three different groups, Dam and a colleague among them, independently reported that the bleeding tendency is due to vitamin K deficiency. As Dam observes: "Since then, the practical utilization of vitamin K in surgery has been tried by a large number of surgeons and its value has been fully established. It is possible by suitable vitamin K treatment, to eliminate completely the risk of bleeding in such patients, provided of course, that the case is not complicated by severe damage of the liver so that vitamin K cannot act."

Furthermore, "a bleeding tendency due to reduced absorption of vitamin K from the intestine can . . . be observed in certain intestinal diseases, where profuse diarrhoea occurs and the intestinal mucosa is damaged. This has been found in cases of sprue, for instance, where the absorption of fat is greatly diminished, or in ulcerative colitis." Here again vitamin K is useful in treatment.

Vitamin K deficiency is also seen in the newborn infant. The low prothrombin level which occurs in the first week after birth may be raised by treatment with vitamin K. Where bleeding actually is noted this is essential; the prothrombin may be raised to approximately normal values in 24 hours. Bleeding almost certainly occurs, however, in many cases where it is not easily detectable, and the administration of vitamin K to parturient women before delivery has reduced the death rate among the newborn.

Both forms of vitamin K are 2-methyl-1,4-naphthoquinones. Vitamin K_1 has a phytyl side chain in the 3-position; vitamin K_2 has the farnesyl group instead. (These side chains are of the isoprenoid series; that is, they are built up of units of the five-carbon, branched-chain hydrocarbon known as isoprene. In this respect they bear a family relationship to the intermediates occurring in the biological synthesis of cholesterol, steroid hormones, and vitamin A.) The compound lacking a side chain is known as menadione; it is effective as a synthetic vitamin K substitute. Menadione diphosphate has the advantage over the natural vitamin of being water-soluble. In the treatment of poisoning or over-dosage with the anticoagulant drug Dicumarol, however, vitamin K_1 must be used.

1 9 4 4

JOSEPH ERLANGER
(1874–1965)

HERBERT SPENCER GASSER
(1888–1963)

"For their discoveries regarding the highly differentiated functions of single nerve fibers."

BIOGRAPHICAL SKETCHES

ERLANGER

JOSEPH ERLANGER WAS BORN IN SAN FRANCISCO, ON JANUARY 5, 1874. He received the B.S. degree in chemistry from the University of California, and in 1899 the M.D. degree from the Johns Hopkins University. After serving for one year as interne in the Johns Hopkins Hospital he was appointed assistant in the Department of Physiology at the Johns Hopkins University Medical School under Dr. William H. Howell, then served successively as instructor, associate, and associate professor at that school. He then went to the University of Wisconsin as the first professor of physiology in the newly organized medical school there, where one of his pupils was Herbert S. Gasser. In 1910 he was appointed professor of physiology and head of the department in the reorganized medical school of Washington University, St. Louis. Gasser later rejoined him there and their work together was carried out in St. Louis. Dr. Erlanger became emeritus professor in 1944.

GASSER

HERBERT SPENCER GASSER WAS BORN IN PLATTEVILLE, A SMALL town in Wisconsin, on July 5, 1888. He was educated in the State Normal School there, and afterward in the State University. He records that "the preclinical years of the Medical School had just started and classes were so small that the faculty became not only teachers but friends." His first course in physiology was with Dr. Joseph Erlanger. The clinical years were completed at the Johns Hopkins Medical School in 1915. Next there followed a year in pharmacology at Wisconsin. He then rejoined Dr. Erlanger, who had meantime become professor of physiology at Washington University, St. Louis. In 1921 Dr. Gasser was made professor of pharmacology at Washington University. Two years later, at the instigation of Dr. Abraham Flexner, of the Rockefeller Foundation, Gasser was granted leave of absence for two years of study in Europe. After his return to the United States he remained at Washington University until 1931, when he left to become professor of physiology at the Cornell Medical School in New York City. In 1935 he was appointed director of the Rockefeller Institute for Medical Research. He held this position until his retirement in 1953, at which time the Institute provided him with a small laboratory in which to initiate new research in neurophysiology. He died on May 10, 1963.

DESCRIPTION OF THE PRIZE-WINNING WORK *

[It has been mentioned earlier (p. 164) that Gasser was one of the pioneers in the use of amplifiers in physiology. Whereas Adrian combined the amplifier with the capillary electrometer, Erlanger and Gasser combined it with the cathode-ray oscillograph, invented by F. Braun in 1897. (Braun received the Nobel Prize in Physics in 1909.) A stream of electrons is given off from the negative

---

* Joseph Erlanger and Herbert S. Gasser, "The Compound Nature of the Action Current of Nerve as Disclosed by the Cathode Ray Oscillograph," *American Journal of Physiology*, Vol. 70 (1924), p. 624.

electrode (cathode) in a Crookes tube; in Braun's cathode-ray tube, otherwise the same, these rays are narrowed into a threadlike beam which is subjected to the influence of external electric currents. It is then focused on a screen so that the oscillations caused by these outside potentials may be recorded. Erlanger and Gasser, in their first publication on this subject (1922), pictured and discussed the changes which the action current in nerve was sometimes found to undergo in its course. The record of this potential close to its source was a triangular wave with a rounded peak. Later it exhibited one or more humps on the descending limb. In a subsequent paper, quoted below, Erlanger and Gasser presented a partial explanation, afterward greatly elaborated, of the nature of these waves.]

"Light upon the fundamental nature of the waves which the cathode ray oscillograph has disclosed in the amplified action current was first obtained in experiments designed to ascertain whether altering the distance the action current is propagated along the nerve affects the relative positions of the waves. In these experiments the nerve is mounted in a moist chamber and kept at a constant temperature. . . . The stimulus is delivered through pairs of platinum electrodes of which several, 3 to 5, range along the nerve at measured distances from the proximal lead into the oscillograph. By means of . . . switches situated outside the moist chamber any desired pair of electrodes can be connected with the inductorium. . . . At the longer conducting distances [in the sciatic nerve of the bullfrog] the action current is composed of three waves, though the third in some instances is not very distinct. These waves may be designated alpha, beta and gamma from before backwards in the action current. . . . [Figures derived from an analysis of the waves] give the very definite impression that the shift in the relative positions of the waves that occurs with the change in the conducting distance, is due to differences in the rates with which the waves move along the nerve. . . .

"Every observation we have made indicates that each wave represents a discrete action current started by the one stimulus, but travelling in different groups of nerve fibers. Thus each wave, or better, perhaps, each group of fibers . . . has its own conduction rate. . . . The positions of the starts of the slower waves can not be ascertained with even a reasonable degree of accuracy. We, therefore, have taken the times elapsing between the crests of alpha and of beta . . . [etc.] as the lags between these waves. This is justifiable because . . . these crests at fairly long conducting distances are not materially displaced by summation and because . . . the times to maximum of all the waves are essentially alike. . . . [Each wave, or each group of fibers, was concluded to have not only its own conduction rate but also] its own threshold of stimulation and its own refractory period. . . . ["Threshold of stimulation" refers to the strength of stimulation required to produce an effect. It was found that different stimulation strengths produced different patterns; in one case, for instance, a completely developed action current appeared, while in another there was only an alpha wave, etc. Analysis of the patterns produced by graded action currents therefore contributed to the view that not one but several discrete action currents were being recorded. The "refractory period" is the time that must elapse after delivering an effective stimulus before another response to a second stimulus is obtainable from the same point. By applying stimulation at different intervals and studying the resultant wave patterns, the varying refractory periods of alpha, beta, etc. were revealed.]

"Of even greater . . . interest, however, is the experimental dissociation of the action current into the several processes of which it is composed, that is made possible through the fact that the alpha and beta (and gamma) processes have different stimulation thresholds as well as different refractory phases. If by properly selecting the strength of stimulation, an action current consisting solely of a maximal alpha process is started in a nerve, and if while the nerve still is absolutely refractory to this alpha process it is stimulated a second time through the same electrodes with a strong shock, one that ordinarily would elicit all of the processes, the action current started by the second stimulus will be without an alpha process."

CONSEQUENCES IN THEORY
AND PRACTICE

The work described above, developed in further detail, led to the establishment of a theory of differentiated function. The evidence presented in the last paragraph above was a strong indication that the alpha process resulted from a separate action current in a separate division of the nerve—i.e., in a particular group of fibers. It was concluded as the result of later studies that the thickest, or A-fibers, have the highest conduction velocity; that those of intermediate size, the B-fibers, have a lower rate; and that the lowest rate of all is in the slenderest, the C-fibers. Individual fibers, running in the same nerve, were thought to serve different purposes; for example, the lowest rate of conduction was found in fibers carrying pain impulses. A part of the work, pursued chiefly by Gasser, was concerned with the changes of excitability that occur at a nerve cross section at which impulses arrive. The arrival of one or several impulses to such a region was found to be followed by slow changes of excitability associated with slow changes of electrical potential. These changes of excitability enhance or depress succeeding impulses. It was shown that such "after-potentials" behaved in a different manner in the three main types of fiber, confirming the concept of a high degree of differentiation of the nerve fibers for their various tasks. Gasser, however, in his Nobel lecture, delivered in December 1945, observed in regard to pain, touch, temperature, etc., that "attempts to identify modalities with definite segments of the velocity spectrum have not been very successful. We are left faced with evidence for conduction of single modalities at very different velocities, and inclusion of a number of modalities within a narrow band of fibers. What then is the significance of the wide velocity range? Is it timing? Reflection on this, the most obvious interpretation of all, causes it to loom progressively larger. One need but consider the speed with which posture is controlled in preparation for the reception of oncoming detailed information and adjustment of fine movement; or again the mode of transmission of excitation through any central ganglion. . . . Differential axonal velocities must play their part in the mechanism. Be this their only contribution to integration, it is still a large one."

Adrian and others had studied responses from a single nerve fiber after teasing a nerve until only one fiber remained intact. In the work of Erlanger and Gasser, and especially in the later work of Erlanger and Blair, an intact nerve was selected, such as the frog's phalangeal nerve, likely to contain a fiber of particular excitability so that a threshold stimulus would excite that fiber only. Thus the investigation of a more nearly physiological condition became possible with the refined apparatus used. These studies have been pursued, as Erlanger stated in his Nobel lecture, delivered in 1947, "because it is felt . . . that in the investigation of this comparatively simple structure, the nerve fiber, lies the hope of finding clues to an understanding of the much more complicated mechanisms that determine the activities of peripheral and central nervous mechanisms."

REFERENCES

ERLANGER, J. "A Physiologist Reminisces," *Annual Review of Physiology*, vol. 26 (1964), pp. 1-14.

HINSEY, J. C. (ed.) "Herbert Spencer Gasser, 1888-1963, Scholar, Administrator, Nobel Laureate," *Experimental Neurology*, Supplement 1, 38 pp., May, 1964. This is an autobiographical memoir.

1 9 4 5
ALEXANDER FLEMING
(1881–1955)

ERNST BORIS CHAIN
(1906–)

HOWARD WALTER FLOREY
(1898–)

"For the discovery of penicillin and its therapeutic effect for the cure of different infectious maladies."

BIOGRAPHICAL SKETCHES

FLEMING

ALEXANDER FLEMING WAS BORN ON AUGUST 6, 1881, AT LOCH-field, in Ayrshire, Scotland. He obtained his general education at Loudoun Moor School, Darvel School, Kilmarnock Academy, and the London Polytechnic. Before beginning the study of medicine he worked for four years in a shipping office. He then began his medical education at St. Mary's Hospital Medical School, University of London. He qualified in 1906 and immediately commenced work in Sir Almroth Wright's laboratory in St. Mary's Hospital.

He remained there all his life. In 1929 he became professor of bacteriology. Fleming published many articles on immunology, general bacteriology, and chemotherapy. His most important papers are those dealing with antiseptics, lysozyme (an antibacterial substance discovered in 1922), and penicillin. He made use of variations of Wright's technique of the teat and the capillary tube (see lecture below) in his studies of human blood. He received many honorary degrees and prizes for his research, and was made Knight Bachelor in 1944. Fleming died on March 11, 1955, in London.

CHAIN

SON OF DR. MICHAEL CHAIN, A CHEMIST AND INDUSTRIALIST, Ernst Boris Chain was born on June 19, 1906, in Berlin. Educated at the *Luisengymnasium,* Berlin, he early became interested in chemistry and in 1930 was graduated as a chemist from the Friedrich-Wilhelm University. After several years of research work on enzymes at the Pathological Institute of the Charité Hospital in Berlin he emigrated to England; this was early in 1933, soon after the access to power of the Nazi regime in Germany. He spent two years in the Cambridge School of Biochemistry, the domain of Sir Frederick Gowland Hopkins, whom he greatly admired. In 1935 he was invited to Oxford by H. W. Florey to develop a chemical section in the Department of Pathology. In 1938 he initiated jointly with Florey a systematic investigation of antibacterial substances produced by microorganisms. This work led to the reinvestigation of penicillin, described nine years earlier by Fleming, and to the discovery of its chemotherapeutic action. From 1949 to 1961 Chain was Professor of Biochemistry and Scientific Director of a research center in chemical microbiology at the Superior Institute of Health in Rome. But in 1961 he returned to England to become Professor of Biochemistry at the Imperial College of Science and Technology in London.

FLOREY

HOWARD WALTER FLOREY WAS BORN ON SEPTEMBER 24, 1898, at Adelaide, South Australia. After attending local schools and

Adelaide University (1916-1921), he went to Magdalen College, Oxford, in 1922, as a Rhodes Scholar. He later studied at Cambridge and at the London Hospital, and was Rockefeller Travelling Fellow in the United States, 1925-1926. He became Huddersfield Lecturer in Special Pathology, Cambridge, 1927; professor of pathology, University of Sheffield, 1931; and professor of pathology, Oxford, 1935. In 1935 he invited Chain to join him at Oxford. In 1941 he was elected Fellow of the Royal Society and in 1944 was made Knight Bachelor. He has received many prizes and honorary degrees. In 1944 he was Nuffield Visiting Professor to Australia and New Zealand. The subjects of his research have included inflammation, capillary blood circulation, and the functions of the lymphocyte. His work on lysozyme led to a general study of antibiotics, in association with Chain; this in turn led to the discovery of the chemotherapeutic value of penicillin. Florey was elected President of the Royal Society in 1960.

DESCRIPTION OF THE PRIZE-WINNING WORK

FLEMING *

"The origin of penicillin was the contamination of a culture plate of staphylococci by a mould. [Staphylococci are among the common pus-forming bacteria. A culture plate is a flat, shallow glass dish containing a gelatinous solid, commonly agar, on the surface of which the bacteria are grown.] It was noticed that for some distance around the mould colony the staphylococcal colonies had become translucent and evidently lysis [solvent action] was going on. This was an extraordinary appearance and seemed to demand investigation so the mould was isolated in pure culture and some of its properties were determined.

"The mould was found to belong to the genus penicillium and it was eventually identified as penicillium notatum. . . .

"Having got the mould in pure culture I planted it on another culture plate and after it had grown at room temperature for 4 or

---

* From Alexander Fleming, "Nobel Lecture on Penicillin," *Les Prix Nobel en 1945*, pp. 155-164.

5 days I streaked different microbes radially across the plate. Some of them grew right up to the mould—others were inhibited for a distance of several centimetres. This showed that the mould produced an antibacterial substance which affected some microbes and not others. . . .

"Then the mould was grown on fluid medium to see whether the antiseptic substance occurred in the fluid. After some days the fluid on which the mould had grown was tested . . . by placing it in a gutter in a culture plate and then streaking different microbes across the plate. The result [indicated] that the microbes which were most powerfully inhibited were some of those responsible for our most common infections. . . .

"All the experiments I have cited showed that [penicillin] was bacteriostatic, that is, it inhibits the growth of microbes. But I showed also that it was bactericidal—that it actually killed them. Then the very first observation . . . showed that it induced lytic changes in the bacteria. Thus it was bacteriostatic, bactericidal and bacteriolytic. . . .

"I had since the war of 1914/18 been interested in antiseptics and in 1924 I described what I think is probably the best experiment I ever did. This showed up in a dramatic fashion the relative activity of a chemical on bacteria and on human leucocytes [white blood cells].

"Normal human blood has a strong bactericidal power on the ordinary cocci . . . but this power is completely lost if the leucocytes are removed from the blood. If defibrinated blood is infected with a small number of staphylococci . . . and incubated in a capillary space [e.g., a fine glass tube with a hairlike bore] the cocci which survive grow out into colonies which can easily be enumerated. But only about 5 per cent grow out. If however, phenol [carbolic acid] is added to a concentration of 1 in 600 all the cocci grow out freely. Here the phenol in a concentration which does not interfere with bacterial growth has destroyed the leucocytes which constitute one of our most powerful defenses against infection.

"I had tested all the chemicals which were used as antibacterial agents and they all behaved in the same way—in some concentration they destroyed leucocytes and allowed bacteria to grow. When I tested penicillin in the same way on staphylococcus it was quite a different story. The crude penicillin would completely inhibit the growth of staphylococci in a dilution of up to 1 in 1000 when tested in human blood [phenol loses its inhibitory power when diluted more than 300 times] but it had no more toxic effect on the leucocytes than the original culture medium in which the mould had been grown. I also injected it into animals and it had apparently no toxicity.

"A few tentative trials [on hospital patients] gave favourable results but nothing miraculous and I was convinced that . . . it would have to be concentrated. . . .

"We tried to concentrate penicillin but we discovered . . . that penicillin is easily destroyed . . . and our relatively simple procedures were unavailing. . . .

"In 1929 I published the results which I have briefly given."

CHAIN AND FLOREY *

"It was first established that penicillin was an acid . . . [which, extracted from the culture fluid with ether and shaken up with dilute aqueous alkali, formed stable salts]. In addition to ether, a number of organic solvents . . . could be used to extract the free acid form of penicillin. The salts of penicillin were much more soluble in water than in the organic solvents, and therefore penicillin was removed from the organic solvent by about 1/5 to 1/10 the volume of alkali solution. A concentration of penicillin was thereby achieved, and by repeating the extraction several times with different solvents and at a suitable pH, a considerable purification of penicillin and simultaneous reduction of the bulk of liquid was obtained. . . . [By drying at low temperature and pressure] a preparation of a salt of penicillin was obtained, in powder form, which kept its antibacterial activity unchanged for a long time.

"Chemically, however, the preparation was far from pure, containing, as is now known, not more than a small percentage of pure

* From Ernst Chain and H. W. Florey, "The Discovery of the Chemotherapeutic Properties of Penicillin," *Caribbean Medical Journal,* Vol. 7 (1945), pp. 151-155.

penicillin. The isolation of penicillin in the pure state from this mixture proved a difficult problem because of its instability towards many reagents and the unfavourable solubilities of the free acid and its salts. . . . [By distribution between different solvents and water, by adsorption methods, and by a variety of other means, later much elaborated, it became possible] to produce penicillin preparations from which crystalline salts could be made. The purest material obtained at Oxford [1945] has an activity of about 1,000 Oxford units per mg., and is capable of inhibiting the growth of certain bacteria at a dilution of about 1:50,000,000. . . . [The Oxford unit, also called Florey unit, was an arbitrary amount determined by comparison with a standard preparation.]

"For the first biological experiments very crude preparations were used. . . . So great was the antibacterial power of even the crudest extracts that at that time—not realizing the extraordinary potency of penicillin—we believed them to be fairly pure. In actual fact we know now that they contained about 1 per cent of pure penicillin. . . .

"It was shown that the extracts were remarkably non-toxic to mice. . . . Not only were the extracts relatively innocuous to the whole animal, but leucocytes and tissue cultures withstood many hundreds of times the concentration needed to inhibit such organisms as the streptococcus. In light of present knowledge of the gross impurity of the original extracts, one can only be thankful that the mass of impurities, as well as the penicillin, were so little toxic.

"Penicillin was readily absorbed in animals after intramuscular or subcutaneous injection, and from the small intestine. It could not of course be given by mouth because the acid of the gastric juice destroyed it, nor by rectum as the bacteria there inactivated it. It was largely excreted, still in an active form, in the urine . . . and to a certain extent in the bile and saliva. . . . Though penicillin was readily soluble and diffusible, it did not pass in detectable quantities from the blood into the cerebro-spinal fluid.

"In agreement with Fleming's observations it was found that the action of penicillin was bacteriostatic, in that it merely inhibited the growth of organisms and did not kill them quickly, as did poisonous antiseptics. . . . Most antibacterial substances such as ordinary antiseptics and the sulphonamides are . . . not active in the presence of pus, and hence their therapeutic efficacy is severely limited. It was therefore a particularly fortunate property of penicillin that pus, tissue autolysates [products of the self-digestion of cells, called autolysis], blood and serum had no inhibitory effect on its activity. It was found too that the number of organisms present had little effect on its inhibitory power—again a contrast with the sulphonamides. . . .

"In terms of the labour involved it was . . . a big step from experiments on mice to making observations on the human subject, for the mould produces very little of the active substance. Months elapsed before enough material could be accumulated to try the first injection on man.

"Injection in the human subject disclosed that some substance was present in the crude penicillin preparations which caused a rigor and sharp rise of temperature. This had not been suspected from observations on animals. By good fortune the pyrogenic effect was not due to the penicillin but to an impurity which could be removed.

"Insufficient material had been accumulated for the first 2 cases treated, and although both patients, who were seriously ill, did well for a time, they relapsed and further treatment could not be carried out for lack of material. In the course of some months enough was accumulated . . . to treat by parenteral injection a further 18 patients. . . . Toxic reactions, apart from pyrogen, were not observed and some striking recoveries of patients infected with staphylococci were obtained. Suitable dosage was worked out and the principles of treatment were formulated. At the same time penicillin was shown to be valuable for local application in various septic conditions. . . ."

CONSEQUENCES IN THEORY
AND PRACTICE

Chain and his colleagues at Oxford began the long and difficult task of elucidating the structure of penicillin; this problem was subsequently taken up elsewhere, chiefly in the United States. Meanwhile the job of producing penicillin in quantity from the mold was undertaken by a number of American pharmaceutical houses, at first independently, later under the aegis of the War Production Board. The manifold production problems were solved in a surprisingly short time.

Penicillin could be used on many cases in which sulfonamides would be ruled out, as on patients with kidney damage and those reacting allergically to the "sulfa" drugs. Its effectiveness was at first hard to evaluate, for insufficient supplies and insufficient experience often resulted in inadequate dosage. It proved effective against pneumonia and other diseases due to staphylococci and largely beyond the reach of the "sulfas" or any other form of treatment. It showed itself a powerful weapon against streptococci and the bacilli of gas gangrene. It cured gonorrhea rapidly and without the sometimes unpleasant reactions due to "sulfa" therapy. It transformed the treatment of syphilis. It cured a large percentage of cases of bacterial endocarditis, a disease previously regarded as almost 100 per cent fatal. Although powerless against tuberculosis, typhoid fever, and such nonbacterial diseases as malaria and infantile paralysis, it was shown to have a wide "bacterial spectrum" and to be the most powerful microbe-killer yet discovered.

Penicillin nevertheless has its limitations. It is primarily active against gram-positive organisms—those which take a blue or deep violet stain when treated by Gram's differential staining method. It has little activity against the gram-negatives—the red-staining organisms which cause cholera, typhoid, dysentery, and other diseases. Many of these have since proved susceptible to streptomycin and other new agents. Penicillin has acted as a spur to the search for these newer antibiotics, of which about half a dozen are now in fairly general use, most of them the products of soil bacteria. It is now quite common for physicians to give penicillin orally, means having been found to prevent its destruction before it can act. It was at first supposed that penicillin was quite innocuous and that all bad effects would vanish as soon as a pure product had been obtained. Although it is true that penicillin is remarkably nontoxic for a drug of such potency, it is nevertheless not entirely free of noxious side effects; these are seldom so serious, however, as those which sometimes complicate the use of the sulfonamides.

A not uncommon, and certainly highly unpleasant, allergic symptom is a severe urticaria (a reaction in the nature of hives) which may persist for days, or even for weeks, after the discontinuance of penicillin therapy. Bad reactions to penicillin are annoying, and sometimes dangerous, but they are neither frequent enough nor serious enough to constitute any considerable limitation on the use of the drug. As in the case of the sulfonamides, 'bacterial generations may arise which are penicillin-resistant.

Despite its various limitations and drawbacks, penicillin remains the most important of antibiotic drugs.

REFERENCES

RATCLIFF, J. D. *Yellow Magic: The Story of Penicillin* (New York: Random House, 1945).

1 9 4 6
HERMANN JOSEPH MULLER
(1890–   )

*"For his discovery of the production of mutations
by means of X-ray irradiation."*

BIOGRAPHICAL SKETCH

HERMANN JOSEPH MULLER WAS BORN IN NEW YORK CITY, ON
December 21, 1890. He attended a public primary school in Har-
lem and the Morris High School in the Bronx. In 1907 he won a
scholarship for entry into Columbia College, where he became interested in biology. He attributes his particular interest in genetics
to reading a book on this subject by R. H. Lock. In 1909 he
founded a students' biology club, in which Altenburg, Bridges, and
Sturtevant participated, all destined to be distinguished geneticists.
After graduation he held first a scholarship, then a teaching fellowship, in physiology, the latter at Cornell Medical College; he then
taught zoology at Columbia, 1912-1915. From 1910 on he was a
member of Morgan's research group (see above, p. 169) and in
1912 he began to do original research in genetics. From 1915 to
1918 he was an instructor in the Rice Institute, Houston, under
Julian Huxley. During this time and the two years following, when
he instructed at Columbia, he elaborated methods for quantitative
mutation study. In 1920 he went to the University of Texas as
associate professor, becoming professor in 1925. His first evidence
of mutations produced by X rays was obtained in 1926 and published in 1927. In 1932 he was awarded a Guggenheim Fellowship

for a year in Oscar Vogt's institute in Berlin, in Timoféeff's Department of Genetics. He then spent more than three years as Senior Geneticist at the Institute of Genetics of the Academy of Sciences of the U.S.S.R., first in Leningrad, later in Moscow. Then followed work in the Institute of Animal Genetics, University of Edinburgh (1937-1940), Amherst College (1940-1945) and Indiana University, where he accepted a professorship in the Zoology Department in 1945. In 1953 he was elevated to the rank of Distinguished Service Professor at that university. He was a member of the City of Hope Medical Center, Duarte, California, in 1964-1965, and is now Director of Genetic Biology at Quadri-Science, Inc., in Washington, D.C.

DESCRIPTION OF THE PRIZE-WINNING WORK*

"If . . . mutations were really non-teleological, with no relation between type of environment and type of change, and above all no adaptive relation, and if they were of as numerous types as the theory of natural selection would demand, then the great majority of the changes should be harmful in their effects, just as any alterations made blindly in a complicated apparatus are usually detrimental to its proper functioning, and many of the larger changes should even be totally incompatible with the functioning of the whole, or, as we say, lethal. . . .

"To get exact evidence . . . required the elaboration of special genetic methods, adapted to the recognition of mutations that ordinarily escape detection—(1) lethals, (2) changes with but small visible effects, and (3) changes without any externally visible effects but influencing the viability more or less unfavourably. . . .

"It was possible in the first mutation experiments, which [Edgar] Altenburg and the writer conducted, partly in collaboration, in 1918-19, to get definite evidence in *Drosophila* that the lethal mutations greatly outnumbered those with visible effects, and that among the latter the types having an obscure manifestation were more numerous than the definite conspicuous ones used in ordinary

---

* From H. J. Muller, "The Production of Mutations," *Les Prix Nobel en 1946,* pp. 257-274.

genetic work. Visible or not, the great majority had lowered viability. Tests of their genetic basis . . . showed them to be most varied in their locus in the chromosomes, and it could be calculated . . . that there must be at least hundreds, and probably thousands, of different kinds arising in the course of spontaneous mutation. . . .

"Objectivity of recognition, combined with [their greater number] . . . made it feasible for lethals to be used as an index of mutation frequency. . . . In the earliest published work, we . . . attempted not only to find a quantitative value for the 'normal' mutation frequency, but also to determine whether [temperature] . . . affected the mutation frequency. . . . The results . . . indicated that a rise of temperature, within limits normal to the organism, produced an increase of mutation frequency of about the amount to be expected if mutations were, in essentials, orthodox chemical reactions.

". . . Mutations, when taken collectively, should be subject to the statistical laws applying to mass reactions, but the individual mutation . . . should be subject to the vicissitudes of ultramicroscopic or atomic events. . . . This is a principle which gives the clue to the fact . . . that differences in external conditions . . . do not appear to affect the occurrence of mutations, while on the other hand, even in a normal and sensibly constant environment, mutations of varied kinds do occur. It is also in harmony with our finding, of about the same time, that when a mutation takes place in a given gene, the other gene of identical type present nearby in the same cell usually remains unaffected, though it must of course have been subjected to the same macroscopic physicochemical conditions. On this conception, then, the mutations ordinarily result from submicroscopic accidents, that is, from caprices of thermal agitation, that occur on a molecular and submolecular scale. . . .

"Now this inference . . . led naturally to the expectation that some of the 'point effects' brought about by high-energy radiation like X-rays would also work to produce alterations in the hereditary material. For if even the relatively mild events of thermal agitation can . . . have such consequences, surely the energetically far more potent point changes caused by powerful radiation should succeed. And, as a matter of fact, our trials of X-rays . . . proved that such radiation is extremely effective, and inordinately more so than a mere temperature rise, since by this method it was possible to obtain, by a half hour's treatment, over a hundred times as many mutations . . . as would have occurred . . . spontaneously in the course of a whole generation. These mutations too were found ordinarily to occur pointwise and randomly, in one gene at a time, without affecting an identical gene that might be present nearby in a homologous chromosome.

"In addition to the individual gene changes, radiation also produced rearrangements of parts of chromosomes. As our later work . . . has shown, these latter were caused in the first place by breakages of the chromosomes, followed afterwards by attachments occurring between the adhesive broken ends, that joined them in a different order than before. The two or more breaks involved . . . may be far apart, caused by independent hits, and thus result in what we call *gross* structural change. . . . By the rejoining, in a new order, of broken ends resulting from two . . . nearby breaks, a *minute* change of sequence of the genes is brought about."

CONSEQUENCES IN THEORY AND PRACTICE

Possibly the most obvious lesson of Muller's important discovery is that "the great majority of mutations being undesirable . . . their further random production in ourselves should so far as possible be rigorously avoided." It thus "becomes an obligation for radiologists . . . to insist that the simple precautions are taken which are necessary for shielding the gonads. . . . And, with the coming increasing use of atomic energy, even for peacetime purposes, the problem will become very important of insuring that the human germ plasm . . . is effectively protected from this additional and potent source of permanent contamination."

Other agents were soon found to produce mutations—alpha rays, neutrons, ultraviolet and infrared light, mustard gas and related chemical compounds. The latter were investigated by J. M. Robson and C. Auerbach, because Robson had noticed a similarity between the effects of mustard gas on the body and those produced by X ray and radium. Muller had already inferred that "a large proportion . . . of the somatic effects of irradiation . . . arise secondarily as consequences of genetic effects produced in the somatic cells. The usefulness of this interpretation has been shown in recent studies . . . dealing with improved methods of irradiation of mammalian carcinoma." Dr. Muller is also of the opinion that studies in this field are "helping to clear the way for an understanding of the mechanism by which radiation acts in inhibiting growth, in causing sterilization, in producing necrosis [local death of tissue] and burns, in causing recession of malignant tissue, and perhaps also, on occasion at least, in inducing the initiation of such tissue."

The importance of the discovery in aiding scientists to understand the mechanism of evolution has been hinted in the principal quotation. Its importance for further studies in genetics is suggested by Muller's assertion that "every natural mutation, when searched for long enough, is found to be producible also by radiation." The abundant, if random, production of mutations has enormously extended the materials of the geneticist's work. For instance, "position effect" (implying that the function of a gene is to a certain extent dependent upon what other genes are near by) had been observed previously, but it was not known to what extent the effect might be a special one until numerous rearrangements could be studied; this was made possible by irradiation, and there is now evidence that "position effect" is a general principle. This is one instance only of the way in which Muller's discovery has affected genetics. Analysis of the properties of the chromosomes and their parts has gained a great deal from studies in which parts have been removed, added, or rearranged. Mutations are produced at random, but they are so numerous that it is possible to pick out those best suited for successive steps in analysis, and the method has been applied not only to "pure" genetics but also to studies in the biochemical synthesis of amino acids, vitamins, purines, etc. By means of induced mutations it has been possible to develop strains of fungi which have lost the power to synthesize certain substances. Such studies promise to shed more light on synthetic processes in the organism and to improve our understanding of certain hereditary metabolic disturbances. Hereditary diseases in general are ultimately due to mutations. Mutations also determine the development of new properties in bacteria, such as resistance to particular drugs.

The possibility of applying any influence which will change individual genes to order seems very remote, but there has been evidence that induced mutations may at times be used for selection in artificial breeding.

1 9 4 7
BERNARDO ALBERTO HOUSSAY
(1887–   )

"For his discovery of the part played by the hormone of the anterior pituitary lobe in the metabolism of sugar."
(*The award for 1947 was shared with C. F. and G. T. Cori; see below, pp. 254-260.*)

BIOGRAPHICAL SKETCH

BERNARDO ALBERTO HOUSSAY WAS BORN IN BUENOS AIRES, ON April 10, 1887. His early studies were in a private academy. In 1901 he was admitted to the School of Pharmacy of the University of Buenos Aires, where he was graduated in 1904. He had already commenced his work at the medical school, from which he obtained his M.D. in 1911 for his thesis on the hypophysis, or pituitary body. Before he had completed his medical studies he was appointed professor of physiology in the University of Buenos Aires School of Veterinary Medicine. In 1919 he resigned this position to occupy the chair of physiology in the medical school, as the first full-time professor in an Argentine university; he remained as professor and director of the Institute of Physiology until 1957, with interruptions in 1944 and 1946-1955. During those periods he worked as Director of the Institute of Biology and Experimental Medicine in Buenos Aires, a privately financed laboratory. He has worked in almost every field of physiology, but has given particular attention to endocrinology.

DESCRIPTION OF THE PRIZE-WINNING
WORK*

"The production and consumption of glucose and hence the blood sugar level are controlled by a functional endocrine equilibrium. [The endocrine glands are ductless glands secreting hormones into the bloodstream.] This mechanism acts on the liver— the organ which produces and stores glucose—and on the tissues which are the consumers of glucose, by means of hormones which play a part in the chemical processes of carbohydrate metabolism.

"The secretion of each endocrine organ is controlled by a physiological mechanism. For instance, the pancreas secretes insulin in adequate quantities so as to maintain a normal blood sugar level and the blood sugar level regulates the amount of insulin secreted. Thus hyperglycemia [high blood sugar] increases the secretion of insulin [which lowers the blood sugar], and hypoglycemia [low blood sugar] diminishes or completely inhibits it. . . . The extrinsic innervation of the pancreas is not necessary for the regulation of insulin secretion [i.e., cutting the nerves has little effect on the control of the endocrine part of the gland].

"Not only is the secretion of each gland regulated according to the organic needs of each moment, but there is also an equilibrium between the secretions of the different glands [e.g., those which raise blood sugar and those which lower it]. . . .

"In 1907, when I was a medical student, I was attracted to the study of the hypophysis because the microscopic picture showed glandular activity and its lesions were accompanied by serious organic disturbances, such as acromegaly, dwarfism, etc. [The hypophysis, or pituitary body, is a small two-lobed body at the base of the brain. Both parts produce hormones. Those of the anterior lobe control the thyroid, the sex glands and cortex of the suprarenal glands, regulate the formation of milk and the growth of the whole body; Houssay has shown that this anterior lobe also has a part in the conversion of sugar. Disordered function in the secretion of the growth hormone causes acromegaly, a disease described

---

* B. A. Houssay, "The Rôle of the Hypophysis in Carbohydrate Metabolism and in Diabetes," *Les Prix Nobel en 1947*, pp. 129-136.

by Pierre Marie in 1886, in which there is progressive enlargement of the head and face, the hands, feet, and thorax.]

"The frequency of glycosuria [sugar in the urine] or diabetes in acromegaly has been reported many times. . . . Moreover extracts of the posterior lobe of the hyphosis produce . . . a transitory hyperglycemia. Therefore it was commonly accepted that if the hypophysis played a part in carbohydrate metabolism, it would be due to the activity of its posterior lobe.

"One year after the discovery of insulin a systematic study of the influence of endocrine glands on its activity was organized in my laboratory. [When the hypophysis had been removed from dogs, a difficult surgical procedure, they were found to be excessively sensitive to the action of insulin; this was also found in a large kind of toad, plentiful in Argentina, which Houssay used in many of his experiments. Later he found that administration of extract of anterior lobe prevented or corrected this hypersensitiveness to insulin.] The next step consisted in the removal of the pancreas in hypophysectomized dogs and toads. . . . [A dog without a pancreas is diabetic; but removal of the hypophysis or its anterior lobe] produced a considerable attenuation of the severity of pancreatic diabetes. The injection or implantation of anterior hypophyseal lobe reestablished or even increased the usual severity of diabetes. . . .

"Later the diabetogenic [diabetes-producing] effect was also demonstrated in dogs with a surgically reduced pancreas or [by other workers] with an intact pancreas. A permanent diabetes was produced by prolonged treatment with the extract of anterior lobe. . . . [This was shown to be due to the damage caused to the β cells, or insulin-secreting cells, of the pancreas.] If after a few days the anterohypophyseal treatment is discontinued the diabetic condition disappears, the blood sugar returns to a normal level, and later the β cells regain their normal aspect. If daily injections . . are continued for several weeks . . . the animals remain permanently diabetic."

CONSEQUENCES IN THEORY
AND PRACTICE

The far-reaching importance in animal metabolism of the tiny hypophysis has been realized only in the present century. Its relation to body growth was first clearly appreciated during the first decade of the century, but not until 1944 did H. M. Evans and C. H. Li produce the growth hormone in pure form. In the same way the influence of the pituitary body on sex functions, although perceived about fifty years ago, was not worked out in detail until much later. The effect of the hypophysis on the pancreas, although surmised, was little investigated or understood before the work of Houssay. Beginning in 1924, Houssay demonstrated that an animal deprived of its pituitary is abnormally sensitive to insulin; that a pituitary extract will offset this effect, showing an anti-insulin property; that this influence emanates from the anterior lobe of the pituitary; that diabetes caused by removal of the pancreas is distinctly relieved by removal of the pituitary body too; and that the diabetogenic (diabetes-producing) capacity of the anterior lobe is so great that sufficient quantities of extract injected into a test animal will evoke the symptoms of diabetes.

In 1930 P. E. Smith discovered that the anterior lobe of this vital organ also has an adrenocorticotropic function—i.e., that it produces a hormone which stimulates the functional activity of the adrenal cortex. This hormone was later isolated and is known as ACTH. One of its effects, and doubtless the principal one, is to cause the adrenal cortex to secrete cortisol, a hormone whose metabolic actions include stimulation of the conversion of protein to carbohydrate and the elevation of the blood sugar concentration.

Carbohydrate metabolism is of such enormous importance to the body's economy that whatever serves to throw light upon it is a useful contribution. Hope of determining the basic cause of diabetes must depend upon increasing knowledge of this exceedingly complex mechanism. Houssay has demonstrated a link in the cycle. He has also helped to attract further attention to the importance of the anterior pituitary, a subject of ever-increasing interest.

CARL F. CORI
(1896–   )

GERTY T. CORI
(1896–1957)

"For their discovery of how glycogen is catalytically converted."
(The award for 1947 was shared with B. A. Houssay; see above, pp. 250-253.)

BIOGRAPHICAL SKETCHES

CARL F. CORI

CARL FERDINAND CORI WAS BORN IN PRAGUE, THEN PART OF Austria-Hungary, on December 5, 1896. His father was director of the Marine Biological Station in Trieste, and his maternal grandfather, Ferdinand Lippich, professor of theoretical physics at the German University of Prague, so that he was early subjected to influences deriving from both the physical and the biological sciences. He attended the *Gymnasium* at Trieste and studied medicine at Prague, where he was graduated in 1920. His wartime studies were interrupted by service as a lieutenant in the Sanitary Corps of the Austrian Army on the Italian front. His collaborative scientific work with Gerty Theresa Cori (née Radnitz) began when they were classmates, with a publication on the complement of human serum. They were married in 1920. At the Universities of Vienna and Graz, Cori devoted the next two years chiefly to pharmacology. In 1922 he moved to the United States, becoming an American citizen in 1928. From 1922 to 1931 he served as biochemist at the State Institute for the Study of Malignant Diseases in Buffalo, New York. He then joined the faculty of Washington University Medical School in St. Louis, first as professor of pharmacology and later as professor of biochemistry. His work has been centered on enzymes and hormones, particularly in relation to carbohydrate metabolism. He has been elected a Foreign Member of the Royal Society, and in 1958 was President of the Fourth International Congress of Biochemistry, held in Vienna. In 1965 he was named Distinguished Service Professor of Biological Chemistry at Washington University School of Medicine.

GERTY T. CORI

GERTY THERESA CORI (NÉE RADNITZ) WAS BORN IN PRAGUE, on August 15, 1896. She was privately tutored until the age of ten, when she entered a school for girls. In 1914 she enrolled in the medical school of the German University of Prague, and in 1920 she received her doctorate. In the same year she married her classmate, Carl F. Cori, with whom she had already published an immunological study. After two years at the Carolinen Children's Hospital in Vienna she joined her husband at the State Institute for the Study of Malignant Diseases in Buffalo, New York; in 1931 she accompanied him to the Washington University School of Medicine as research associate, and in 1947 she was appointed professor of biochemistry. Their joint work has dealt with the catalytic and hormonal metabolism of the carbohydrates. Gerty Cori died in 1957.

DESCRIPTION OF THE PRIZE-WINNING
WORK*

"The discovery of polysaccharide phosphorylase and glucose-1-phosphate [Cori ester] can be traced to systematic work on the formation of hexose-6-phosphate in muscle. Of particular importance was the fact that the method used for the determination of hexose-6-phosphate consisted of two independent measurements, one based on the reducing power of the compound and the other on its phosphate content, and that there was generally good agreement between these two measurements. In this manner it was found that a number of procedures led to an increase in the hexose-6-phosphate content of muscle, among which may be listed anaerobiosis, injection of epinephrine in intact animals, incubation of isolated frog muscle in Ringer's solution containing epinephrine, and gastric stimulation of mammalian or frog muscle.

"Balance experiments during aerobic recovery of previously stimulated and isolated frog muscle indicated that the hexose-6-phosphate which disappeared was in large part reconverted to glycogen; hence it was made probable that the reaction, glycogen → glucose-6-phosphate, was reversible. The next step was the finding that the increase in hexose-6-phosphate in isolated frog muscle incubated anaerobically with epinephrine was accompanied by a corresponding decrease in inorganic phosphate. . . . Phosphocreatine and adenosine triphosphate (ATP) remained unchanged, suggesting that they were not involved in the formation of hexose-6-phosphate, but since their regeneration through lactic acid formation was not excluded, the experiments were repeated with muscles poisoned with iodoacetate. The results were the same as with unpoisoned muscle and it was therefore concluded that hexose-6-phosphate was formed from glycogen by esterification with inorganic phosphate. . . .

"The following experiments led to the detection and isolation of glucose-1-phosphate. Minced frog muscle was extracted 3 times

---

* From Carl F. Cori and Gerty T. Cori, "Polysaccharide Phosphorylase," *Les Prix Nobel en 1947*, pp. 216-235. The first quotation is from Part I, by Carl F. Cori; the second is from Part II, by Gerty T. Cori.

with 20 volumes of cold distilled water, a procedure which removed most of the acid-soluble phosphates normally present in muscle, but did not remove glycogen. When the washed residue was incubated anaerobically at 20° in isotonic phosphate buffer at pH 7.2, some hexosemonophosphate was formed. On addition of a catalytic amount of muscle adenylic acid, the formation of hexosemonophosphate was very markedly increased. When phosphate was replaced by isotonic KCl, no ester formation occurred. The glucose part of the ester could have come only from glycogen, and the phosphate part only from the added inorganic phosphate, thus confirming the reaction postulated for intact muscle.

"After short periods of incubation there was much more organic phosphate present in the hexosemonophosphate fraction than corresponded to the reducing power of hexose-6-phosphate. Such a discrepancy had not been encountered before in analyses of the hexosemonophosphate fraction, and since the discrepancy became smaller or disappeared completely after longer periods of incubation, the formation of a precursor of glucose-6-phosphate was suspected. Short hydrolysis in NH_2SO_4 at 100° (conditions under which hexose-6-phosphate is not hydrolyzed) revealed the presence of a compound which yielded equivalent amounts of fermentable sugar and inorganic phosphate. . . .

"The new phosphate ester was isolated as the crystalline brucine salt in a large-scale experiment . . . and identified as glucose-1-phosphate.

"When glucose-1-phosphate was added to a cell-free frog or rabbit muscle extract, it was converted rapidly to glucose-6-phosphate by an enzyme which was named phosphoglucomutase. It was due to the leaching out of the mutase that glucose-1-phosphate accumulated in minced frog muscle. Mutase is greatly enhanced in its activity by magnesium ions. In order to demonstrate the formation of glucose-1-phosphate from glycogen and inorganic phosphate in muscle extract, it was necessary to remove magnesium ions by dialysis. . . . [The chemical properties of the isolated ester were determined and it was later synthesized.]

"The first clue for a possible reversibility of the reaction, glycogen + phosphate → glucose-1-phosphate, came from the observation that addition of glucose-1-phosphate to a reaction mixture containing enzyme, glycogen and phosphate was strongly inhibitory, while glucose-6-phosphate had only a weak inhibitory effect on the formation of glucose-1-phosphate. Further investigation showed that conditions for reversibility were unfavourable because the concentration of glucose-1-phosphate could not be maintained, owing to the activity of phosphoglucomutase. . . . It became clear that a separation of the two enzymes was necessary in order to investigate reversibility. A partial separation was first achieved by adsorption of phosphorylase on aluminium hydroxide, followed by elution with disodium phosphate and dialysis to remove inorganic phosphate. When glucose-1-phosphate was added to this enzyme preparation, inorganic phosphate was set free and a polysaccharide was formed in equivalent amounts, showing the reversibility of the reaction. . . . Reversibility could also be demonstrated with phosphorylase preparations of heart and brain [and liver]. . . ."

* * *

"The protein fraction of a muscle extract, precipitated by less than 0.5 saturation with $(NH_4)_2SO_4$, showed a marked rise in phosphorylase activity per unit of protein over the unfractionated starting material. This was however the case only when the enzyme was catalyzing the reaction toward the right:

Glycogen + inorganic phosphate $\rightleftarrows$ glucose-1-phosphate

"When enzyme activity was tested in the opposite direction a puzzling difficulty was encountered. Activity set in only after a lag period; refractionation of the enzyme increased this lag period from minutes to hours and in some preparations completely abolished the activity toward polysaccharide formation. . . .

"Liver phosphorylase, upon salt fractionation, was found to retain activity toward polysaccharide synthesis. Such preparations always contained traces of glycogen, while the purified muscle enzyme was free of glycogen. This observation offered a clue. Addition of glycogen to the reaction mixture in as low a concentration as 10 mg. per cent led to immediate activity of muscle phosphorylase preparations, seemingly inactive when tested without glycogen addition. . . . From these observations it followed that glycogen was needed for the activity of the enzyme in both directions. . . ."

CONSEQUENCES IN THEORY
AND PRACTICE

The chemical changes involved in the contraction and relaxation of muscle have long been subjected to careful study (cf. the work of Meyerhof, pp. 107-110 above). It seemed probable that cyclical changes also occur during periods of rest, a conversion of energy taking place in the same way but with less intensity. Ever since the discovery of glycogen, or animal starch, by Claude Bernard, much effort has also been devoted to the study of carbohydrate metabolism. In the work of the Coris these two avenues of research, already merging, were brought together. The discoveries of these workers helped to elucidate specific details of what happens when glycogen is changed into sugar and vice versa. Tissues such as muscle and liver contain enzyme systems which bring about the phosphorylation of both glycogen and glucose. To an understanding of the phosphorylation of glucose, Meyerhof (1927) was the pioneer contributor with his discovery of "hexokinase," which later turned out to consist of two enzymes, both present in muscle. The phosphorylation of glycogen was explained by the Coris on the basis of a somewhat different mechanism.

As indicated above, they were able to produce from muscle an ester of hexose-phosphoric acid in which the phosphoric acid was linked to the sugar near carbon atom 1. In the presence of muscle extract this changed to the 6-ester, the process requiring the presence of magnesium and of a special enzyme, phosphoglucomutase. When the latter had been destroyed in the presence of phosphorylase, which causes phosphoric acid to be split off, they were able to build up glycogen from Cori ester, thus reversing the process; but, as shown in the brief quotation from Gerty T. Cori's Nobel lecture, small quantities of glycogen had to be present in order to bring about the synthesis. The reaction between the Cori ester and the 6-ester was also shown to be reversible. Two of the Coris' associates succeeded in converting glucose into a glucose-6-phosphoric acid.

The Coris' studies of phosphorylase and associated enzymes, carried out in vitro, showed a possible mechanism for the synthesis and breakdown of glycogen. Some years later Luis F. Leloir and C. E. Cardini demonstrated another route of formation of glycogen. In this route the glucose-1-phosphate, or Cori ester, reacts with a derivative of uracil (a pyrimidine base, found also as a component of nucleic acids) to form uridine-diphosphate-glucose. This is the actual substrate from which glycogen is formed in the Leloir system. Indeed, it seems to be the physiological substrate; that is, the one acted upon in vivo, whereas phosphorylase is considered to act in the body upon glycogen, catalyzing its breakdown when conditions call for a replenished supply of glucose in the tissues or in the blood.

Phosphorylase exists in an active and an inactive form in the tissues. Adrenaline, the hormone of the adrenal medulla (the core of the adrenal gland, as distinct from the cortex), increases the proportion of the enzyme existing in the active form. This would favor the breakdown of glycogen and formation of increased blood sugar, two long-known consequences of the injection of adrenaline. Thus, the Coris' work has made it possible to understand the action of still another hormone.

1 9 4 8
PAUL MÜLLER
(1899–1965)

"For his discovery of the high efficacy of DDT as a contact poison against several arthropods."

BIOGRAPHICAL SKETCH

PAUL MÜLLER WAS BORN IN OLTEN, SOLOTHURN CANTON, Switzerland, on January 12, 1899, but lived from the age of four or five in Basel. There he went to school and, during 1916-1917, worked in industrial chemical laboratories, an experience which he considers to have been of great practical value. In 1918 he returned to secondary school, completing the course in 1919. He then began the academic study of chemistry at the University, obtaining his doctorate in 1925, with chemistry as major and physical chemistry and botany as minors. In the same year he accepted a position as managing chemist with the dye works of the J. R. Geigy Company of Basel. There he worked not only on dyes and insecticides but also on disinfectants and tanning agents. DDT was synthesized and its effects discovered in the autumn of 1939, but the first commercial DDT insecticides did not appear until 1942. During the Second World War and since, such insecticides have found world-wide use for a broad range of agricultural and hygienic purposes.

DESCRIPTION OF THE PRIZE-WINNING WORK*

"The composition of important vitamins and hormones, as well as bacteriostatic substances such as penicillin, streptomycin, etc., . . . has been made clear, and some have since been synthesized. But despite all these successes, we are still far from knowing how to predict, with any degree of reliability, what physiological effect to anticipate from a given composition. . . .

"The relationships are still more difficult in the field of artificial, and particularly synthetic, insecticides. . . .

"When I began, about 1935, on behalf of my firm, the J. R. Geigy Company of Basel, to work in the field of insecticides and especially the insecticides important for agriculture, the situation looked hopeless. There already existed an immense literature in this field, and a flood of patents had been taken out. But of the many patent insecticides there were practically none on the market, and special experiments indicated that they were not equal in value to . . . arsenicals, pyrethrum [etc.].

"That gave me the courage to work on. But just the same the chances were very bad, for only an exceptionally cheap or unusually effective insecticide could have any prospect of finding application in agriculture, yet the demands which must be made on an insecticide for agriculture are especially severe. . . . I reflected about what my ideal insecticide must be like and what characteristics it should have. I soon perceived that a contact insecticide would have a far better chance than a food poison. The characteristics of this ideal insecticide must be as follows:

"1. Great toxicity for insects,

"2. Rapid commencement of toxic effect,

"3. Little or no toxicity for warm-blooded animals and plants,

"4. No irritant effect and no smell, or a faint and at any rate not unpleasant one,

"5. The range of effectiveness should be the greatest possible, and extend to the largest possible number of arthropods [joint-

---

* Translated from Paul Müller, "Dichlordiphenyltrichloräthan und neuere Insektizide," *Les Prix Nobel en 1948,* pp. 122-132.

footed invertebrate animals, including crustaceans, insects, centipedes, and arachnoids—spiders, scorpions, mites, and ticks],

"6. Long duration of effect—i.e., great chemical stability,

"7. Low price = economic use. . . .

"To begin with, at all events, it was a question of finding a substance with great effect as a contact insecticide. . . . My biological tests were carried out in a large glass case . . . into which I shot a fine spray of the substance to be tested in a nonpoisonous solvent. . . .

"After the fruitless testing of hundreds of different substances, I realized that it is not easy to find a good contact insecticide. In the field of science one attains something only through obstinacy and steadfast work. . . .

"It was known to me from earlier research that compounds with the group —CH₂Cl . . . often show definite effectiveness. From work on moth repellents carried out in our firm at this time by Dr. H. Martin and his co-workers, in which I myself had no share, it was known to me that compounds with the general formula:

$$Cl—X—Cl, \quad X = SO_2, SO, S, O, \text{ etc.}$$

often showed quite considerable effect as food poison for moths.

"In studying the literature I came across an article by Chattaway and Muir . . . in which the formation of diphenyltrichloroethane is described:

I recollected my old research with substances containing the —CH₂Cl group . . . and I was curious as to what possible influence the —CCl₃ group would have on the contact-insecticide effect.

"The substance was produced in September 1939 and the test gave a very considerable contact-insecticide effect on flies. I began to make derivatives of this basic formula, and, influenced I daresay by the results of the work on moth repellents, I synthesized the p,p′-dichlor-compound:

"This compound, which had already been brought forward by an Austrian student in the course of his dissertation in 1873, had now such a strong contact-insecticide effect as I had never observed in any substance thus far. After a short time my fly chamber was so much poisoned that after it had apparently been carefully cleansed, new flies perished from contact with the walls without spraying of the substance. . . . [This effect persisted for about a month.]

"Other insects were tested later. . . . The new compound was everywhere effective, although often death first occurred after some hours or even days. . . . [DDT was found to fulfill all but the second of Müller's seven desiderata of the ideal insecticide: its action, although very powerful, is not immediate, and it is therefore often combined with a "knockdown" such as pyrethrum.]

"Finally the laboratory results were confirmed by field research . . . and it was found that the effect against Colorado beetles lasts four to six weeks. . . .

"The DDT insecticides have now been introduced into all possible spheres of insect control, for example in hygiene, in the safeguarding of textiles and provisions, and in the protection of plants."

CONSEQUENCES IN THEORY AND PRACTICE

It is hardly necessary to expatiate on the significance of Dr. Müller's discovery. As shown above, the primary aim was to find a good agricultural insecticide; this aspect of the success attained is not without importance, from the nutritional point of view, for world health. Effectual control of flies has had a more direct bearing on medicine in the reduction of fly-borne diseases. Most dramatic of the triumphs of DDT has been its success against typhus. In October 1943 a typhus epidemic broke out in Naples under conditions which made control seem impossible. In January 1944, when sixty new cases were appearing daily, use of DDT was begun on a large scale for delousing the population. In three weeks 1,300,000 persons were deloused and the outbreak was stopped. Never before in history had it been possible to check a winter epidemic of typhus. This experience was repeated in Japan three months after the occupation. Müller thus provided a corollary of the greatest importance to the work of the 1928 Nobel laureate, Charles Nicolle, who discovered that typhus is conveyed by lice (see above, pp. 133-136). DDT has similarly proved of great value in preventing malaria and other diseases spread by arthropods. The discovery has also been a stimulus for further work in synthesizing chemical compounds to control plant and animal parasites and to destroy the vectors of disease.

REFERENCES

WEST, T. F., AND CAMPBELL, G. A. *D.D.T. and Newer Persistent Insecticides* (London, 2nd ed., 1950).

1 9 4 9
WALTER RUDOLF HESS
(1881–)

"For his discovery of the functional organization of the interbrain as a coordinator of the activities of the internal organs."
(*The award for 1949 was shared with Egas Moniz; see below, pp. 270-277.*)

BIOGRAPHICAL SKETCH

WALTER RUDOLF HESS WAS BORN ON MARCH 17, 1881, IN Frauenfeld, a town in eastern Switzerland. He was fortunate in his early training, which combined expeditions into the woods and fields with elementary instruction in physical science by his father, who permitted him great freedom in the use of scientific apparatus. He matriculated in 1900 at the *Gymnasium* of his native town, thereupon beginning the study of medicine, which he pursued in Lausanne, Berne, Berlin, Kiel, and Zurich; his medical doctorate was granted by the latter university in 1906. Although attracted to physiology early in his medical course, he turned to ophthalmology on graduation and practiced his specialty until 1912. In that year, although already the father of a family, he gave up a successful practice to devote himself to the study of physiology, principally in Bonn. In 1917 he was appointed director of the Physiological Institute in Zurich. Further advanced study, postponed by the First World War, took him to England, where he came under the influence of Langley, the great pioneer in the study of the autonomic nervous system, Sherrington, Starling, Hopkins, and Dale. His research was at first directed to hemodynamics (study of the blood pressure), then to the regulation of breathing, and finally to the central control of the internal organs in general through the vegetative, or autonomic, nervous system. He worked out a technique for applying pin-point electrical stimulation to specific areas in the brain, using fine electrodes (0.2 mm. in diameter), insulated except at their very tips. He could thus produce strictly localized stimulation and also localized destruction of brain tissue. His investigations in this field were rewarded by the discoveries for which he was given the Nobel Prize. In addition to the work under review, Hess made early contributions to the study of blood viscosity (1907-1920) and squint (Hess screen, 1911). In 1951 Hess became Professor Emeritus, after 34 years of research and teaching at the University of Zurich.

DESCRIPTION OF THE PRIZE-WINNING WORK*

"In contrast with the very extensive . . . investigation of the vegetative [i.e., involuntary or autonomic] nervous system, there existed relatively limited knowledge of the central organization of the whole regulating apparatus. . . . It had nevertheless become clear that . . . the parts of the brain joined from above directly to the spinal marrow—the medulla oblongata and *the portion lying immediately under the cerebrum, the so-called interbrain*—exert a decisive influence on the vegetative regulations. . . . [Something was known in this connection of the function of a group of nuclei at the base of the brain referred to collectively as the hypothalamus.] But up to the time the special investigations were started, what still lay in the dark was the relation of particular functions to definite morphological substrata. . . . To achieve clarity on this point, so far as possible, was the problem I duly set myself. . . .

"[The autonomic nervous system is divided into two parts: the sympathetic, arising from cells in the thoracic and upper lumbar region of the spinal cord; and the parasympathetic, arising from cells in the midbrain, the medulla oblongata, and the lower, or

---

* Translated from W. R. Hess, "Die zentrale Regulation der tätigkeit innerer Organe," *Les Prix Nobel en 1949*, pp. 115-123.

sacral, region of the spinal cord. There is also evidence that the sympathetic has a control center in the hypothalamus. The two divisions of the system have different, and usually opposite, effects on the organs and vessels they innervate.] Those functions which are mediated by the sympathetic division of the vegetative nervous system are related to a part, extending from posterior to middle . . . of the hypothalamus. This is therefore to be considered the central 'source,' so to speak, of the sympathetic. To give complete physiological meaning to this discovery calls for further explanation. . . . The question has . . . arisen whether a circumscribed effect is associated with the classical sympathetic, defined primarily by the limitation of its root zone to the thoracic spinal marrow. . . . . Where the sympathetic takes effect, it sustains the efficiency of the body and helps the organism to better success through coming to terms with its environment. It is functional insofar as it comprises an *ergotropic or dynamogenic* [i.e., energizing or work-producing] *system*. But with this knowledge further experiences fit in, of particular interest to the psychiatrist, but also to anyone who is aware that behind the diversity of phenomena stands the unity of the organism. Stimulations in a *circumscribed area* of the ergotropic (dynamogenic) zone regularly induce a distinct *change of mood*. Thus a previously good-natured cat becomes angry; she begins to mew and spit, and on someone's approach she turns to a well-directed attack. While the pupils widen markedly, and at the same time the hair stands on end, a picture develops such as the cat shows when she is attacked by a dog and is unable to elude him. The widening of the pupils and bristling of the hair are quite comprehensible as sympathetic effects; but the same does not hold good for the change in psychic attitude. . . .

[Space does not permit listing all the various effects produced by the pin-point electrical stimulation of different centers. When the electrode is placed a little farther forward than in the experiment just described, a general relaxation of skeletal muscles ensues. Not far away is another center which when stimulated soon brings on what appears to be a perfectly natural sleep. From various sharply limited areas it is possible to influence blood circulation and breathing, salivation and heat regulation, etc.]

"In each case *collective symptoms* appear. [Several activities are initiated at the same time, as in the case of the angry cat, to bring about a coordinated response.] *Groups of organs* are called into action, and in such a way that the separate effects are combined. . . ."

CONSEQUENCES IN THEORY AND PRACTICE

Professor Hess is one of the group of modern investigators (students of the nervous system and the endocrine glands) who have contributed to present knowledge of the integrated action of the body—of the way in which the organism mobilizes its force and reacts, as a whole, to routine demands made upon it, and especially to emergencies. The mechanism of the body's reactions, both nervous and hormonal, to unusual stress is today one of the most actively cultivated and most promising fields of research.

Since the internal organs, such as the blood vessels, heart, lungs, and digestive tract, are chiefly controlled by the autonomic nervous system, it is obviously of prime importance to know as much about this system as possible. Dr. Hess has greatly extended the knowledge of the subject contributed by W. H. Gaskell, J. N. Langley, and others. It is such knowledge which underlies modern surgery in this field. Sympathectomies (eradications of parts of the system) have been used in the treatment of angina pectoris, essential hypertension, certain forms of disease in the blood vessels of the extremities, and a variety of other conditions. The regulation of blood pressure to meet the varying demands of the body occasioned by changes in external and internal environment is dependent in large part on sympathetic regulation, and it is known that injuries, encephalitis, and tumors which damage the central control areas occasionally cause profound blood-pressure changes. Other sympathetic effects have also been attributed to such causes.

Current teaching of the functions of the hypothalamus is based largely on American and British work. The distinctive feature of Hess's approach to the problem is his use of the intact, unnarcotized animal. His method is to place steel-needle electrodes in the brain under anesthesia, and to fasten them in place by fixing them to a frame, which in turn is attached to the skull itself. The actual experiments in stimulation of brain centers are performed later without anesthesia. In this way the effects both of anesthesia and of operative trauma are eliminated and the experiments approach more nearly the ideal physiological condition.

Hess' technique for the study of the functions of the hypothalamus in the conscious, unrestrained animal is now widely applied in neurophysiology. A variation of it, used in the study of the action of drugs upon the brain, involves recording of the normal electrical activity at point-sites, through the implanted electrodes. Changes in rhythm and amplitude of the waves generated when the animal receives a drug provide insight into the action of the drug that can be gained in no other way. The method has been used to get at the site of action within the brain of many new and important drugs, like the tranquilizers and stimulants.

REFERENCES

HESS, W. R. *Diencephalon: Autonomic and Extrapyramidal Functions* (New York: Grune and Stratton, 1954).

McDONALD, D. A. "W. R. Hess: The Control of the Autonomic Nervous System by the Hypothalamus," *The Lancet,* vol. 1 (March 17, 1951), pp. 627-629.

EGAS MONIZ

(1874–1955)

"For his discovery of the therapeutic value of prefrontal leucotomy in certain psychoses."
(*The award for 1949 was shared with W. R. Hess; see above, pp. 266-270.*)

BIOGRAPHICAL SKETCH

EGAS MONIZ (ANTÔNIO CAETANO DE ABREU FREIRE) WAS BORN at Avança, Portugal, on November 29, 1874. A student of the medical faculty of Coimbra, he continued his work there, becoming professor in 1902. In 1911 he became the first occupant of the new chair of neurology in Lisbon. For many years, partly in collaboration with Almeida Lima, he devoted himself to angiography, the visualization of blood vessels, especially those of the brain, after the injection into an artery of a substance opaque to X rays. In this field he was a pioneer, for he obtained the first "arteriograph" in man. In 1931 he published a large volume on the diagnosis of cerebral tumors by this method. In 1936 appeared the first memoir on prefrontal leucotomy. He is also the author of several other volumes on various aspects of medicine, including clinical neurology, sexual physiology and pathology, and medical history, and has produced literary and political writings. Dr. Moniz has taken an active part in the political life of Portugal. He was deputy in several legislatures from 1903 to 1917, Portuguese Minister in Madrid in 1917, Minister of Foreign Affairs, 1917-1918, and president of the Portuguese delegation to the Paris Peace Conference, 1918. However, soon after this he left politics. He died on December 13, 1955, in Lisbon.

DESCRIPTION OF THE PRIZE-WINNING WORK*

"It was no sudden inspiration which caused me to work out the surgical operation which I named 'prefrontal leucotomy.' I already laid stress on this fact in my first publication in 1936 and also in my first monograph, which I published in Turin in 1937.

"As an adherent of the doctrine of Ramón y Cajal [see above, pp. 36-37] and on the basis of the theory regarding the connections of the nerve cells, I turned my attention to the origin of normal and pathological psychic activity and its dependence on the neurons. The impulses course along the fibrils through the neurons. Changes are brought about at the synapses which influence many other cells.

"I pondered, along with the activity of the brain in normal psychic life, the changes which are displayed in most psychoses and which heretofore still had no anatomico-pathological explanation. I was particularly struck by the fact that the psychic life in some

---

* Translated from Egas Moniz, "Mein Weg zur Leukotomie," *Deutsche medizinische Wochenschrift*, Vol. 73 (1948), pp. 581-583.

mental diseases—here I thought especially of the compulsive psychoses and melancholia—is constricted to a very small circle of thoughts, which master all others, recurring again and again in the sick brain, and I sought to find an explanation for this.

"[A section on the general anatomy of the nervous system follows.] Starting from [the] anatomical facts I came to the conclusion that synapses, which are found in millions of instances, are the organic foundations of thought. [A synapse is the close approximation or contact of processes of different nerve cells; it is the point of functional linkage between one nerve cell and another.]

"The normal psychic life depends on good synaptic function, and psychic disturbances arise as consequences of synaptic disturbances. . . .

"If the fibrils become sick or the in-between substance suffers a change . . . the passage of the impulses is more difficult as a result of the more or less complete interruption of coherence. In other cases the [terminations] adhere to the cells with abnormal firmness and the impulses then always take their course along the same paths and always find their expression in the same psychic manifestations. I explain in this way the perseverance of the same morbid thoughts, which constantly reinvade the diseased psyche. . . ."

[The author next discusses the nature of the nerve impulse and the factors determining the course it takes. He gives a brief account of Pavlov's work on the conditioned reflex to indicate that new association pathways may be set up. He also discusses the anatomy of the prefrontal lobe, defining it for his own purposes as the region lying in front of the motor area. He points out that its functions are not definitely localized, as are those of the motor area.]

"The prefrontal region is closely associated with the psychic phenomena and has a less autonomous function than the so-called brain centers. Its activity depends on the enormous number of synapses of innumerable neurons which are concerned in the formation of the psychic phenomena.

"The functions of the prefrontal lobe can be established in the higher mammals experimentally and in man through clinical findings.

"The classical experiments of Bechterew and Luzaro are worthy of mention. They found that after removal of the prefrontal lobe in dogs the dogs became aggressive, irritable, and impulsive. Their capacity for adaptation was diminished. These findings were confirmed by the experiments of other authors.

"Very valuable are the experiments of Fulton and Jacobsen with chimpanzees previously trained. They found that a unilateral excision of the prefrontal areas produced no important change. Bilateral removal of this region, however, always produced an alteration in the behavior of the animal. After extensive destruction it became impossible to elicit from the animals the performances of their old training. . . .

"These facts are in accord with what has been established in humans. Clinical experience has yielded valuable results for the solution of this important problem. . . . [Evidence is derived from injuries, tumors, and surgical removals.]

"A whole frontal lobe, as is well known, can be removed without considerable consequences for the psychic life. This can at most bring about for the first few days a disorientation for space and time, which, however, gradually disappears again (Penfield).

"Richard Brickner's case is extremely important. This author made a detailed psychiatric investigation in a patient from whom Dandy had to take out important parts of both anterior lobes in order to remove an extensive meningeoma [a tumor of the membranous envelope of the brain].

"At first there occurred a loss of knowledge earlier acquired. But the patient little by little adapted himself again to his environment, despite clearly existing difficulties: character changes, diminished intelligence, etc. According to Brickner the patient later recovered the same personality as before the operation and retained his 'personality type.'

"Prefrontal leucotomy gave still more exact findings regarding the function of the frontal brain. But that is already history and I should like to speak now of the time before the operation which concerns us here was carried out. I should like, so to speak, standing on this side of the bank, to give an account of the reasons which induced me to cross the river.

"People who suffer from melancholia and are tormented by unhappy compulsive ideas, and for whom a medical treatment, a shock treatment or psychotherapy, is of no use, live in everlasting anguish on account of a thought, perpetually present, which overtops all the cares of daily life.

". . . These morbid ideas are deeply rooted in the synaptic complex which regulates matters of knowledge in the consciousness, stirs these up, and keeps them in constant activity.

"All these considerations led me to the following conclusion: It is necessary to alter the synaptic arrangements and thus the paths which are selected by the impulses in their continual course; thereby the corresponding thoughts are altered and forced into other channels.

"On these grounds, after two years' deliberation, I determined to sever the connecting fibers of the neurons in question. In the conviction that the prefrontal lobes are very important for the psychic life, I chose this region for my experiment. . . . Through complete alteration of the existing fiber arrangements, and organization of other synaptic fiber groups, I believed that I could transform the synaptic reactions and thereby cure the patient.

"Since my plan was to do away with a large number of associations, I preferred to attack the cell-connecting fibers of the anterior parts of both lobes of the frontal brain 'en masse,' in order to obtain positive results. At first alcohol injections were used for the destruction, later I performed incisions with the leucotome, a small apparatus designed for this purpose. The white matter of the brain has only a limited blood supply and the operation ought on that account to be free from danger. Everything was done with the greatest care in order to protect the patient's life.

"Permit me to reproduce here a short paragraph from my book *Tentatives opératoires,* which is a cornerstone of my work.

" 'On the eve of my first experiment I had to begin with a justified anxiety. But all fears were put aside by the hope of obtaining favorable results. If we were able to do away with certain psychic symptom-complexes through destruction of the cell-connecting groups, then we would demonstrate conclusively that the psychic functions and the regions of the brain which contribute to their manifestation are in close relation to one another. That would be a great step forward and a fundamental fact for building the investigation of the psychic functions on an organic basis.'

"And this page concluded thus:

" 'We are sure that this operation will produce a strong discussion in medical, psychiatric, philosophic, and other fields. We expect that, but at the same time we hope that this discussion will serve the progress of science, and above all that it will be of use to mentally ill patients.'

"So we went to work with our outstanding co-worker, Almeida Lima, whom we are obliged to thank for a large part of the pioneer work. The first alcohol injection into the white matter of the prefrontal lobe was made on November 12, 1935, and the first operation with the leucotome was carried out on December 27 of the same year. We obtained cure and improvement, but no mischance which would have compelled us to give up our work."

CONSEQUENCES IN THEORY
AND PRACTICE

As the founder of modern psychosurgery, Egas Moniz opened a new chapter in the surgery of the brain. Sir Victor Horsley (1857-1916), famous for his work on cerebral localization, had devised an operation for resecting an area of brain cortex to relieve convulsive movements of the arm. There had been other operations of like nature, but concerned, as was Horsley's, with the motor part of the brain. Aside from these, the great brain surgeons, such as Harvey Cushing, had been chiefly occupied in operations to minimize the damage of brain injuries, or to remove brain tumors. Interference with the parts of the brain controlling psychic functions had never been attempted in a rational manner before 1935, except when these parts were affected by injury or tumor.

Psychosurgery has since undergone great technical evolution. There are at least six types of operation on the frontal lobe currently in use for the treatment of mental disorders. These are all, however, variations on the basic method of Egas Moniz, for the common feature in all such procedures is the interruption of frontal lobe fibers.

Dr. Walter Freeman and Dr. James Watts, having performed a large number of these operations by the lateral approach through the temple, devised a somewhat simpler procedure, the transorbital lobotomy, so called because the instrument is inserted through the eye socket. "Open" operations have also been worked out, involving greater exposure and aiming at better control through a direct view of the field; these require removal of a piece of the skull rather than the mere drilling of a hole. "Selective cortical under-cutting," developed by Dr. William B. Scoville, of Yale, implies a selective local cut where the grey matter of the brain joins the major white fibers. This is supposed to work as well as the more radical division of the latter, but to cause fewer side effects.

When psychosurgery is used in a long-standing and badly de-generated case of schizophrenia, the side effects may hardly be noticed. In less severe cases they are of great importance and con-stitute psychosurgery's principal drawback. Compulsive worries, morbid thoughts, and terrible anxieties may be abolished or greatly weakened. It appears that the inevitable price for this relief, at least when the more radical measures are used, is a certain blunt-ing of personality. This effect, as Dr. Edward K. Wilk observes, "reveals itself in the higher realms of creative imagination, fore-sight, ambition and social sensitivity." It is for this reason that psychosurgery remains a last resort in mental cases, to be employed only when all other treatments have failed.

The results reported for the different operations vary consider-ably; results also vary in different examples of the same operation. In the last decade the use of lobotomy has diminished. This is partly accounted for by the advent of the tranquilizing drugs, but also by uncertainty as to the value of the operation. Some authori-ties state that lobotomy is very useful in selected patients, and de-plore its indiscriminate use. In spite of experience with thousands of cases, precise indications for the operation have not yet been written. Research in this area is sorely needed.

REFERENCES

ANONYMOUS, "Leucotomy Today," *The Lancet,* vol. ii (November 17, 1962), pp. 1037-1038.

FULTON, J. F. *Frontal Lobotomy and Affective Behaviour, A Neurophysiological Analysis* (New York: Norton, 1951).

———, "Surgery of Mental Disorder," *McGill Medical Journal,* Vol. 17 (1948), pp. 1-13.

GREENBLATT, M., R. ARNOT, AND H. C. SOLOMON, eds. *Studies in Lobotomy* (New York: Grune and Stratton, 1950).

"Symposium: A Psychiatric Evaluation of Psychosurgery," *Surgery, Gynecology and Obstetrics,* Vol. 92 (1951), pp. 601-617. (A popular abstract appeared in *Time,* May 28, 1951, pp. 38-40.)

1950

EDWARD CALVIN KENDALL
(1886–)

PHILIP SHOWALTER HENCH
(1896–1965)

TADEUS REICHSTEIN
(1897–)

"For their discoveries concerning the suprarenal cortex hormones, their structure and biological effects."

BIOGRAPHICAL SKETCHES

KENDALL

EDWARD CALVIN KENDALL WAS BORN IN SOUTH NORWALK, Connecticut, on March 8, 1886. His advanced education was pursued at Columbia University, where he received the B.S. degree in 1908 and the M.S. the following year. He was Goldschmidt Fellow in 1909-1910, and obtained his Ph.D. in chemistry in 1910. For a short time (1910-1911) he was research chemist with Parke, Davis and Company in Detroit. From 1911 to 1914 he worked in St. Luke's Hospital, New York City. Since 1914 he has been professor of physiological chemistry and head of the Section of Biochemistry in the Graduate School at the Mayo Foundation, Rochester, Minnesota.

In 1914 Kendall was able to isolate the active constituent of the thyroid hormone, a substance he called thyroxin. Its structure was determined partly by Kendall, partly by C. R. Harrington; Harrington and G. Barger were responsible for its definitive synthesis in 1926. Apart from his work in this field, Kendall has been occupied chiefly with studies of oxidation in the animal organism, glutathione,* and the isolation and synthesis of hormones of the adrenal cortex. In 1951 Kendall became Professor Emeritus at the Mayo Clinic.

HENCH

PHILIP SHOWALTER HENCH WAS BORN IN PITTSBURGH, February 28, 1896. He was graduated (A.B.) from Lafayette College in 1916 and took the M.D. in 1920. From 1921 to 1924 he was fellow at the University of Minnesota. He received the M.S. degree in 1931. In 1928-1929 he worked in Freiburg and in von Müller's Clinic in Munich. At the Mayo Clinic he was first assistant in medicine from 1923 to 1925, associate from 1925 to 1926, consultant and head of the Section for Rheumatic Diseases from 1926 on. At the Graduate School of the Mayo Foundation he was instructor in medicine from 1928 to 1932, assistant professor from 1932 to 1935, and associate professor from 1935 to 1947. He became professor in 1947. Dr. Hench devoted the greater part of his career to the study of rheumatic diseases, and was honoured by dozens of scientific and medical societies for his achievements. He was considered an authority on the history of yellow fever. He died on March 30, 1965, in Jamaica.

REICHSTEIN

TADEUS REICHSTEIN WAS BORN ON JULY 20, 1897, IN WLOCLA-wek, Poland. He passed most of his early childhood at Kiev, where his father worked as an engineer. In 1905 the family moved to

---

* An important substance in oxidation-reduction, discovered by another Nobel laureate, F. G. Hopkins. See above, p. 139.

Berlin and later to Zurich, where they settled permanently and acquired Swiss citizenship in 1914. After private tutoring, Reichstein entered the Zurich Oberrealschule (technical school of junior college grade) and then the Eidgenössische Technische Hochschule (state technical college), where he obtained his first degree, in chemical engineering, in 1920. After a year in industry he returned to E.T.H., receiving the doctor's degree in organic chemistry in 1922. He then worked for some years on an industrial project, a study of the aromatic substances of roasted coffee. In 1930 he became a part-time instructor at E.T.H., and in 1931 was appointed Leopold Ruzicka's assistant. His later appointments in the Department of Organic Chemistry at E.T.H.—assistant professor, 1934, and associate professor, 1937—were followed by his selection in 1938 as head of the Department of Pharmacology and director of the Pharmaceutical Institute, University of Basel. Since 1946 he has been head of the Organic Division in the same university and director of its organic laboratories. Independently of Sir Norman Haworth and his associates in Birmingham, Reichstein succeeded in synthesizing ascorbic acid (vitamin C) in 1933. This was his best-known work prior to his Nobel Prize investigations in the chemistry of adrenal cortical hormones.

DESCRIPTION OF THE PRIZE-WINNING WORK

KENDALL *

"The first investigations which contributed to the development of cortisone came in 1929 from physiologists. Two groups of workers, Hartman and his associates at the University of Buffalo, and Swingle and Pfiffner at Princeton University, were the first to prepare extracts from the adrenal cortex [the outer portion of the adrenal, or suprarenal, gland] which successfully controlled the symptoms of adrenal insufficiency both in adrenalectomized animals and in patients who had Addison's disease.

"Cortisone was first separated as a new compound in 1935 [in

---

* From E. C. Kendall, "The Development of Cortisone as a Therapeutic Agent," *Les Prix Nobel en 1950.*

Kendall's laboratory]. Investigations concerned with the isolation and determination of the chemical structure of cortisone were carried out simultaneously and independently by Wintersteiner and Pfiffner at Columbia University, by Reichstein and his associates at Zurich, Switzerland, and by my associates and myself at the Mayo Clinic.

"[Through the work of the above-named and many others, a large number of compounds, closely related chemically, were isolated from the adrenal cortex. Many were available only in minute amounts. At the time of Kendall's address, 29 compounds were known.] All these compounds belong to the family of steroids and are closely related one to the other. For the detailed investigation of this large group of compounds science is indebted to the very significant contributions which have come from the laboratory of Professor Tadeus Reichstein. Some of these compounds contained two, some three, some four, and a few contained five atoms of oxygen in the molecule. In certain of these steroids there was a double bond adjacent to a ketone, and this small group of compounds soon acquired special interest because they were the only ones which possessed physiologic activity. If the double bond was removed the physiologic activity was abolished. This fact focused attention on four compounds which were designated in my laboratory as A, B [corticosterone], E [cortisone], and F [17-hydroxycorticosterone, dihydrocortisone, cortisol.] Because of the limited supply, it was decided that all of the material separated from the gland should be used on small animals and that none should be employed for investigations in clinical medicine.

"Work on the adrenal cortex was confined to a few physiologists, and several years were required to accumulate evidence concerning the physiologic activity of these compounds. Eventually, it was shown that compounds A, B, E and F had little effect on the metabolism of electrolytes [in particular, sodium, potassium and chloride ions, and water] but that they had a marked effect on the metabolism of carbohydrates and protein. In addition, it was found that the muscles in adrenalectomized animals soon lost the power to contract when they were stimulated but that these compounds would restore the ability of the muscle to respond. Finally, it became evident that the adrenalectomized animals could not resist in the normal manner toxic substances such as typhoid vaccine. Compounds A, B, E and F restored the resistance of the animals to these toxic substances.

"On the basis of these experiments on animals the hope was raised that these compounds . . . might be of help to patients who had suffered trauma including burns or who had certain types of infection. But when this hypothesis was tested with extracts of the adrenal cortex encouraging results were not obtained. . . . For many years there were few who believed that any product of the adrenal cortex would find a place in clinical medicine other than in the treatment of the relatively few patients who had Addison's disease [resulting from failure of the adrenal cortex to provide normal amounts of its hormones to the body]. Under these conditions, it is not surprising that pharmaceutical manufacturers were not interested in the commercial aspects of the adrenal cortex.

"In October, 1941, this situation changed suddenly and completely. The shadow of war was advancing and the medical departments of the army and navy approached the National Research Council of the United States with the request that the hormones of the adrenal cortex be made available. [At the first conference it was decided to attempt the synthesis of compound A because, of the four substances under consideration, this had the simplest structure. Nevertheless, despite strenuous efforts in many laboratories in the United States, none was forthcoming.]

"In Switzerland, Lardon and Reichstein prepared [1943] the first sample of compound A from desoxycholic acid [a steroid found in bile] but the method which they used could not be employed on a large scale.

"[Later on,] compound A was produced by a practical method devised in my laboratory in 1944. Merck and Co., Inc., using the same method, prepared a large sample of this compound in 1945. It was tested on adrenalectomized laboratory animals and was found to have physiologic activity identical with compound A which had been isolated from the adrenal glands of beef. [A patient with Addison's disease, under the care of Dr. Randall G. Sprague, was the first to receive the material, but it had] little influence either subjectively or objectively on the symptoms. . . . After all the work that had been expended this result came as a surprise and was a great disappointment.

"In spite of [this result], attempts to convert a compound closely related to compound A into compound E were carried out both in the laboratories of the Mayo Foundation and in those of Merck and Co., Inc. Dr. Lewis H. Sarett, in the research laboratory of Merck and Co., Inc., first accomplished this conversion, and in the summer of 1947 it became evident that a practical method to make compound E soon would be available. From that time onward the work progressed smoothly. The first few grams of compound E made their appearance in May, 1946, and more was produced during the summer.

"During the summer of 1948 compound E was administered . . . by Dr. Sprague of the Mayo Clinic to a patient who had Addison's disease and the result was encouraging. There was a notable improvement in the condition of the patient.

". . . On September 21, Dr. Charles H. Slocumb, Dr. Hench's associate, administered the first injection of this hormone to a patient who had rheumatoid arthritis. During the following seven months compound E was given by Dr. Howard F. Polley, another associate of Dr. Hench, to many more patients who had rheumatoid arthritis and rheumatic fever and the adrenocorticotropic hormone [ACTH] of the anterior portion of the pituitary body also was shown to produce similar results. [Because of the expansion of use of compound E in medicine and the possibility of its confusion with vitamin E, its name was changed to cortisone.]"

HENCH AND KENDALL *

"Since 1929 one of us (P. S. H.) has studied the beneficial effects of pregnancy and jaundice on rheumatoid arthritis. Results of these and other studies led us to the following conclusions. Even

---

* Philip S. Hench, Edward C. Kendall, Charles H. Slocumb, and Howard F. Polley, "The Effect of a Hormone of the Adrenal Cortex (17-hydroxy-11-dehydro-corticosterone: compound E) and of Pituitary Adrenocorticotropic Hormone on Rheumatoid Arthritis," *Proceedings of the Staff Meetings of the Mayo Clinic*, Vol. 24 (1949), pp. 181-197. This is the original "preliminary report."

though the pathologic anatomy of rheumatoid arthritis is more or less irreversible, the pathologic physiology of the disease is potentially reversible, sometimes dramatically so. Within every rheumatoid patient corrective forces lie dormant, awaiting proper stimulation. Therefore, the disease is not necessarily a relentless condition for which no satisfactory method of control should be expected. The inherent reversibility of rheumatoid arthritis is activated more effectively by the intercurrence of jaundice or pregnancy than by any other condition or agent thus known. Regardless of the supposed 'validity' of the microbic theory [i.e., the theory that arthritis is caused by microbes] rheumatoid arthritis can be profoundly influenced by phenomena which are primarily biochemical.

"It became increasingly difficult to harmonize the microbic theory of the origin of rheumatoid arthritis with the phenomenon of relief of the disease by jaundice or pregnancy. It became easier, rather, to consider that rheumatoid arthritis may represent, not a microbic disease, but some basic biochemical disturbance which is transiently corrected by some incidental biologic change common to a number of apparently unrelated events. It seemed logical to suppose that what causes relief of rheumatoid arthritis in pregnancy is closely related to, if not identical with, that which relieves the same disease in jaundice; if so, it could be neither hyperbilirubinemia [the presence in the blood of an excessive amount of bilirubin, a reddish bile pigment found in large amount during jaundice] nor a unisexual (female) hormone since neither of these is common to both pregnancy and jaundice. It was believed that the discovery of some biochemical denominator common to various agents or states beneficial in rheumatoid arthritis, but common especially to jaundice and pregnancy, would provide us with an improved treatment or control of the disease.

"Finally, it was conjectured that the hypothetic common denominator or 'antirheumatic substance X' was not a disintegration product from a damaged liver, but probably was a biologic compound specific in nature and function, a compound which was normal to the human organism. But if this was true, we had no certain clue as to its chemical nature or the organ of its origin.
. . . [There follows an account of the attempts to relieve arthritis with female hormones, biliary products associated with jaundice, etc.]

"In time we conjectured that the antirheumatic substance X might be an adrenal hormone. This conjecture was strengthened by the knowledge that temporary remissions of rheumatoid arthritis are frequently induced by procedures which are now known to be capable of stimulating the adrenal cortices, such as general anesthesia or surgical operation. In 1938 we administered to several rheumatoid volunteers lecithin [one of a group of compounds containing two fatty acid molecules and a molecule each of glycerophosphoric acid and choline] separated from the adrenal gland, not as an adrenal product per se, but in an attempt to induce hyperlipemia [an excessive degree of lipemia, or fat droplets in the blood] such as may occur in association with pregnancy and jaundice. In January, 1941, we recorded our interest in adrenal cortical fractions in general and in Kendall's compound E in particular, and we used briefly Kendall's cortical extract. But compound E was not available to us until September, 1948. . . .

"Since the fall of 1948 [this report is dated April 13, 1949] we have given compound E more or less continuously to 5 rheumatoid patients, and for periods of eight to sixty-one days to 9 other patients; a total of 14 patients. None had mild or moderate disease. All had 'moderately severe' or 'severe' chronic polyarticular rheumatoid arthritis of four and a half months to five years' duration. . . .

"To provide adequate controls, the intragluteal injection of compound E [i.e., injection into the buttocks] was in some cases preceded, and in other cases replaced, by the injection of a fine aqueous suspension of cholesterol . . . indistinguishable in appearance from compound E. The times when the control solution and the adrenal hormone were interchanged were unknown to the patients and were, for five weeks, unknown even to the three clinical authors who were evaluating the results. . . . [The dosage was more or less guesswork at first but fortunately turned out to be about right from the beginning. Progress was checked not only by appearance and symptoms but by the sedimentation rate of the red blood cells and other objective tests.]

"In each of the 14 patients the initial results were as follows. Within a few days there was marked reduction of stiffness of muscles and joints, lessening of articular aching or pain on motion and tenderness, and significant improvement of articular and muscular function. . . . Articular swellings generally diminished, sometimes fairly rapidly and completely. . . . [Some flexion deformities disappeared.]

"Those who found the following maneuvers difficult or impossible often were able within a few days to do them much more easily or even 'normally': getting in or out of bed unassisted, rising from chairs or toilets, shaving, washing the hair or back of the neck, opening doors with one hand, lifting a cup or book with one hand, and climbing stairs.

"The appetite often was rapidly improved. Several patients gained weight on routine general diets. . . . Improved strength was frequently noted. Several patients stressed the loss of the 'toxicity' of the disease and experienced a marked sense of wellbeing. . . .

"[On discontinuance of injections] the arthritis returned slowly in most cases, and rapidly in two . . . and again improved strikingly after use of the hormone was resumed."

REICHSTEIN *

"If a chemist wishes to attempt the isolation of a physiologically active substance, he is advised to have the collaboration of a physiologist, who will help him to control the purification of his material by animal experimentation. When, in 1934, I began the investigation of adrenal extracts with my colleague J. von Euw, we found ourselves in an unfavorable position. The most important consequences of adrenalectomy were indeed known, but there were relatively few quantitative methods for determining the activity of extracts. There were really only three:

1) The survival test (especially as carried out in the rat). [The adrenal cortex is necessary to survival of the otherwise untreated animal.]

2) The dog test, according to Swingle and Pfiffner (elevation of the endogenous nitrogen content of the blood).

3) The Everse-de Fremery test (failure of muscle to contract after only a brief period of stimulation).

---

* Translated from T. Reichstein, "Chemie der Nebennieren-Rinden-Hormone," *Les Prix Nobel en 1950.*

"Of these the dog test was the most sensitive and, also, could give relatively exact results; but it was not available to us. On the other hand, the first and third tests could be carried out in the laboratories of colleagues. Both test methods, however, required relatively large amounts of material. Because of this, the purification could be controlled biologically only in the initial phases. The following figures present some idea of the purification process:

"One thousand kilograms [i.e. more than a ton] of beef adrenals extracted on an industrial scale by a modification of the method of Swingle and Pfiffner, yielded an extract containing about one kilogram of dry residue. By careful partition, most of the activity of this extract could be retained in about 25 grams of material that had been carried through additional steps. Further experiments with physical methods of separation always gave a partition of activity in several fractions. On the other hand, using chemical methods with the aid of the ketone reagent 'T' of Girard and Sandulesco, the 25 grams of extract already mentioned could be separated into the following two parts: about 7-8 grams of a ketonic fraction [i.e. the fraction containing steroids that bear a ketone group, $R'R''C=O$] which possesses practically the whole activity, and about 15-16 grams of ketone-free material that is biologically inactive. From this point on, further biological control on the above basis was no longer possible. The whole of the material present (ketonic and non-ketonic fractions) were therefore separated into individual constituents as carefully as possible. The following methods served for this purpose:

Solvent partition (using water, benzene, ether, chloroform).

Fractional crystallisation.

Chromatography of the acetate derivatives on alumina.

At first prepared as pure, crystalline, individual substances, they were tested biologically as far as possible [but,] because of the small amounts available, the exact determination of their chemical constitution was given priority. This goal was accomplished in nearly all cases.

"When I began the investigation of the extracts of adrenal glands I thought that I would be dealing with a hormone (or mixture of hormones), but surely not a steroid. The solubilities were very different from those of other steroids. My assumption proved wrong.

Even in the first chemical degradation experiments we were able to establish that we were apparently concerned with steroids, and were able to prove it soon afterwards. The relatively great solubility in water stems from the high content of oxygen [in these steroids.]

"Up to the present time 29 steroids have been isolated from adrenal extracts. [Their structures are given in a table, to which Reichstein now refers.]

"It is neither possible nor necessary to go into the details of these formulas. They demonstrate chiefly that all these substances are very closely related to one another. . . . Out of these 29 steroids five were already known; they occur elsewhere in nature. The remainder are characteristic of the adrenals. They differ from one another mainly through the presence or absence of certain oxygen atoms, or in the presence or absence of a double bond. Of the 29, six were found to be biologically active in the sense that they could prolong the life of adrenalectomized animals as well as relieve one or more symptoms. These are [deoxycorticosterone, corticosterone, 17-hydroxycorticosterone (cortisol), 11-deoxy-17-hydroxycorticosterone, 11-dehydrocorticosterone, and 17-hydroxy-11-dehydrocorticosterone (cortisone).]

"In the life-maintenance test [in adrenalectomized animals] as well as in activity on electrolyte and water balance deoxycorticosterone is by far the most active, and 17-hydroxycorticosterone and cortisone are the weakest. . . . In other tests, for example those based upon carbohydrate metabolism, the relation is reversed; 17-hydroxycorticosterone and cortisone are by far the most active, and deoxycorticosterone is the weakest."

CONSEQUENCES IN THEORY AND PRACTICE

The adrenal cortex long resisted all efforts to probe its secrets. "Addison's disease," a chronic insufficiency resulting from any one of several adrenal lesions but chiefly from tuberculosis, was first described by Thomas Addison in 1849. Toward the end of the century and early in the present one, a series of investigations resulted in the isolation of adrenaline, product of the adrenal medulla; W. B. Cannon then demonstrated the "emergency function" of this hormone. But no relevance to Addison's disease was shown and efforts to obtain active extracts from the cortex were at first unsuccessful. The work of Hartman, Swingle, and Pfiffner led to the production of "cortin," which was used in the treatment of Addison patients. This was only the beginning. In 1937 Reichstein and von Euw reported the synthesis of deoxycorticosterone, an adrenal cortical steroid with its primary action on electrolyte metabolism (and classified as a "mineralocorticoid" in the terminology introduced by Hans Selye). Deoxycorticosterone proved useful in the management of Addison's disease, but its actions left open the question of which steroids of the adrenal are responsible for the other important metabolic functions. The above excerpts from the lectures of Kendall and Reichstein tell of the preparation of representative steroids of the "glucocorticosteroid" type, such as cortisone.

In the preliminary report on the treatment of rheumatoid arthritis, Hench and his colleagues had already recorded their experience not only with cortisone but also with ACTH, or "adrenocorticotropic hormone." This is a product of the anterior lobe of the so-called "master gland," the pituitary body or hypophysis, situated at the base of the brain. (This important organ was the chief object of study of the 1947 Nobel laureate in medicine, B.A. Houssay. See above, pp. 250-253.) ACTH was found to produce effects which are in general quite similar to those of cortisone. It acts on the adrenal cortex, stimulating it to action, and the consequences are therefore indirect. While Merck and Company were busy with the production of cortisone, chemists of Armour and Company were occupied in the extraction of ACTH, following the pioneer work of Smith, Collip, and others, and likewise stimulated by wartime pressure.

It is not too much to say that a revolution in medicine was in preparation. As other scientists and clinicians took up the study of these compounds, it was found that both agents not only influenced a few relatively rare endocrine conditions, but might profoundly alter many diseases which appeared to be nonhormonal and to have no connection with the pituitary or adrenal gland. Both were shown to be antirheumatic, first in rheumatoid arthritis and then in acute rheumatic fever. Beyond this they possess marked · anti-allergic activity and have limited influence on certain blood dyscrasias— i.e., diseased states of the blood with abnormal cells. A variety of skin conditions, inflammatory diseases of the eye, intestinal diseases such as ulcerative colitis, and even respiratory infections are greatly improved by the use of these extraordinary drugs. In Addison's disease and in hypopituitarism (a condition in which the pituitary gland produces insufficient hormones, including ACTH) cortisone is used as "replacement therapy." In no case do cortisone and ACTH "cure" disease; they simply suppress symptoms or reduce them temporarily, i.e. as long as the hormone is taken.

Many new steroid derivatives have been synthesized by varying the cortisone molecule slightly. Some of these contain, for example, an extra methyl group (CH_3-), others a fluorine Atom. A select number have come into clinical use because of their greater potency. Furthermore, new non-steroidal anti-rheumatic drugs have become available.

Once the nature of the adrenal glucocorticoids had been clarified, chemists turned again to the problem of the mineralocorticoid, or salt-retaining, factor of the gland. Deoxycorticosterone was present in this fraction, but in insufficient concentration to explain the great activity of glandular extracts. In 1953, the steroid responsible was identified and named "aldosterone." Thus, the major chemical and physiological mysteries of the cortex were at last solved.

1 9 5 1
MAX THEILER
(1899–)

"For his discoveries concerning yellow fever and how to combat it."

BIOGRAPHICAL SKETCH

MAX THEILER WAS BORN IN PRETORIA, SOUTH AFRICA, ON January 30, 1899. His father, Sir Arnold Theiler, had been Director of the Institute of Veterinary Research at Onderstepoort. Max Theiler obtained his early schooling in South Africa, except for a year in Switzerland. He studied medicine at St. Thomas's Hospital in London, and in 1922 became a licentiate of the Royal College of Physicians, London. In the same year he also obtained the Diploma of the London School of Tropical Medicine, but instead of practising in that field, he was induced by Professor Andrew W. Sellards to take a research post in the Department of Tropical Medicine at Harvard Medical School in Boston. During his eight years in Boston he studied a number of infective diseases, including yellow fever. These studies, including his demonstration of the susceptibility of the mouse to the virus, were continued, from 1930, at the International Health Division of the Rockefeller Foundation in New York City, where he and his colleagues developed the 17D strain of virus. In 1951 Theiler was made Director of the Laboratories of the Division of Medicine and Public Health of the Rockefeller Foundation.

DESCRIPTION OF THE PRIZE-WINNING
WORK*

"It was shortly after monkeys were found susceptible that, in searching for a less expensive and more readily available experimental animal, I found that the common white mouse was susceptible to the virus if inoculated by the intracerebral route [i.e. into the brain]. This method of inoculation was chosen as it was generally conceded that the common laboratory animals could not become infected if inoculated by the usual routes. The strain of virus with which this work was done was isolated by Mathis, Sellards and Laigret in 1928 in Dakar, French West Africa, is known as the French strain and, like the Asibi, is highly virulent for rhesus monkeys. The disease in mice was an encephalomyelitis [inflammation of the brain and spinal cord] with no involvement of the visceral organs, in contrast to that induced in man and monkey, in which the liver, kidney and heart are involved. By serial passage in mice . . . [there was] evidence of a progressive loss of virulence for rhesus monkeys when inoculated parenterally. This loss of virulence for monkeys first suggested the possibility of the use of an attenuated [weakened] active virus for the immunization of man.

"In considering the possibility of using the modified mouse-adapted virus for human immunization, although it was clear that it had become markedly attenuated for monkeys when inoculated by parenteral routes, the discovery was made by Sellards, and Lloyd and Penna that the virus had acquired marked neurotropic affinities [i.e. an affinity for the nervous system] for these animals and produced a fatal encephalitis when inoculated into their brains. There was thus the possibility that the virus, if used as a vaccine, although it had lost the power of inducing a serious visceral disease, might induce an infection of the nervous system.

"In the development of vaccines for human beings, using my mouse-adapted virus, two paths were followed. In the first, used chiefly by French workers, virus alone was inoculated; and in the

---

* From M. Theiler, "The development of vaccines against yellow fever," *Les Prix Nobel en 1951.*

second, used by American and English workers, virus and human immune serum were inoculated simultaneously. The first immunizations of humans using mouse-adapted neurotropic virus alone were reported by Sellards and Laigret (1932). Several reactions were reported. . . . Further investigations by French workers, however, finally led to a safe and efficient method of vaccination, which is at present used on a very large scale in the French territories in Africa. This method, introduced by Peltier and his co-workers (1939), consists of applying the mouse-adapted virus to the scarified skin. In retrospect, it seems probable that the early severe reactions were due to the use of a virus which, although it had undergone a considerable degree of modification, was nevertheless not sufficiently attenuated for safe use in man. At the present time this method of vaccination is usually combined with vaccinia virus [against smallpox]. A mixture of both viruses is applied to the scarified skin, and the individual is thus immunized to the two agents at the same time. Many millions of people have been immunized thus without any very serious reactions having been reported.

"The other early method of vaccination using the mouse-adapted virus consisted in the simultaneous inoculation of the virus and human immune serum. This method was based on the observation that an active immunity was readily induced in monkeys by the simultaneous inoculation of highly virulent yellow fever virus and immune serum. After extensive experiments in monkeys, using the mouse-adapted virus and immune serum, Sawyer, Kitchen and Lloyd introduced this method for the immunization of persons working with yellow fever virus, thus bringing to an end the long series of laboratory infections that had taken such a heavy toll. Though the reactions to the vaccine were, in general, very mild, it should be noted that one very serious reaction with signs of involvement of the brain occurred like those reported by the French workers following the use of the virus alone. This method, however, had a very serious disadvantage in that it could not be used on an extensive scale because of the large quantities of human immune serum required.

"Investigations were accordingly undertaken—on the one hand to find a substitute for the human immune serum and on the other hand to develop a more attenuated strain of virus. The first was readily achieved, and various workers succeeded in producing high titer horse, rabbit, goat, and monkey immune sera. Experiments in monkeys by Whitman and myself showed that by the use of a hyperimmune serum the quantity used for human vaccination could be considerably reduced. . . . Only a few cubic centimeters were necessary for each individual vaccinated, whereas previously from 35 to 40 cc. of human serum were needed. . . . [Large-scale immunization] had become an urgent problem as the epidemiological entity known as jungle yellow fever had been discovered. Classical urban yellow fever, transmitted by the common yellow fever mosquito, *Aedes aegypti,* can be readily controlled by anti-mosquito measures. Jungle yellow fever, on the other hand, occurs in country districts, sometimes in vast epidemics, and in the absence of *Aedes aegypti.* The only rational method of protection of the exposed population called for large-scale vaccination."

[Theiler then describes the attempts to attenuate yellow fever virus by growing it in tissue culture using chick and mouse embryonic tissue. During the first set of sub-culture experiments an event occurred that augured well for the outcome of his work.]

"Before these new culture experiments had progressed very far, a very marked change in pathogenicity was observed in the Asibi virus grown in the medium, the tissue component of which was chick embryo containing minimal amounts of nervous tissue. This is called the 17D strain. This attenuation consisted in a partial loss of neurotropism for mice and monkeys, as well as a marked loss of viscerotropism [affinity, in this case, for heart, liver and kidneys] for monkeys. Monkeys inoculated intracerebrally developed a mild encephalitis which as a rule was non-fatal. This was the much hoped for change.

"After extensive experiments in monkeys by Smith and myself, the 17D strain was used for human vaccination without the simultaneous inoculation of immune serum. . . . In a preliminary study we showed that reactions in man were either absent or minimal and that satisfactory antibody response was obtained.

"The reason for the rapid change noticed in the 17D strain, which occurred between the 89th and 114th subcultures, was and still is completely unknown. However, these experiments indicate that once the mutant had occurred, it was relatively stable.

"In comparing the two vaccines at present in use—*viz.* the French vaccine and the 17D, it may be stated that both vaccines produce an actual infection and a resulting immunity. The infection produced by the French vaccine is more severe than that produced by the 17D, as manifested both by subjective symptoms as well as by the amount of circulating virus. As a consequence of this relatively severe infection induced by the French vaccine, antibody production is more regular than after the extremely mild infection induced by the 17D vaccine. Only time will tell which of the two is to be preferred.

"By the intelligent application of anti-mosquito measures combined with vaccination, public health officials have now the means available to render what was once a prevalent epidemic disease to one which is now a comparatively rare infection of man."

CONSEQUENCES IN THEORY AND PRACTICE

Yellow fever, known by scores of different names since the fifteenth century, is an acute infection caused by a virus. The disease varies in severity from a relatively mild illness with fever up to the "black vomit," including jaundice (which gives the disease its name). There is a high mortality, and many scientists engaged in the study of yellow fever, for example, Noguchi, have been its victims. So devastating is the disease that in the past it forced armies to retreat in disarray; it ensured the defeat of Napoleon's Haitian army at the turn of the nineteenth century and convinced him of the wisdom of retiring from Louisiana. Later in that century it defeated another type of army, attempting to cut a link between the Pacific and Atlantic Oceans across the Isthmus of Panama.

The first period in the study of yellow fever began at the time of the Spanish-American War, when the toll of lives due to yellow fever led to the establishment by the Surgeon-General of the United States of a Yellow Fever Commission headed by Walter

Reed, with the participation of James Carroll, a bacteriologist, and Jesse W. Lazear, an entomologist. The Commission established that neither bacteria nor contamination by a patient or his clothing causes yellow fever, but that the disease is transmitted by the mosquito *Aedes aegypti,* as had been claimed twenty years earlier by Dr. Carlos Finlay, a Cuban, in a report to the Spanish Royal Academy. A further result of the Commission's work was the discovery that the immediate cause of yellow fever is a filterable virus, the first of this type of organism known to cause disease in man. The new knowledge now provided the basis for eradication of yellow fever from its focal points. In Havana, this was accomplished by William C. Gorgas. Similar anti-mosquito measures soon wiped out yellow fever as an endemic disease in the South of the United States, the Canal Zone (permitting completion of the canal), Brazil, Mexico, and elsewhere.

Gorgas eventually became head of a Yellow Fever Commission set up by the Rockefeller Foundation for the purpose of eradicating the disease. The discovery that the disease is endemic among the monkey population of jungle and forested areas introduced a new dimension in the proposed campaign. A traveller might be infected in such areas through the bite of a mosquito and then bring the "jungle yellow fever" back to civilization. The new approach, then, was the search for some form of immunization.

The discovery by Adrian Stokes, J. H. Bauer, and N. P. Hudson of the Rockefeller African Unit at Accra in 1928 that the Indian rhesus monkey can be infected experimentally introduced the second phase of yellow fever studies. "The first strain of yellow fever established by [Stokes, Bauer, and Hudson] is known as the Asibi strain, named after the patient from whom it was isolated. It has been used extensively in yellow fever work and . . . was the parent strain from which the 17D vaccine was eventually produced" (Theiler, op. cit.). Theiler's discovery at Harvard University in 1930 that the inexpensive mouse can conveniently be used to carry the infection in laboratory studies provided the next big advance. His demonstration that the mouse can be protected by prior administration of serum from a patient who had recovered from the disease (thus, "immune serum") made it possible to determine which individuals had already been exposed to the disease, so that the occurrence of yellow fever could readily be mapped out. The test—determining whether or not a particular serum can protect mice from the infection—also made it possible to establish the role of the forest monkeys and mosquitoes in maintaining yellow fever.

The difficulty of obtaining sufficient immune serum from recovered patients for protection of others was overcome by Theiler's finding that other species could be used to prepare such serum in the laboratory. Strangely enough, in the history of a research carried out over so many years and registering one solid advance after another, it was an unexpected mutation in the attenuated virus, rendering it much less pathogenic, that provided the basis for the present immunization program and dispensed with the need to inject immune serum concomitantly with the vaccine. The 17D vaccine, prepared when Theiler was already established in the laboratories of the International Health Division of the Rockefeller Foundation in New York City, was tested widely in Brazil for three years beginning in 1937, and millions of doses have since been distributed by the Rockefeller Institute. It is estimated that well over 100 million persons have now received the vaccine.

The use of vaccines against viral disease dates to Edward Jenner (1749-1823), who demonstrated how to protect man against smallpox. Theiler's discovery is essentially the same in principle. The special significance of his work lies in the freeing of mankind from a centuries-old scourge and giving hope that other widespread viral diseases will be similarly conquered. The reduction of yellow fever to the status of one of the minor diseases of man will undoubtedly display important political and social consequences through, for example, the increased vitality now guaranteed to the peoples of the new nations of Africa and to those of tropical America.

REFERENCE

Strode, G. K. (ed.), *Yellow fever* (New York: McGraw-Hill, 1951).

1 9 5 2
SELMAN ABRAHAM WAKSMAN
(1888–   )

"For his discovery of streptomycin, the first antibiotic effective against tuberculosis."

BIOGRAPHICAL SKETCH

SELMAN ABRAHAM WAKSMAN WAS BORN ON JULY 2, 1888, IN Priluka in the Ukraine, the son of Russian-Jewish parents. He received his early education from private tutors in Russia, and went to the United States in 1910 for university work. He took his bachelor's and master's degrees, the latter with the soil microbiologist J. G. Lipman, at Rutgers College, New Brunswick, New Jersey, and then spent the next two years (1916-1918) at the University of California where he obtained the Ph.D. degree in biochemistry. Except for brief periods from 1918 until his retirement he was associated with Rutgers and the New Jersey Experiment Station. In 1930 he became professor of microbiology and head of that department at Rutgers. He is especially noted for his work on microbiological populations of the soil, his research on a "new" group of soil organisms, the actinomycetes, and on antibiotics. In 1949 the University established a special research institute, funded largely from royalties on antibiotics discovered by Waksman and his colleagues. Selman Waksman was the first director of this institute. In 1958 he retired from his university posts. He has been awarded numerous honors by universities, research foundations, scientific societies, and governments. He became a citizen of the United States in 1916.

DESCRIPTION OF THE PRIZE-WINNING
WORK*

"Streptomycin belongs to a group of compounds known as antibiotics, which are produced by microorganisms and which possess
the property of inhibiting the growth and even of destroying other
microorganisms. Antibiotics vary greatly in their chemical nature,
mode of action upon different organisms, and effect upon the animal body. The selective action of antibiotics upon bacteria and
other microorganisms is known as the antibiotic spectrum. Some
antibiotics are characterized by a very narrow spectrum, whereas
others possess a wide range of activity. Some are active only against
certain bacteria and not upon others, whereas some are active
against fungi, and some against viruses. There is not only considerable qualitative variation in the activity of different antibiotics,
but also wide quantitative differences. Antibiotics are produced by
bacteria, fungi, actinomycetes, and to a limited extent by other
groups of microorganisms.

"It has been known for more than six decades that certain fungi
and bacteria are capable of producing chemical substances which
have the capacity to inhibit the growth and even to destroy pathogenic organisms. Only within the last 12 or 13 years, however,
have antibiotics begun to find extensive application as chemotherapeutic agents. . . .

"The isolation of streptomycin was the culminating point of a
painstaking search for antimicrobial agents produced by actinomycetes, a group of organisms closely related to the bacteria. This
was preceded by long and continuous research, dating back to
1915, on actinomycetes, their occurrence and abundance in nature,
their systematic or taxonomic position, their role in soil processes
. . . and finally their associative and antagonistic effects upon
bacteria and fungi. It was finally established that as many as 20 to
50 per cent of all the actinomycetes found in the soil and in other
natural substrates had the capacity to inhibit the growth of other
microorganisms. . . .

---

* From S. A. Waksman, "Streptomycin: background, isolation, properties, and
utilization," *Les Prix Nobel en 1952.*

"The first true antibiotic to be derived from a culture of an actinomyces was isolated in our department in 1940. The organism, *Actinomyces antibioticus,* yielded a substance which was designated as actinomycin. . . . It proved to be extremely toxic to experimental animals. . . . This practical failure was followed by a comprehensive program of screening actinomycetes for their ability to produce different antibiotics. . . . A new type of substance, designated as streptothricin, was soon isolated, in 1942. It showed distinct promise as a chemotherapeutic agent. . . . It was active against a number of bacteria, not only *in vitro,* but also *in vivo,* as well as against various fungi. . . . A study of its pharmacology, however, brought out the fact that streptothricin exerted a residual toxic effect upon the animal body; its use in the treatment of infectious diseases was, therefore, limited. . . .

"It was, of course, desirable that any new substance should possess a spectrum which would be broader than that of streptothricin, that it be particularly active against a greater variety of bacteria which were resistant to penicillin, and, if possible, that it be active against tuberculosis. . . . Less than six months after many freshly isolated cultures of actinomycetes were screened, an organism was obtained which appeared to produce the long looked-for antibiotic. . . . Thus *streptomycin* was born.

"Recovery of the streptomycin was accomplished in a series of operations involving removal of the mycelium by filtration, adsorption of the streptomycin on activated carbon or on some other adsorbent, elution by dilute acid, neutralization of the eluate, concentration by evaporation and dehydration or by solvent precipitation, and filtration and drying. Various methods have been used for further purification and crystallisation of the antibiotic. . . .

"Streptomycin is active against a large number of bacteria found among the gram-negative [see page 242], gram-positive, and acid-fast groups [among which is the organism causing tuberculosis] and among the spirochaetes; it has relatively little activity against anaerobic bacteria, fungi, protozoa, and viruses. . . . Its bacteriostatic and bactericidal action upon different strains of *Mycobacterium tuberculosis* is particularly significant. . . .

"Of particular importance was pioneering work done by Feldman and Hinshaw [working at the Mayo Clinic] on the effectiveness of streptomycin in experimental tuberculosis in guinea pigs. On the basis of an arbitrarily established index of infection, microscopically determined, 100 represented the maximum possible amount of tuberculosis. The control animals, sacrificed after 61 days, exhibited an index of 67 as contrasted to 5.8 for those which had received streptomycin. In another experiment, the corresponding values were 81.9 for the untreated and 2.8 for the treated animals. The daily administration of streptomycin per guinea pig varied from 1387 to 6000 micrograms [10^6 micrograms = one gram]. Two different strains of the human tubercle bacillus were equally sensitive to streptomycin. *M. tuberculosis* was recovered from the spleens of only one of the guinea pigs treated with streptomycin, the animal having received 1387 mcg streptomycin daily for 54 days.

"The conclusion was reached that streptomycin is the most effective tuberculochemotherapeutic agent so far studied. Its relatively low toxicity for guinea pigs, its high efficacy in resolving and suppressing what would otherwise be lethal tuberculosis, established streptomycin as a drug worthy of serious consideration for the treatment of tuberculosis. . . .

"A variety of human and animal diseases caused by various bacteria respond readily to streptomycin treatment. . . . These include tularemia, urinary tract infections, especially those resistant to sulfa drugs and to penicillin [pulmonary infections], bacteremia ["blood poisoning"] due to penicillin-resistant organisms, various forms of meningitis, and whooping cough. . . .

"Various forms of tuberculosis were soon found to respond promptly to streptomycin. . . .

"I need hardly survey the subsequent developments in the use of streptomycin for the different infectious diseases, especially tuberculosis. . . . Suffice to say that streptomycin pointed the way, both through the planned screening programs and through its specific activity against the gram-negative bacteria and tuberculosis, to many of [the newer] antibiotics."

CONSEQUENCES IN THEORY
AND PRACTICE

Waksman's singular achievement in a lifetime spent in microbiology has been the domestication of a new type of microorganism, the actinomycetes. He defines these as "a group of microbes, filamentous in nature; in size and physiology they are more closely related to the bacteria; in structure they are similar to the fungi; may be considered as intermediary between these two groups of microbes." About 1939 Waksman turned from morphological and physiological work to search systematically among the actinomycetes for antibiotics. The discovery of gramicidin by René Dubos and the beginning development of penicillin for therapeutic purposes at this time were focusing scientific attention on a new aspect of microbiology. It was Waksman's extensive background in developing a new branch of microbiology that culminated in the isolation of streptomycin and the characterization of its properties. As in many branches of scientific endeavor nowadays the research on streptomycin was a cooperative piece of work, and when the discovery of the antibiotic was reported in the *Proceedings of the Society of Experimental Biology and Medicine* in January, 1944, the article carried the names of Albert Schatz, Elizabeth Bugie, and Waksman. In a second paper later that year in the same journal, detailing the test-tube work on the effect of streptomycin and other antibiotics on the tubercle bacillus, Schatz and Waksman mentioned that they had suggested the need for tests of the efficacy in animals to colleagues at the Mayo Foundation. The results of these tests, using guinea pigs, were duly reported by Drs. W. H. Feldman and H. C. Hinshaw. An extensive literature rapidly grew around streptomycin, particularly its clinical actions and uses: almost ten thousand scientific papers and twenty volumes in the first ten years.

"Streptomycin proved to be the first chemotherapeutic agent ever discovered which had the capacity of controlling the dreadful 'white plague' of man. It was not a perfect agent, it had its limitations; it certainly was not a cure for tuberculosis. But it pointed a way toward the final solution of this dreadful disease.

"Streptomycin also opened many other new fields of chemotherapy, notably in the treatment of infections not subject to penicillin therapy. This was true of urinary tract infections, tularemia, plague, influenza, meningitis, brucellosis, and many others. Although later other antibiotics were found that could replace streptomycin, it pointed the way to the control of numerous diseases not previously subject to treatment." *

In the same year that Waksman was awarded the Nobel Prize, new synthetic chemicals, showing considerable promise in the treatment of tuberculosis, were found. One of them, isoniazid, has become the mainstay of anti-tubercular drug treatment and has proved to be very effective for out-patient use. Another chemical, knowns as PAS (para-aminosalicylic acid) is an important adjunct in therapy. Both isoniazid and PAS can be given by mouth, but streptomycin must be injected for treatment of tuberculosis. This represents a limitation on its use, but the antibiotic is of great value in tuberculosis of the lung, central nervous system, genitourinary tract and bone. Tubercular meningitis and miliary TB, previously considered to be fatal diseases, may now be treated successfully. Other forms of the disease are now rarely encountered. Streptomycin is also used orally to reduce the bacterial count in the intestine, as a preparation for surgery of that organ.

In spite of the advances in the treatment of tuberculosis by chemical and other means, over fifty million people have the disease. Factors such as the persistence of social conditions favoring tuberculosis, the ready communicability of the disease and possible development of resistance to the drugs by the tubercle bacillus, combined with an incorrect appraisal by the public that the disease has been "conquered," have recently led to warnings by many public health leaders of the continuing tuberculosis problem. And research for an ideal antitubercular drug continues.

---

* From S. A. Waksman, *My Life with the Microbes* (New York: Simon and Schuster, 1954).

1 9 5 3
HANS ADOLF KREBS
(1900–   ).

"For his discovery of the citric acid cycle."
(*The award for 1953 was shared with Fritz Lipmann; see below,*
pp.308-314.)

BIOGRAPHICAL SKETCH

HANS ADOLF KREBS WAS BORN IN HILDESHEIM, GERMANY, ON
August 25, 1900. His father was an otolaryngologist there. He studied medicine from 1918 to 1923 at various universities—in Göttingen, Freiburg, Munich, and Berlin. After interning and devoting a
year to chemistry, he became assistant to Otto Warburg at the
Kaiser Wilhelm Institute from 1926 to 1930. He returned to
clinical work, but was forced to leave his hospital appointment
under the Nazi racial laws. He emigrated to Cambridge, with the
aid of Sir Frederick Gowland Hopkins, and in 1935 he moved to
Sheffield where in a few years he was placed in charge of the
Department of Biochemistry. He was appointed director of a
Medical Research Council Unit for Studies of Cell Metabolism at
Sheffield in 1945, and at the same time became professor of bio-
chemistry at the University. In 1954 he was appointed Whitley
Professor of Biochemistry at Oxford. His M.R.C. Unit now func-
tions at that University.

DESCRIPTION OF THE PRIZE-WINNING
WORK*

"Very little was known in the earlier 1930ies about the intermediary stages through which sugar is oxidised in living cells. When, in 1930, I left the laboratory of Otto Warburg (under whose guidance I had worked since 1926 and from whom I have learnt more than from any other single teacher), I was confronted with the question of selecting a major field of study and I felt greatly attracted by the problem of the intermediary pathway of oxidations. These reactions represent the main energy source in higher organisms, and in view of the importance of energy production to living organisms (whose activities all depend on a continous supply of energy) the problem seemed well worthwhile studying.

"The first major investigation into the intermediary metabolism of oxidation was that of Thunberg who examined systematically the oxidisability of organic substances in isolated animal tissues. . . . He discovered the rapid oxidation of the salts of a number of acids, such as lactate, succinate, fumarate, malate, citrate and glutamate. Thunberg's results were confirmed and extended by Batelli and Stern and later investigators. . . .

"However the data of Thunberg and Batelli and Stern remained isolated observations because they could not be linked to the chief oxidative process of muscle tissue, the oxidation of carbohydrate. Another twenty years had to elapse before they could be incorporated into a coherent account of respiration.

"An important development came from the laboratory of Szent-Györgyi of Szeged in 1935, who discovered that pigeon breast muscle . . . is especially suitable for the study of oxidative reactions. . . . He confirmed on this material the rapid oxidation of the C_4-dicarboxylic acids—succinic, fumaric, malic and oxaloacetic acids—and arrived at the new conclusion that part of the action of these substances was of a catalytic nature. Final proof of this *catalytic* effect (as opposed to the oxidation in which the acids

---

* From H. A. Krebs, "The citric acid cycle," *Les Prix Nobel en 1953.*

serve as substrate) was provided by Stare and Baumann in Wisconsin in December 1936.

"The next step was the discovery, made in Sheffield early in 1937, that citrate can act as a catalyst in the same way as succinate. A decisive contribution to the field was made in March 1937 by Martius and Knoop, who . . . discovered α-ketoglutarate as a product of citrate oxidation.

"Further relevant observations were made in the Sheffield laboratory between March and June 1937. Firstly, the reaction which Martius and Knoop had demonstrated in liver was found to occur at a rapid rate in muscle and other tissues. The rate was found to be sufficient to justify the assumption that the reaction constitutes a component of the main respiratory process of that tissue.

". . . Succinate was found to be a major product of the oxidation of citrate. Of major significance was another new observation: citrate was not only broken down at a rapid rate but was also readily formed in muscle and in other tissues provided that oxaloacetate was added. This could be explained by the assumption that some oxaloacetate was broken down to pyruvate, or acetate, and that the formation of citrate was the result of a combination between the remaining oxaloacetate on the one hand, and pyruvate or acetate on the other. The discovery of the synthesis of citrate from oxaloacetate and a substance which could be derived from carbohydrate, like pyruvate or acetate, made it possible to formulate a complete scheme of carbohydrate oxidation. According to this scheme, pyruvate, or a derivative of pyruvate, condenses with oxaloacetate to form citrate. By a sequence of reactions . . . one acetic acid equivalent is oxidized and the oxaloacetic acid required for the condensing reaction is regenerated. The concept explained the catalytic action of the di- or tricarboxylic acids, the oxidizability of these acids in tissues which oxidise carbohydrates, and the similarity of the characteristics of the oxidation of these substances and of the main respirations already noted by Batelli and Stern in 1910. . . .

"[The essential feature of the metabolic scheme] is the periodic formation of a number of di- and tricarboxylic acids. As there is no term which would serve as a common denominator for all the various acids, it seemed reasonable to name the cycle after one, or some, of its characteristic and specific acids. It was from such considerations that the term 'citric acid cycle' was proposed in 1937. . . .

"The evidence in support of the cycle mentioned so far comes under two main headings: firstly, all the individual stages of the cycle have been demonstrated to occur in animal tissues, and their rates are high enough to comply with the view that they are components of the main respiratory process. Secondly, di- and tricarboxylic acids have been shown under suitable conditions to stimulate oxidations catalytically. . . .

"The concept of the citric acid cycle was originally put forward as a scheme of the oxidation of carbohydrate. It was however clear from the beginning that the cycle must also play a major part in the oxidation of a considerable fraction of the protein molecule. . . . A substantial proportion of protein molecules pass through the citric acid cycle when undergoing oxidation.

"Since 1943 it has become evident that the citric acid cycle also comes into play in the later stages of the oxidation of fatty acids. . . . [The use of compounds 'labeled' by an isotope, beginning about 1944 in the United States showed] conclusively that the carbon atoms of fatty acids, and of acetoacetate, appear in the acids of the citric acid cycle, and that these acids are thus intermediates in the complete oxidation of fatty acids.

"It is indeed remarkable that all foodstuffs are burnt through a common terminal pathway. About two-thirds of the energy derived from food in higher organisms is set free in the course of this common pathway; about one-third arises in the reactions which prepare foodstuffs for entry into the citric acid cycle. The biological significance of the common route may lie in the fact that such an arrangement represents an economy of chemical tools. . . .

"The main experiments on which the concept of the citric acid cycle is based were carried out on striated muscle, chiefly of pigeon breast muscle, and on pigeon liver. The crucial experiments have been repeated with many other animal materials and they suggest that the cycle occurs in all respiring tissues of animals, from protozoa to the highest mammal. . . . The component reactions of the citric acid cycle have also been shown to occur in many microorganisms and in plants."

FRITZ ALBERT LIPMANN

(1899–)

"For his discovery of coenzyme A and its importance for intermediary metabolism."

(The award for 1953 was shared with H. A. Krebs; see above, pp. 304-307)

BIOGRAPHICAL SKETCH

FRITZ LIPMANN WAS BORN ON JUNE 12, 1899, IN KOENIGSBERG, Germany. His medical studies were made at the University there, as well as in Berlin and Munich. He received the M.D. degree from the University of Berlin in 1922. During the next four years he studied chemistry in Amsterdam with Ernest Laqueur, in Koenigsberg with Hans Meerwein, and in Berlin with Otto Meyerhof. He was awarded the Ph.D. degree in 1927 by the University of Berlin. He then spent a further three years of "apprenticeship" with Meyerhof in Heidelberg. With the aid of a Rockefeller Fellowship Lipmann was able to spend a year with P. A. Levene at the Rockefeller Institute in New York City. In 1932 he went to work as assistant to Albert Fischer at the newly opened Biological Institute of the Carlsberg Foundation. His work there dealt with the Pasteur reaction and the non-fermentative metabolism of sugar. In 1939 Lipmann went to the United States and worked initially at the Cornell Medical School, but then (1941) at the Massachusetts General Hospital in Boston where he was head of the Biochemical Research Laboratory. It was here that he and his students discovered coenzyme A and identified pantothenic acid as one of its constituents. In 1949 he received a professorship in biological chemistry at Harvard Medical School. Since 1957 he has been a member· and professor of the Rockefeller Institute for Medical

Research in New York City. His research has dealt with the biological transfer of the sulfate group and with protein synthesis.

DESCRIPTION OF THE PRIZE-WINNING WORK*

[After a three-year apprenticeship with Otto Meyerhof in Berlin and Heidelberg, Lipmann began his independent scientific career. His first interest was the 'Pasteur effect,' a phenomenon whereby a tissue may switch its metabolism from fermentative processes in which various organic acids are produced, to respiration when a source of oxygen is provided. Because fermentation utilises only a part of the foodstuff or nutrient, whereas respiration results in the complete oxidation of these substances to carbon dioxide and water, the former process is regarded as metabolically wasteful, the latter economical.] "By looking for a chemical explanation of this economy measure on the cellular level, I was prompted into a study of the mechanism of pyruvic acid oxidation, since it is at the pyruvic acid stage where respiration branches off from fermentation. For this study I chose as a promising system a relatively simple looking pyruvic acid oxidation enzyme in a certain strain of *Lactobacillus delbrueckii*. The decision to explore this particular reaction started me on a rather continuous journey into partly virgin territory to meet with some unexpected discoveries, but also to encounter quite a few nagging disappointments.

"The most important event during this whole period, I now feel, was the accidental observation that in the *L. delbrueckii* system, pyruvic acid oxidation was completely dependent on the presence of inorganic phosphate.

". . . The phospate balance did not at first indicate any phosphorylative step [i.e. combination of inorganic phosphate with an organic compound]. Nevertheless, the suspicion remained that phosphate in some manner was entering into the reaction and that a phosphorylated intermediary was formed. [After completing certain experiments, I] concluded that the missing link in the reaction chain was acetyl phosphate.

"At the time when these observations were made . . . there was

---

* From F. Lipmann, "Development of the acetylation problem," *Les Prix Nobel en 1953*.

. . . a tendency to believe that phosphorylation was rather specifically coupled with the glycolytic reaction [conversion of sugars to lactic or pyruvic acid]. Here, however, we had found a coupling of phosphorylation with a respiratory system. This observation immediately suggested a rather sweeping biochemical significance, of transformations of electron transfer potential, respiratory or fermentative, to phosphate bond energy and therefrom to a wide range of biosynthetic reactions.

"These . . . novel aspects of the energy problem . . . prompted me to propose not only the generalization of the phosphate bond as a versatile energy distributing system, but also to aim from there towards a general concept of transfer of activated groupings by carrier as the fundamental reaction in biosynthesis. . . . It soon turned out that the relationship between acetyl phosphate and acetyl transfer was much more complicated than anticipated.

"In looking for a sensitive method to study acetyl transfer, the acetylation of aromatic amines [e.g. sulfanilamide] was chosen eventually as a most promising and technically easy procedure. We were furthermore quite confident that any results obtained with this method could be generalized over the whole metabolic territory concerning the transfer of active acetate including such reactions as citrate, acetoacetate and lipid synthesis. . . . Pigeon liver homogenate was tried and found to harbour an exceedingly potent acetylation system. This finding of a particularly active acetylation reaction in cell-free pigeon liver preparations was most fortunate and played a quite important part in the development of the acetylation problem.

"We had now eventually arrived at the point where the desired test for acetyl phosphate as an acetyl precursor could be performed. . . . It became, nevertheless, clear to us that in this preparation, acetyl phosphate did not furnish active acetate. Under anaerobic conditions with massive concentrations of acetyl phosphate, no acetyl groups for the acetylation of sulfonamide could be derived under conditions where an easy acetylation occurred with a respiring homogenate.

"During these studies we became aware of the participation of a heat-stable factor which disappeared from our enzyme extracts on aging or dialysis. This cofactor was present in boiled extracts of all organs, as well as in microorganisms and yeast. It could not be replaced by any other known cofactor. Therefore, it was suspected that we were dealing with a new coenzyme. From then on, for a number of years, the isolation and identification of this coenzyme became the prominent task of our laboratory.

"Parallel with this slow but steady elaboration of the structure, all the time we explored intensively metabolic mechanisms in the acetylation field.

"The first example of a generality of function was obtained [when it was found that the purified coenzyme activated the acetylation of choline and sulfonamides by their respective enzymes, in exactly the same way].

"The next most significant step toward a generalization of CoA [the name given to the newly found coenzyme of acetylation] function for acetyl transfer was made by demonstrating its functioning in the enzymatic synthesis of acetoacetate. [Thus, three important biological acetylations required the coenzyme. Other acetylation reactions were then examined, and] in the course of these various observations, it became quite clear that there existed in cellular metabolism an acetyl distribution system centering around CoA as the acetyl carrier. . . .

"A most important, then still missing, link in the picture was supplied through the brilliant work of Feodor Lynen [Nobel Prize Winner, 1964] who chemically identified acetyl CoA as the thioester of CoA. Therewith the thioester link was introduced as a new energy-rich bond and this discovery added a very novel facet to our understanding of the mechanisms of metabolic energy transformation."

CONSEQUENCES IN THEORY AND PRACTICE

The award of the Nobel Prize to Krebs and Lipmann, whose researches were clearly supplementary to one another, was a recognition of the maturity of biochemistry in its ability to perform detailed chemical dissections of processes that for so many years had been known simply by the starting materials and the end products. This type of work is known as "intermediary metabolism"; its aim is to elaborate the specific chemical reactions whereby each substance in the body is formed, converted to other compounds, or broken down to simpler materials. Many phases of research in intermediary metabolism are today aided greatly by the use of isotopes which then act as markers. For example, organic compounds can be synthesized in the laboratory with radioactive carbon-14 substituted for the ordinary carbon-12. When this compound is administered to an animal, it mixes with the non-radioactive compound of the same composition already in the body. The radioactive atoms always accompany the inactive ones and, to all intents and purposes, the body does not distinguish the two types of molecule. They are considered to exist now in the same "pool" of molecules. They will be distributed and metabolized in the same manner. The biochemist can then search for substances containing radioactive carbon, which is detected relatively easily, and he knows that these must have derived their carbon-14 from the compound he administered. The comparative ease of following intermediaries in metabolism through isotopic labeling of compounds makes Krebs' contribution all the more remarkable because his work on the citric acid cycle was carried out without benefit of this extraordinary technique.

Lipmann's work on the "acetyl distribution system centering around CoA as the acetyl carrier" illustrates the function of "pools," as conceived by modern biochemistry. Acetate, or acetyl groups, entering the cell from no matter what source, are brought into metabolic processes, i.e. are "activated," once they have combined with coenzyme A. From that point on, each acetyl CoA molecule is the same as any other, and an acetyl group that has originated from foodstuffs, from the breakdown of sugars to pyruvic acid, and the latter to acetyl CoA, from the metabolism of fatty acids or certain amino acids, may follow any of a large variety of metabolic paths, including complete combustion to carbon dioxide and water.

Other cycles besides the citric acid cycle are recognized. Indeed, in 1932 Krebs and Kurt Henseleit, working in the Department of Medicine at the University of Freiburg, outlined a "cycle" whose operation results in the conversion of carbon dioxide and ammonia to urea. These cycles are the "chemical tools" of metabolism, but they are *dynamic,* as the late Rudolf Schoenheimer (1946) had stressed. For, like the phoenix, they are constantly being consumed in the fire of metabolism out of which they arise once more, regenerated. Each turn of the citric acid cycle results in the combustion of an acetyl group and the regeneration of oxaloacetic acid, available once more for the introduction of another acetyl group into the process (see figure).

The discoveries of Krebs and Lipmann explain much about the workings of metabolism and the fundamental nature of certain biochemical processes in the cell. Thus, if any of the enzymes of the citric acid cycle were missing through mutation or genetic defect, the protean result would be incompatible with life. The key reaction, conversion of pyruvic acid to acetyl CoA, is very sensitive to arsenicals, that is, organic substances containing arsenic, such as the war gas lewisite. Research at the University of Oxford at the beginning of the Second World War led to the development

The citric acid cycle and related reactions. A, the formation of acetyl CoA from pyruvate. B, conversion of citric acid to related tricarboxylic acids. C, various pathways funneling into the citric acid cycle. D, the dicarboxylic acids of the cycle. (From W. W. Umbreit, *Metabolic Maps,* Vol. 2. Minneapolis: Burgess Publishing Company, 1960.)

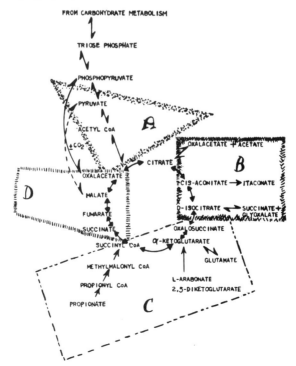

of the antidote "British anti-lewisite," or BAL. Again, pyruvic acid oxidase requires many cofactors, among them a phosphoric acid derivative of thiamine (vitamin B_1). In thiamine deficiency, pyruvic and lactic acids pile up in the blood and tissues because of the reduced rate of oxidation of the former, and this phenomenon can be used as an aid to the diagnosis of beri-beri and of Wernicke's encephalopathy. Medicinal chemists have in some cases sought drugs that would interfere with reactions of the citric acid cycle; a drug that could interfere selectively with metabolism of an invading organism without affecting a corresponding reaction in the tissues of the host might prove of great value in therapy.

The study of intermediary metabolism has great evolutionary significance. As Krebs put it, "The basic metabolic processes, in particular those providing energy, and those leading to the synthesis of cell constituents are also shared by all forms of life.

"The existence of common features in different forms of life indicates some relationship between the different organisms, and according to the concept of evolution these relations stem from the circumstance that the higher organisms, in the course of millions of years, have gradually evolved from simpler ones. The concept of evolution postulates that living organisms have common roots, and in turn the existence of common features is powerful support for the concept of evolution. The presence of the same mechanism of energy production in all forms of life suggests two other inferences, firstly, that the mechanism of energy production has arisen very early in the evolutionary process and secondly that life, in its present forms, has arisen only once."

REFERENCE

Schoenheimer, Rudolf. *The Dynamic State of Body Constituents* (Cambridge: Harvard University Press, 1946).

1 9 5 4
JOHN F. ENDERS
(1897–   )

FREDERICK C. ROBBINS
(1916–   )

THOMAS H. WELLER
(1915–   )

"For their discovery of the ability of poliomyelitis viruses to grow in cultures of various types of tissue."

BIOGRAPHICAL SKETCHES

ENDERS

JOHN FRANKLIN ENDERS WAS BORN ON FEBRUARY 10, 1897, IN West Hartford, Connecticut. His undergraduate studies at Yale College, begun in 1915, were interrupted by service in the armed forces of the United States during the First World War. He obtained his B.A. degree in 1920 and, after a short and dissatisfying sojourn in business, he began a four-year study of English literature and language at Harvard University. An early interest in biology, contact with medical students and others, and encouragement by Hans Zinsser, then head of the Department of Bacteriology and Immunology at Harvard Medical School, and of Hugh K. Ward, he entered upon bacteriological studies for the Ph.D. The degree was awarded him in 1930 for his immunological research. During the next sixteen years as a member of the Harvard faculty he continued his studies in immunology and initiated work on viruses affecting mammals, including the mumps virus. In 1946 he was invited to set up a laboratory for research in infectious diseases at the Children's Medical Center in Boston. One of the projects there led to the Prize-winning work.

ROBBINS

FREDERICK CHAPMAN ROBBINS WAS BORN IN AUBURN, ALAbama, on August 25, 1916. He studied as an undergraduate at the University of Missouri, and trained in medicine at the Harvard Medical School, receiving his degree in 1940. He worked in bacteriology at the Children's Hospital, Boston, from 1940 to 1942, and during four years in the United States armed services he conducted research in viral diseases, working in the United States, North Africa, and Italy. After completing his training at the Children's Hospital, he commenced research with J. F. Enders and T. H. Weller on the cultivation of poliomyelitis virus, as well as investigating other viruses. He left the Children's Medical Center and Harvard in 1952 to become professor of pediatrics at Western Reserve University Medical School and director of the Department of Pediatrics and Contagious Diseases at Cleveland City Hospital.

WELLER

THOMAS HUCKLE WELLER WAS BORN IN ANN ARBOR, MICHIgan, on June 15, 1915. He received his early schooling in that city and then his B.A. degree in 1936 from the University of Michigan, where his father was a member of the medical faculty. He entered Harvard Medical School, continuing work on a part-time basis in the Department of Pathology and Tropical Medicine and during two summers at the University of Michigan Biological Station, for which he earned the M.S. degree in 1937. He received the M.D. degree in 1940, and began his internship at the Children's Hospital in Boston. From 1942 to 1945 he served in the United States Army Medical Corps as chief of a laboratory in Puerto Rico concerned with bacteriology, virology and parasitology. Shortly after Dr. Enders established the infectious diseases laboratory at the Children's Medical Center in Boston Weller joined him, and was assistant director from 1949 to 1955. In 1954 he was given the Richard Pearson Strong Chair in Tropical Public Health at the Harvard School of Public Health, and was made head of the department. He has continued his research on the propagation of viruses.

DESCRIPTION OF THE PRIZE-WINNING WORK*

"In 1937 Dr. Enders working in the Department of Bacteriology and Immunology at the Harvard Medical School turned from the study of bacterial immunity to an investigation of the growth of herpes simplex virus [an organism causing a certain type of skin eruption]. Experience with the herpes virus served to establish an enduring preoccupation with pathogens of this class and was followed by attempts to isolate the agent of measles [another virus]. In these experiments the tissue culture method was employed with uncertain results. [This technique consists in maintaining actively metabolizing tissue, or rather its cells, in a nutrient fluid, and transferring the tissue periodically to a new tube containing fresh salts, serum, and other nutrients. Usually an extract of embryonic tissue, such as the amniotic membrane of the chick, must be included in the suspending medium to provide necessary growth factors.] But the conviction was gained that it represented a basic tool for the study of viruses of which the possible applications were almost unlimited. For this as well as other reasons the roller tube method used about this time by Gey and

---

* From J. F. Enders, F. C. Robbins and T. H. Weller, "The cultivation of the poliomyelitis viruses in tissue culture," *Les Prix Nobel en 1954*.

Bang for the cultivation of the virus of lymphogranuloma ven-
ereum was selected as an ideal means of investigating over a prolonged period the relationships between a virus and its host cells.
One of the participants in this research in which the agent of
vaccinia was employed was Thomas Weller, then a fourth year
medical student at Harvard.

"These preliminary explorations of the value of the tissue culture
method were interrupted by the war, [but in 1946] . . . Dr.
Enders was asked to establish a laboratory for research in infectious diseases at the Children's Hospital [in Boston]. Dr. Weller
participated in the establishment of the laboratory and we were
soon joined by Dr. Robbins who had recently returned from duty
in Italy where under his direction an epidemiologic study of a
disease resembling Q fever had resulted in the identification of
the responsible rickettsia for the first time in that country. Under
these circumstances congenial to the free implementation of our
interests the first experiments in the new laboratory were begun
in April of 1947."

[The group had been interested previously in using the tissue
culture technique to study the effect of the virus upon the cells
of the host tissue. Now they became concerned with the possibility
of actually growing viruses on such tissue in culture.] "Viral increase was easily followed by measuring the amount of hemagglu-
tinin that emerged in the culture fluid after inoculation of small
quantities of the agent [of mumps, the first one selected for
study]. A modification of the usual technique for handling such
cultures was introduced that permitted the demonstration of the
slow-growing mumps virus. Instead of transferring material from
one culture to another after an interval of 3 or 4 days as had been
the procedure of most previous investigators, the tissues were
preserved while the nutritive medium was removed and replenished at frequent intervals. In this way viability of the cells could
be maintained for 30 days or longer and full opportunity allowed
for viral growth to occur while a substantial dilution of the original viral inoculum was effected.

"In 1948 when this work was completed we had no immediate
intention of carrying out experiments with poliomyelitis viruses.

Nevertheless from time to time we had considered the mounting evidence . . . in favor of the possibility that these agents might not be strict neurotropes [i.e. viruses with a specific affinity for nervous tissue]. Thus, for us, along with others it was becoming increasingly difficult to visualize the nervous system as site of manufacture of the enormous quantities of virus that was found in the feces of many patients. Such ideas were in our minds when the decision was taken to use a mixture of human embryonic skin and muscle tissue in suspended cell cultures in the hope that the virus of varicella [chicken pox] might multiply in the cells of its natural host. In this way such cultures were made available while close at hand in the storage cabinet was the Lansing strain of poliomyelitis virus. Thereupon it suddenly occurred to us that everything had been prepared almost without conscious effort on our part for a new attempt to cultivate the agent in extraneural tissues.

"Accordingly the virus in the form of an infected suspension of mouse brain was introduced into several of these cultures of human tissue. . . . By inoculation of mice with the fluids removed from the original cultures as well as with those taken from subsequent serial passages in vitro it soon became apparent that multiplication of the virus regularly occurred. Introduction of fluid from the third passage into the brains of monkeys was followed by the appearance of typical flaccid paralysis of the legs. These findings, surprising as they were in the light of the failure of our predecessors to propagate the virus in extraneural tissue, left no doubt in our minds that this could be accomplished.

"Since the tissue employed in these experiments was removed from the extremities it was considered to be free of intact nerve cells. It was concluded, therefore, that growth of poliomyelitis virus in cultures of this material occurred in cells of extraneural origin. This conclusion has been amply supported by direct observations of the effect of the viruses on various types of cells. . . . It has been made evident, then, that in vitro at least poliomyelitis viruses are not strict neurotropes.

"Signs of viral activity in the cultures themselves were observed soon after it was established that multiplication took place. Examination of stained sections of fragments of human embryonic intestine and skin and muscle removed from the early suspended cell subcultures of the Lansing strain revealed widespread cellular degeneration. In contrast, uninoculated tissues maintained under the same conditions were found to contain many cells in apparently excellent condition.

"At about the same time these cytopathogenic effects of the virus . . . were observed, we perceived an indirect manifestation of cell injury. It consisted of an accelerated decline in the metabolic rate of tissues infected with virus as expressed by a progressive reduction of acid formation.

"These indices of viral multiplication in suspended cell cultures, useful as they were in our earlier investigations, proved inconvenient in two respects. The direct observations of cell injury required the fixation, sectioning and staining of the fragments—a laborious process, while the difference in pH [the measure of acidity] required the lapse of about 2 weeks or longer before it became evident. Accordingly, other means were sought by which viral cytopathogenicity might be conveniently and rapidly demonstrated.

"Could not the same phenomena, we inquired, be elicited more simply and more rapidly in roller tube cultures which we knew provided large sheets of proliferating cells? Accordingly viruses representing the three types were inoculated in roller tube cultures of human embryonic skin and muscle. Within 3 to 5 days degenerative changes were evident which hereafter involved the entire cell population. . . . Because of the speed with which these changes develop and the readiness with which they may be observed the roller tube technique was used in most of our subsequent investigations.

"The isolation and typing of poliomyelitis viruses from man has been in the past a laborious and time-consuming procedure since it depended upon the intracerebral inoculation of monkeys. Therefore, we sought to determine whether these agents might not be recovered from feces or suspensions of the spinal cord. It was soon learned that through the addition of the antibiotics streptomycin and penicillin followed by centrifugation contaminating bacteria and other microorganisms could be suppressed. . . .

Roller tube cultures were adopted as routine for isolation as well as typing of the virus since the procedure is less complicated and the results are obtained more rapidly."

CONSEQUENCES IN THEORY
AND PRACTICE

The discovery by the Boston group that polio virus can grow on non-nervous tissue raised the question anew of where the virus ordinarily resides in the body and how it reaches nervous tissue. It was found that it enters the body through the mouth, and that it persists in the intestines, occasionally passing through the lining to be absorbed into the bloodstream and pass to the lower part of the brain and parts of the spinal cord controlling the action of muscles.

With large amounts of virus readily available by the tissue culture technique a number of investigators set themselves the task of preparing an immunizing agent against polio virus, three strains of which were identified: the Brunhilde, Lansing, and Leon strains. Two approaches were employed. The first was to prepare a weakened strain of the virus by frequent transfers and other methods, so that ultimately one would have a strain that was "live" but incapable of producing disease, much like the 17D strain of yellow fever virus. Three scientists succeeded in doing this, quite independently: Albert B. Sabin, Hilary Koprowski, and Herald Cox. Their strains are given by mouth, the virus multiplies in the intestines and induces the formation of protective antibodies. The second approach was employed by Jonas Salk, and it involved treating the live virus with formalin. After the injection of three doses of his vaccine, there was a great increase in the antibody titer. The vaccines of these four American investigators received massive field trials in the 1950's: Salk's in the United States and Western Europe, Sabin's in the USSR, Koprowski's in Poland, and Cox's in Latin America and parts of the United States. All were found effective and millions of doses of these vaccines have now been administered.

The simple techniques for growing the polio virus made it possible to map out the incidence of the various strains in the world's population. Other investigators have employed the tissue culture *cum* antibiotics method to detect previously unknown viruses inhabiting the human intestinal tract.

In their Nobel lecture Enders, Robbins, and Weller stated that "the discovery of the antibiotics has, as in so many other areas, worked a revolution in the field of tissue culture. Through the use of these substances it is now not only possible to apply tissue cultures to the routine isolation of viruses from materials heavily contaminated with microorganisms, but it has become feasible to use them under conditions and in numbers which in the past would have been unthinkable. Here then we have another example of how one discovery leads to many others often of quite a different nature."

REFERENCE

Calder, Ritchie. "Man's struggle against poliomyelitis," *World Health*, Vol. 14 (1961), pp. 29-35.

1 9 5 5
HUGO THEORELL
(1903–   )

"For his discoveries relating to the nature and mode of action of oxidizing enzymes."

BIOGRAPHICAL SKETCH

AXEL HUGO TEODOR THEORELL WAS BORN IN LINKÖPING, Sweden, on July 6, 1903. He took his early schooling in his home town, and entered the Caroline Institute in 1921. He received the Bachelor of Medicine degree in 1924, but even before he had completed the requirements he had joined the staff of the Institute. Working under Einar Hammarsten on plasma lipids and their influence on the sedimentation of red blood cells, he was awarded the research degree of M.D. in 1930. Following this he was appointed docent at the Caroline Institute and began an investigation of the molecular weight of the muscle pigment, myoglobin. He made use in his work of the ultracentrifuge that had recently been built by The Svedberg in Uppsala. During the next few years, Theorell was on the faculty of the University of Uppsala, but was given leave to work in Berlin and Stockholm. With Otto Warburg in Berlin, he purified a yellow enzyme, and split it reversibly into protein and coenzyme portions. In 1936 he went to the Nobel Medical Institute in Stockholm to open and head the Department of Biochemistry. He has received many honors for his work on oxidizing enzymes.

DESCRIPTION OF THE PRIZE-WINNING WORK*

"When in 1933 I went on a Rockefeller fellowship to Otto Warburg's institute in Berlin Warburg and Christian had in the previous year produced a yellow-coloured preparation of an oxidation enzyme from yeast. It was obviously very impure. . . . The yellow colour was of particular interest: it faded away on reduction and returned on oxidation with e.g. oxygen, so that it was evident that the yellow pigment had to do with the actual enzymatic process of oxido-reduction. It was possible to free the yellow pigment from the high molecular carrier substance, whose nature was still unknown, for example by treatment with acid methyl alcohol, whereupon the enzyme effect disappeared. Through simultaneous works by Warburg in Berlin, Kuhn in Heidelberg and Karrer in Zürich the constitution of the yellow pigment (lactoflavin, later riboflavin; = vitamin B_2) was determined.

"It was here for the first time possible to localize the enzymatic effect to a definite atomic constellation: hydrogen freed from the substrate (hexose monophosphate) is with the aid of a special enzyme system (TPN-Zwischenferment), whose nature was elucidated somewhat later, placed on the nitrogen atoms of the flavin (1) and (10), giving rise to the colourless leucoflavin. This is reoxidized by oxygen, hydrogen peroxide being formed, and may afterwards be reduced again, and so forth. This cyclic process then continues until the entire amount of substrate has been deprived of two hydrogen atoms and been transformed into phosphogluconic acid, and a corresponding amount of hydrogen peroxide has been formed. At the end of the process the yellow enzyme is still there in unchanged form.

"There now remained some extremely important questions to elucidate: why was the flavin in free form completely inactive, but active when it was anchored to a high-molecular carrier? And what was this carrier? In order to find out I decided to try to purify the yellow enzyme, using for the purpose electrophoretic

---

* From H. Theorell, "The nature and mode of action of oxidation enzymes," *Les Prix Nobel en 1955.*

methods worked out by myself. At this time Tiselius had not yet worked out his technically more perfected electrophoretic methods [selective migration of charged molecules in a voltage gradient], but my own proved surprisingly useful.

"The polysaccharides, which constituted 80-90% of the entire weight, were completely removed, together with some inactive colourless proteins. After fractionated precipitations with ammonium sulphate I produced a crystalline preparation which on ultracentrifuging and electrophoresis appeared homogeneous. The enzyme was a protein with the molecular weight 75000 and strongly yellow-coloured by the flavin part. The result of the flavin analysis was 1 mol flavin per 1 mol protein. With dialysis against diluted hydrochloric acid at low temperature the yellow pigment was separated from the protein, which then became colourless. In the enzyme test the flavin part and the protein severally were inactive, but if the flavin part and the protein were mixed at approximately neutral reaction the enzyme effect returned and the original effect came back when one mixed them in the molecular proportions 1:1. That in this connection a combination between the pigment and the protein came about was obvious, moreover for other reasons: the green-yellow colour of the flavin part changed to pure yellow, and its strong yellow fluorescence disappeared with linking to the protein.

". . . In my electrophoretic experiments lactoflavin behaved as a neutral body, while the pigment part separated from the yellow enzyme moved rapidly towards the anode and was thus an acid. An analysis for phosphorus showed 1 P per mol flavin, and when after a time (1934) I succeeded in isolating the natural pigment component this proved to be a lactoflavin phosphoric acid ester, thus a kind of nucleotide, and it was obvious that the phosphoric acid served to link the pigment part to the protein.

"[Theorell goes on to discuss a second group of oxidizing enzymes, the alcohol dehydrogenases. These] consist of colourless protein in reversible combination with a coenzyme, which in the present case is the diphosphopyridine nucleotide, earlier generally referred to as cozymase, now 'DPN' [and most recently as NAD, nicotinamide adenine dinucleotide]. . . . It contains as active atomic group nicotinic acid amide, which analogously with the flavin in the yellow enzyme functions by taking up hydrogen from one direction and giving it off in another. . . .

"Alcohol dehydrogenases occur in both the animal and the vegetable kingdoms. . . . The yeast enzyme was crystallized by Negelein and Wulff (1936) in Warburg's Institute, the liver enzyme (from horse liver) by Bonnichsen and Wassen at our institute in Stockholm in 1948.

"[The alcohol dehydrogenases of yeast and horse liver] have come to play a certain general role in biochemistry on account of the fact that it has been possible to investigate their kinetics [i.e. the velocities of the reactions they catalyze and the factors affecting velocity] more accurately than is the case with other enzyme systems. . . . For all reactions with a DPN-system it is possible to follow the reaction $DPN^+ + 2H \leftrightarrows DPNH + H^+$ spectrophotometrically, since DPNH [the reduced form of the coenzyme] has an absorption-band in the longer-wave ultra-violet region, at 340 $m\mu$, and thousands of such experiments have been performed all over the world. A couple of years ago, moreover, we began to apply our fluorescence method, which is based on the fact that DPNH but not DPN^+ [the oxidized form] fluoresces, even if considerably more weakly than the flavins. As regards the liver enzyme there is a further effect, which proved extremely useful for certain spectrophotometrical determinations of reaction speeds; together with Bonnichsen I found in 1950 that the 340 $m\mu$ band of the reduced coenzyme was displaced, on combination with liver alcohol dehydrogenase, to 325 $m\mu$.

"After my return home [from Berlin] I set about purifying . . . cytochrome c [page 156]. . . . In 1936 we had obtained the cytochrome approximately 80% pure, and in 1939 close to 100%.

"It is a beautiful red, iron-porphyrin-containing protein which functions as a link in the chain of the cell-respiration enzymes, the iron atom now taking up and now giving off an electron, and the iron thus alternating valency between the 3-valent ferri and the 2-valent ferro stages. It is a very pleasant substance to work with, not merely because it is lovely to look at, but also because it is uncommonly stable and durable. From 100 kilograms of heart-meat of horse one can produce 3-4 grams of pure cytochrome

c. The molecule weighs about 12000 and contains one mol iron porphyrin per mol.

". . . Reduced cytochrome c cannot react with molecular oxygen. In a chain of oxidation enzymes it will thus not be able to be next to the oxygen. The incapacity of cytochrome to react with oxygen was a striking fact that required an explanation. Another peculiarity was the extremely firm linkage between the red hemin pigment and the protein part: in contradistinction to the majority of other hemin proteids, the pigment cannot be split off by the addition of acetone acidified with hydrochloric acid. . . . In 1938 we succeeded in showing that the porphyrin part of the cytochrome was linked to the protein by means of two sulphur bridges from cysteine residues in the protein of the cytochrome in such a way that the vinyl groups were saturated and were converted to a-thioethyl groups. The firmness of the linkage . . . [was] herewith explained. This was the first time that it had been possible to show the nature of chemical linkages between a 'prosthetic' group (in this case iron porphyrin) and the protein part in an enzyme."

[With Anders Ehrenberg, Theorell constructed models of hemin peptides to try to match what was then known of the structure of cytochrome c, and thus arrive at a three-dimensional picture of the molecule. They made extensive use of models designed by Linus Pauling, Nobel laureate in chemistry, 1954, and in peace, 1962, and by his colleague R. B. Corey.]

". . . We now consider it extremely probable that the hemin plate in cytochrome c is surrounded by peptide spirals on all sides in such a way that the hemin iron is entirely screened off from contact with oxygen; here is the explanation of our experiment in which we were unable to oxidize reduced cytochrome c with oxygen-gas. The oxygen simply cannot get at the iron atom. There is, on the other hand, a possibility for electrons to pass in and out of the iron atom via the imidazole [group of histidine, which appeared to fit closely to the iron atom]."

CONSEQUENCES IN THEORY
AND PRACTICE

Theorell's demonstration of the reversible splitting of the coenzyme from the yellow enzyme merited him the title "Master of Enzyme Research" from Otto Warburg, in whose laboratory this classic work was accomplished. Theorell explained the significance of this work, as follows:

"1. The reversible splitting of the yellow enzyme to apo-enzyme + coenzyme in the simple molecular relation 1:1 proved that we had here to do with a pure enzyme.

"2. This enzyme was thus demonstrably a protein. In the sequel all the enzymes which have been isolated have proved to be proteins.

"3. The first coenzyme, FMN [flavin mononucleotide], was isolated and found to be a vitamin phosphoric acid ester. This has since proved to be something occurring widely in nature: the vitamins nicotinic acid amide, thiamine and pyridoxine form in an analogous way nucleotide-like coenzymes, which like the nucleic acids combine reversibly with proteins."

Thus, Theorell introduced novel experimental proof backing up the protein character of enzymes, as had been maintained for many years by J. B. Sumner and J. H. Northrop (who shared the Nobel Prize in chemistry with W. M. Stanley in 1946). Although the American biochemists had crystallized various enzymes and found the crystals to consist of protein, the old criticism by Richard Willstätter (Nobel Prize Winner in chemistry, 1915) hung on. He had maintained that the protein is just an inert carrier (*Träger*) of a small catalytic molecule. Theorell's test showed that neither portion of the enzyme was active without the other and that one of these portions was a pure protein. His test of reversible dissociation of the complex is now routinely applied in experimental work with new enzymes suspected of possessing a coenzyme. We do not yet understand how the protein-coenzyme linkage facilitates, or makes possible, the rapid movement of hydrogen on and off the molecule, but Theorell's work on the structure and function of cytochrome c, described above, is an outstanding example of pioneer work in this direction, i.e. in taking the mystery out of enzymic catalysis.

In 1955 Theorell said that the first stage of the final goal of enzyme research is "to investigate the entire steric constitution of all enzymes—a nice little job! So far we know the *most easily* accessible sixth part of the smallest enzyme model, cytochrome c." But at this very time methods were being developed that would make possible the relatively facile analysis of even large proteins; best known among the investigators in this field is Frederick Sanger, winner of the Nobel Prize in chemistry in 1958, for his work on the structure of proteins, especially insulin. These procedures have now enabled biochemists to unravel the structure of cytochrome c crystallized from the tissues of many species, and of ribonuclease, not to mention many biologically active peptides.

The studies of alcohol dehydrogenase have many important technical aspects for enzymologists, particularly with respect to the study of pyridine nucleotide-linked enzymes. But the study of kinetics, abstract as it may seem, nevertheless led to the development of a very sensitive and virtually specific method for the determination of ethyl alcohol, as in blood samples. This method is now recognized in forensic practice in Sweden and West Germany, and is being considered by other governments.

1 9 5 6

ANDRÉ FRÉDÉRIC COURNAND

(1895–)

WERNER FORSSMANN

(1904–)

DICKINSON WOODRUFF RICHARDS

(1895–)

"For their discoveries concerning heart catheterization and pathological changes in the circulatory system."

BIOGRAPHICAL SKETCHES

COURNAND

ANDRÉ FRÉDÉRIC COURNAND WAS BORN ON SEPTEMBER 24, 1895, in Paris. He studied at the Sorbonne for his undergraduate training in the humanities and science. His medical studies, begun in 1913, were interrupted by the First World War and were completed in 1925 in Paris. He was awarded the M.D. degree in

1930, with a thesis on acute disseminated sclerosis. On coming to Bellevue Hospital in New York City for further training, he was offered the opportunity to carry on research on respiratory physiology under D. W. Richards. He decided to follow this course, and remained in the United States, becoming a citizen in 1941. His university association has been with Columbia, where he became professor of medicine in 1951.

FORSSMANN

WERNER FORSSMANN WAS BORN ON AUGUST 29, 1904, IN BERlin. He was graduated from the Askanic Gymnasium in 1922 and began his medical studies, which were completed in 1928. In 1929 when he was registrar in the surgical department of the Augusta-Viktoria Hospital in Eberswalde, to the north of Berlin, he began his experiments on cardiac catheterization, described below. He had postgraduate training in Berlin and Mainz in urology, and began his professional career in Dresden. During the Second World War he served as a health officer in the German Army, until taken prisoner on the western front. When he was released at the end of 1945 he entered into urological practice, together with his wife, who was similarly trained. In 1950 he settled in Bad Kreuznach. He received the Leibniz Medal of the German Academy of Science in 1954, and was made an Honorary Professor of Surgery and Urology at the Johannes Gutenberg University in Mainz. In 1958 he became chief of the Surgical Clinic at the Düsseldorf Evangelical Hospital.

RICHARDS

DICKINSON WOODRUFF RICHARDS WAS BORN ON OCTOBER 30, 1895, in Orange, New Jersey. His early schooling was taken in that state and in Connecticut. At Yale University he took a degree in languages, receiving the A.B. shortly after leaving to join the United States Army in 1917. After the War, he studied medicine and physiology at Columbia (M.A., 1922; M.D., 1923). He interned for four years in New York City at Presbyterian Hospital, and then went to England for a year where he worked with Sir Henry

Dale at the National Institute for Medical Research. Back in New York he entered the field of research for which he was to share the Nobel Prize: the physiology of the heart and lungs, and their circulatory supply. He began his work with Dr. André Cournand in 1931. During the Second World War they studied traumatic shock in man, and since then have devoted themselves to a large number of fundamental and clinical problems of cardiac and pulmonary diseases. Richards was Lambert Professor of Medicine in Columbia University from 1947 to 1961.

DESCRIPTION OF THE PRIZE-WINNING WORK*

FORSSMANN**

"In emergency conditions which menace patients by interruption of cardiac activity, such as in acute collapse in cardiac patients or in anesthetic episodes and poisoning, one is forced to undertake a rapid local drug treatment. In such cases, the sole remedy is often an attempt at intracardiac injection which then occasionally can be life-saving. Nevertheless, intracardiac injection always remains a dangerous measure on account of the numerous cases in which death occurs by damage to the coronary vessels and their branches, and therewith by hemorrhage into the pericardial sac and by cardiac tamponade [i.e. the accumulation of fluid, causing pressure, in the sac enclosing the heart]. Furthermore, damage to the pleura can also lead to a fatal pneumothorax. . . . These considerations have led me to seek a new way whereby one can penetrate into the heart without danger, and so I have investigated the probing of the right heart, approaching it from the venous system. . . .

---

* The three laureates were named by the Prize Committee in alphabetic order. On December 11, 1956, Forssmann presented his lecture first; he was followed by Richards and then Cournand. For historical and narrative reasons the work is presented here in the order: Forssmann, Cournand, Richards.
** The major quotation is translated from Werner Forssmann, "Die Sondierung des rechten Herzens," Klinische Wochenschrift, Vol. 8 (1929), pp. 2085-2087. The second one is translated from W. Forssmann, "Die Rolle der Herzkatheterung und Angiocardiagraphie in der Entwicklung der modernen Medizin," Les Prix Nobel en 1956.

"These reflections have been verified by investigations on cadavers. I have probed from an arbitrarily selected vein of the
elbow towards the heart, and by means of a very gentle sliding
process, without meeting resistance, have reached into the right
heart chamber where the probe was offered its first resistance.
The position of the sound [i.e. the probe] was afterwards established by dissection. . . .

"After the success of the experiments on cadavers, I undertook the first investigation in living humans through self-experi-
mentation. First of all, in a preliminary experiment I allowed
myself to be punctured in the right elbow vein using a large-bore
needle. One of my [surgical] colleagues kindly placed himself at
my disposal for this purpose. I then introduced, as in the experiments on cadavers, a well-oiled ureteral catheter through the
cannula into the vein. The catheter was then easily introduced for
a distance of 35 cm. of height. Because further catheterisation appeared to my colleague to be risky, we interrupted the experiment,
although I felt completely well. After one week I undertook alone
a further experiment. Because venipuncture with a thick needle
in oneself appeared technically too difficult, I made a venesection
after local anesthesia in my left elbow and introduced the catheter
without resistance for its whole length, 65 cm. This distance appeared to correspond to the path from the left elbow as far as
the heart. During the introduction of the catheter, I had the feeling of gentle warmth only during the sliding along the wall of
the vein, similar to the feeling during an intravenous injection
of calcium chloride. By intermittent movement the catheter beat
against the upper and rear wall of the clavicular vein, I noticed
an especially intense heat behind the collarbone under the insertion of the muscles of rotation of the head; at the same time,
probably through irritation of vagal branches, there was a gentle
cough.

"The position of the catheter was proven by x-ray and indeed
I observed the tip of the catheter itself in a mirror held in front
of the illuminated screen by a nurse. . . .

". . . The trip from operating room to x-ray department, which
is an unusually long distance in our establishment and during
which I had to ascend stairs, covering the distance on foot with

the probe lying in the heart, was not associated with unpleasantness. The introduction and removal of the catheter was completely painless, only being associated with the above described sensations. Later on I could not establish anything detrimental to myself apart from a mild phlebitis at the site of venesection; this occurred apparently because of an imperfect asepsis at the site of operation. I consider that injury to the wall of the vein, carrying with it a danger of coagulation or of thrombosis, is excluded by the gentle, easy mobility of the well-oiled probe. There is certainly a sufficient number of known cases, especially from the war and post-war literature in which a month-long stay of foreign bodies in the heart produced no disturbance. . . . Further, the blood pressure measurements undertaken by Chauveau and Marey as early as 1861 are known; these measurements were made in animals with introduction of the manometer into the heart from the jugular vein and carotid artery. *The entire work demonstrates the safety of this type of intervention in the heart.* . . .

"The first occasion offered to me for clinical application was a case of generalized purulent peritoneal inflammation in connection with a perforating inflammation of the appendix.

"The patient was in an exceptionally bad condition and gave the picture of a severe general disturbance of the circulation—a very weak variable pulse, bluish spots on the limbs, difficult and superficial respiration, clouding of consciousness. At 9:30 A.M. a venesection in the right arm was undertaken and the catheter introduced. Resistance met with at approximately 30 cm. was easily overcome by raising of the arm, and the catheter was introduced further for 60 cm. An hour-long infusion of 1 litre of dextrose solution containing 0.002 suprarenin hydrochloride and 0.001 strophanthin was given, with a visible improvement showing inside of minutes. The pulse was slow and powerful, respiration and consciousness normal. After the infusion ¼ of a cc. of citrate solution was injected through the catheter and the mandrel was introduced. At 12:30 there occurred a very severe deterioration of the condition of the patient, whereupon I repeated the infusion without strophanthin. After some transient improvement death intervened at 3:10 P.M. Cardiac activity outlasted respiration by 6 minutes. I left the catheter in position and found, by dissection of the cadaver, that it reached as expected from the vena cephalica as far as the right auricle; thence it passed another 2 cm. into the lower vena cava. No change in the lining of the blood vessel or in the valves was detected, and no thrombosis formation; there was only some coagulum in the vessels exactly as in the other arm.

"The evidence shows that even a six and one-half hour-long stay of the catheter in a weakened organism evokes no disease changes in the major blood vessels and in the heart. . . .

"I recommend that the method worked out by me be checked, using where suitable, venipuncture and in difficult untoward episodes venesection. . . .

"I regard as advantageous the further use of the method for carrying out slow intravenous injections as, for example, in the administration of . . . contrast media, or also for infusions. . . .

"In conclusion I might point out that the method applied by me opens up numerous prospects for new possibilities in the investigation of metabolism and investigation of cardiac activity, which I am already pursuing."

* * *

"The further development of the method was inhibited not only by the lack of a technical hypothesis and lack of understanding that followed therefrom. In addition to [this], weighty ethical considerations were thrown into the balance. And if one considers with what difficulties people like Cournand and McMichael in 1941 and later had to put up with, one will perhaps understand what obstacles had stood in my way 12 years earlier.

"A decisive point for the further development of cardiology is the year 1941 in which Cournand and Ranges presented, as is known, their first investigations with the heart catheter as a clinical method of investigation."

COURNAND*

"Because [cardiac catheterization] is apparently the soundest method for obtaining mixed venous blood for respiratory gas deter-

---

* The first quotation is from A. Cournand and H. A. Ranges, "Catheterization of the right auricle in man," *Proceedings of the Society for Experimental Biology and Medicine*, Vol. 46 (1941), pp. 462 ff. The second is from Cournand, "Control of the pulmonary circulation in man with some remarks on methodology," *Les Prix Nobel en 1956.*

minations and because of the numerous problems of hemodynamics it might help to solve, a method of right heart catheterization was developed that attempts to overcome objections to former methods. The principle objections included the possibility of venous thrombosis and thrombophlebitis that might be associated with introduction of a foreign body in the blood stream, the formation of thrombi within the catheter, and the psychic effects accompanying the procedure with possible alterations in the cardiac output."

[The method is then described, and represents some improvements over Forssmann's procedure.]

"In our experience we have found no evidence of blood clotting on the smooth outside walls of the catheter. Nor have there been any thrombi seen at the holes of the catheter or within the catheter when it is flushed with saline after being withdrawn. We do not believe that the results are affected by any psychic disturbance. There is no pain involved in the operation, once the needle is in place in the arm vein. The pulse rate does not vary significantly before and during the procedure, and cardiac output determinations as measured by the ballistocardiograph before, during and after the procedure are quite constant."

* * *

"An important progress in technique was the development of a double lumen catheter through which simultaneous procedures in two contiguous heart chambers and large vessels could be recorded. The first two tracings of blood pressure pulses recorded simultaneously within the right ventricle and the pulmonary artery . . . served to illustrate a paper published in 1945 in collaboration with Henry Lauson and Richard Bloomfield, on the use and advantages of this newly designed double-lumen catheter. For me this tracing holds a unique place, since it is the first demonstration that the tip of a catheter was placed in the pulmonary artery of man in order to record pressure pulses. Subsequent progress in our knowledge of the dynamics of the pulmonary circulation in man owes much to the technique of catheterization of the pulmonary artery. The part played by Lewis Dexter and his associates in this latter technical development deserves special mention.

". . . Considerable attention was also required for proper operation of the Hamilton manometer. . . . Although [it] was subsequently replaced by a strain gauge in association with electronic recorders, it is well to recall that most of our early knowledge of pressure pulses was obtained by using this device.

"An estimation of the pressure drop across the entire pulmonary vascular system has been of particular concern to physiologists interested in the dynamics of the pulmonary circulation. Catheterization of the pulmonary artery supplied the necessary data, concerning pressures at the origin of the system; but the pressure at the end of the system, that is, in the left atrium . . . could not be accurately determined. A first step in the proper direction was made when pressures were recorded from the left atrium and large pulmonary veins in human subjects under the abnormal conditions provided by interatrial septal defects [i.e., a hole in the heart wall separating the two auricles, thus permitting some flow of blood from one side to the other. This work was published by Cournand and his colleagues in 1947].

"To summarize our present knowledge, it can be said that we have acquired some understanding of the relations between pressure and flow in the pulmonary vessels of normal man. We know also that these relations can be influenced by mechanical factors and by at least two chemical stimuli—hypoxia [oxygen insufficiency] and acetylcholine. However, the mechanism of action of these stimuli is but poorly understood. And, when we come to fit them into an integrated concept of the control of the pulmonary circulation, we are troubled by several doubts. The first doubt is, how far such unphysiological concentrations of inspired oxygen and doses of acetylcholine throw any light on what happens under normal circumstances. The second is how to extrapolate into indefinite time the results from very short-term observations. The final doubt is whether these notions may be justifiably extended to the solution of physiopathological problems, when the physical properties of pulmonary vessels, and of the surrounding pulmonary tissue have been greatly altered."

RICHARDS*

". . . Dr. Cournand and I . . . began our work in 1931. . . . There was nothing original in our approach. We simply tried, as others had done before, to establish gaseous equilibrium between lungs and inflowing blood by rebreathing procedures, and to do this especially in patients with chronic pulmonary disease. . . . By the late nineteen-thirties, we were able to describe ventilatory functions of the lungs, and with pulmonary measurements supplemented by arterial blood studies, in rest and exercise, define to some extent the mixing and the diffusional aspects of pulmonary alveolar or alveolar-capillary functions. But we still could not measure blood flow through the lungs, and could not therefore move into those broader concepts of cardiopulmonary function which now began to be our goal.

"We were aware of the earlier experiment of Forssmann and had followed closely its isolated uses in Germany, Portugal, South America and France. . . . Late in 1940, Cournand and Ranges took up the catheterization technique, showing in their initial studies that consistent values for blood gases could be obtained from the right atrium, that with this, cardiac output could be reliably and fairly accurately determined by the Fick principle, and furthermore that the catheter could be left in place for considerable periods without harm. Not long after, through the interest of Homer Smith [Professor Emeritus of Physiology, New York University College of Medicine], and the assistance of Bradley, pressure recordings by a Hamilton manometer were added to the other techniques. Blood volumes by Gregersen's method were also included.

". . . Therefore, after ten years of work [i.e. 1931-1941], we had assembled a fairly comprehensive group of methods for the analysis of cardiopulmonary function, methods which could be applied not only to normal man but to patients even in the most severe and acute stages of decompensation.

---

* From D. W. Richards, "The contributions of right heart catheterization to physiology and medicine, with some observations on the physiopathology of pulmonary heart disease," *Les Prix Nobel en 1956.*

"The stage was now set for study of cardiac and pulmonary functions in many forms of clinical disease.

"First to be undertaken was an investigation of traumatic shock in man. The United States was by this time at war, and further information on the hemodynamics of shock, quantitative measurements of this, and of the effects of treatment, were urgently needed. These studies proceeded quite rapidly. It was demonstrated: that with a deficit of 40 to 50 per cent in blood volume, there was critical depressions in cardiac output and in return of blood to the right heart, worsening as shock continued unrelieved; that peripheral resistance tended to be maintained in hemorrhage and skeletal trauma, and greatly increased in severe burns; that an important corollary of this was reduced peripheral blood flow, demonstrated particularly in the case of the kidneys; that whole blood offered great advantages over plasma as sustaining therapy. Other forms of treatment were evaluated. Vasomotor factors, problems of so-called irreversible shock were approached but not solved. In certain cases of severe burn, the catheter was left in place for more than 24 hours, to provide a means of intravenous treatment, with no harm resulting, a further indication of the safety of the procedure.

"The application of cardiac catheterization to the diagnosis of congenital heart lesions was an obvious one, and a number of investigators became interested and pursued this inquiry with great skill. . . . The great advance represented by the surgery of congenital heart disease, under such men as Gross [in 1939 R. E. Gross and J. P. Hubbard reported the first successful case of surgical closing of a patent ductus arteriosus], Blalock [who pioneered, with Helen B. Taussig, in the surgical correction of malformations of the heart], Crafoord, and Brock [the last two having introduced operations for the relief of congenital narrowing of the aorta and pulmonary artery, respectively], was under way before cardiac catheterization, and has moved fundamentally on its own. The cardiac catheter has been, however, a primary aid. Sharing with angiocardiography the ability to define the anatomical lesions, the catheter also quantitates the volumes and pressures of abnormal flow, thus defining for the surgeon both the nature and extent of the disorder. By repeated catheterization can be determined postoperatively the degree to which a normal circulation has been restored.

"An important contribution . . . was the analysis of the action of digitalis glycosides, by Ferrer and Harvey in our laboratory, also by McMichael and Sharpey-Schäfer, by Bloomfield, and others. It was established that digitalis acts favorably only upon ventricles overdilated, with excessive filling pressures and inadequate emptying; that in such hearts it acts rapidly to increase the energy of contraction, increase stroke volume, and promote adequate emptying, thus relieving the congestive state; that it performs with regular as well as irregular cardiac rhythms."

CONSEQUENCES IN THEORY AND PRACTICE

Forssmann's paper describing his "probing of the heart" was published in 1929. In this article he suggested the catheter technique as a means of administering drugs directly into the heart, without having to pass through the chest wall, pericardium, and heart muscle. He also recommended the method for the administration of contrast media in the visualization of the gall bladder and kidney by x-ray. Many years before Fritz Bleichroeder, the medical director of a hospital for women in Berlin, had inserted catheters into the veins and arteries of animals and man without ill effects. Although he published a description of his experiments in 1912, he did not demonstrate penetration of the heart chambers by the catheter, nor did he clearly realize the significance of his technical achievement. He certainly must be credited with being the first to insert a catheter into the blood vessels of man, but Forssmann pioneered a new era in studies of cardiac function.

Forssmann's method was subsequently used, with success, in Czechoslovakia, Portugal, and elsewhere, but was generally considered somewhat dangerous. Other factors hindering the application of Forssmann's finding have been suggested: the contrast media available at that time were not themselves entirely nontoxic, and the radiological techniques being used were unable to take advantage of the possibilities that cardiac catheterization offered. Perhaps Forssmann's youth—he was twenty-five at the time, and training in surgery—and his isolation from an academic research environment detracted from a proper appreciation of his findings. The awarding of a share of the Prize to Forssmann, whose work had been done so long before, was provided for by a rule that had at one time been inserted in the Nobel Prize Statutes, permitting the award to be made "for older works only if their significance has not become apparent until recently."

A decade after Forssmann, Cournand and Richards introduced his technique into their research on the physiology of the heart and lungs, and from then on they and their colleagues demonstrated its usefulness in one brilliant study after another. It was used to elucidate the changes taking place in the circulatory system in shock due to blood loss and burns. It was an aid in the assessment of the results of cardiac surgery in patients with congenital heart defects, and more recently in those with "acquired defects" involving the valves of the heart (e.g. mitral stenosis). It was used to study heart failure and the actions of the important drug digitalis in that condition. It has made possible exact analysis of the functions of the pulmonary circulation, especially the relations between blood pressure and flow in the vessels serving the lungs of normal man. The study of chronic pulmonary diseases (e.g. emphysema), often progressing to involve the heart secondarily, has also profited; these diseases are becoming of greater importance in medicine today because patients suffering from them live longer, protected when necessary by antibiotics and other anti-infective agents, and otherwise aided by symptomatic treatments.

Finally, the technique of organ catheterization has been used successfully in exploring the hepatic renal veins. Forssmann's suggestion that his probe might prove useful in the investigation of metabolism was brought to fruition by Bing, who catheterized a coronary vein [the coronary vessels serve the heart muscle itself] and was thereby able to study the metabolism of the cardiac tissue.

REFERENCE

Benatt, A. J. "Cardiac catheterisation, a historical note," *The Lancet,* Vol. 1 (1949), pp. 746-747.

1 9 5 7
DANIEL BOVET
(1907–   )

"For his discoveries relating to synthetic compounds that inhibit the action of certain body substances, and especially their action on the vascular system and the skeletal muscles."

BIOGRAPHICAL SKETCH

DANIEL BOVET WAS BORN AT NEUCHÂTEL, SWITZERLAND, ON March 23, 1907. His father was professor of pedagogy at the University of Geneva. He had his secondary schooling in Geneva, going on to the University there until 1929, when he was graduated with the D.Sc. degree. During his university studies he assisted F. Battelli in the Department of Physiology and E. Guyenot, professor of zoology and anatomy. In 1929 he went to the Pasteur Institute in Paris to work in the Department of Chemical Therapeutics, under Ernest Fourneau. During this period he married Philomena Nitti, who has been his collaborator in many researches. In 1947 he was invited to establish a Laboratory of Chemotherapeutics at the Superior Institute of Health in Rome, a task that he and his wife undertook. Bovet's division combines laboratories for chemical synthesis of potential new drugs and pharmacological laboratories for testing these substances. The Bovets have published an extensive monograph on chemical structure of drugs related to their pharmacodynamic activity on the vegetative nervous system (1948).

DESCRIPTION OF THE PRIZE-WINNING WORK*

"Taking advantage of the vast possibilities offered by synthetic organic chemistry numerous scientists have directed their efforts towards the domain of applied therapeutics, and have sought to establish the basic principles of a pharmaceutical chemistry or, more exactly perhaps, a chemical pharmacology worthy of the name. Even if so ambitious a program has not yet been fully realized one may nevertheless recognize in studies carried on over the last fifty years the appearance of some guiding principles. . . . for example, the concepts of isosterism [literally, *equivalent shape* of molecules] and of competition.

"Although the antimetabolite concept [a metabolite is a simple bodily substance, such as an amino acid, vitamin, hormone or chemical mediator undergoing metabolism or influencing the metabolism of other materials] stems from experiments that are now old, it is chiefly in the realm of the 'antivitamins' that it has been stated precisely; the researches of Woods (1940) and of Fildes (1940) on the component of yeast that antagonizes the action of sulfanilamide and its identification with para-aminobenzoic acid have had vast repercussions. The concept, according to which a product whose properties approximate those of a normal constituent of the organism is liable to modify the functions normally exercised by this metabolite, has been shown to have a number of applications. The success that it has encountered, particularly in enzymology—where it was first clearly formulated by [J. H.]

---

* Translated from Daniel Bovet, "Rélations d'isostérie et phénomènes compétitifs dans le domaine des médicaments du système nerveux végétatif et dans celui de la transmission neuromusculaire," *Les Prix Nobel en 1957*.

Quastel (1925-1928)—in chemotherapy, vitaminology and endocrinology relieves me of enlarging upon the physicochemical and biological bases upon which the idea of competition rests today. On the contrary, I wish to draw your attention to the importance that the study of competitive phenomena provides in pharmacodynamics, especially in the field of drugs acting on the vegetative [autonomic] nervous system [see page 197]. Such a study will show an extensive branch of therapeutic chemistry linking many alkaloids and synthetic products to certain hormones, chemical mediators, and products of tissue metabolism possessing quite simple chemical structures: adrenaline and noradrenaline, acetylcholine, histamine, and 5-hydroxytryptamine."

[Bovet's first examples are taken from the series of adrenaline-like substances.]

"Sympatholytic agents constitute a group of substances characterized by common pharmacological properties. They act, considered as 'competitive agents' or else as 'blocking agents' . . . by opposing the effects of adrenaline and noradrenaline, so that their most characteristic property consists in the fact that they prevent the hypertension [elevated blood pressure] and vasoconstriction [narrowing of the caliber of blood vessels] brought about by adrenaline.

"The studies carried out at the Superior Institute of Health by Marini-Bettolo and Chiavarelli on the chemical aspect, and by my wife, Longo, Marotta and Guarino on the pharmacological, illustrate how the concepts of isosterism and competition help in investigations of this type.

"If one considers the [lysergic acid moiety] of the ergot alkaloids, its structure at first sight seems to be very different from that of adrenaline or sympathomimetic derivatives of the phenylethylamine series. However, having recognized the existence of the skeleton of β-tetrahydronaphthylamine [a powerful vasodilator substance] in the lysergic acid molecule, we decided to take up the study of substances of this group.

"The pharmacological tests carried out with relatively simple derivatives demonstrated the sympatholytic activity of β-tetrahydronaphthyldiethylamine (843 I.S.S.). . . . Through a series of

a) Adrenaline (epinephrine). b) Amphetamine. c) Tetrahydronaphthylamine.
d) 843 I.S. (N-diethyl-tetrahydronaphthylamine). e) Lysergic acid amide
(R′ = R″ = H) and its derivatives. E.g., for LSD, R′ = R″ = C₂H₅.

molecules of increasing complexity, one passes successively from phenylethylamine to tetrahydronaphthylamine, or to 916 I.S.S. and the alkaloids of ergot; at each one of these steps there is a progressive diminution in sympathomimetic properties and the appearance of sympatholytic properties [i.e. the properties to be expected of substances opposing the action of the sympathetic nerves or of noradrenaline. Some of the structures mentioned are shown in the figure on p. 345].

"The study of synthetic curares furnishes us . . . with a succession of examples comparable to those that we have already reviewed in the sympatholytic series. These researches began in 1946. [It will be recalled that] in 1935 [H.] King had elucidated the structure of one of the physiologically active constituents of Amazonian curares [d-tubocurarine], and that in 1942 [H. R.] Griffith and [G. E.] Johnson had introduced the chemically pure alkaloid as an anesthetic adjuvant.

"The research conducted with my colleagues Viaud, Horclois and de Lestrange was initially directed towards molecules chemically similar [to tubocurarine]; but by successive transformations we synthesized relatively simple derivatives endowed with analogous properties. From a series of derivatives of a new type, whose molecule possesses two quinolinic nuclei with quaternary ammonium function, we have selected the di-iodoethylate of 8', 8''-diquinoleyloxy-1,5-pentane (3381 R. P.); this compound represents the first synthetic substance whose curare-like action is manifested on mammals with a specificity comparable to that of the natural alkaloids. [This compound was described in 1946 and was followed in the next year by a new synthetic agent, gallamine (Flaxedil).]

"In England Barlow and Ing, and Paton and Zaimis (1948) brought forward extremely interesting data concerning the curarizing action of decamethylene-ω-bis-trimethylammonium hydrate (decamethonium). In our laboratory . . . the curare-like action of succinylcholine, synthesized originally by R. Hunt in 1911, was recognized for the first time. . . . The introduction of short-acting curares, in particular succinylcholine, constitutes an important advance. The relative ease with which succinylcholine is hydrolyzed by pseudocholinesterases [enzymes found in serum and various tissues], and the very low toxicity of choline and succinic acid which are formed, explains the brevity of the curarizing action and the remarkable tolerance of the organism to this compound. . . .

". . . Today we recognize two types of application of succinylcholine: its use as a single injection in conditions requiring an especially short action (endoscopy, electroshock), and its use as a continuous intravenous infusion in surgical operations of a longer duration. . . .

"The last of the examples with which I shall illustrate the concept of competition concerns substances antagonistic to a third local hormone, histamine. This is a particularly rich chapter, because therapeutic interest in these substances has given rise to numerous and varied researches in the course of only a few years. In 1937 in E. Fourneau's laboratory and with the collaboration of Miss [A. M.] Staub . . . we began research on substances that exert an antagonism to histamine comparable to that manifested by the sympatholytic drugs against adrenaline, or the parasympatholytics against acetylcholine. The first positive result, the antagonism of thymoxyethyl diethylamine (929F) toward histamine, dates from 1939. [These observations were extended to derivatives of phenylethylenediamine, and then to dimethylaminoethylbenzylaniline, or Antergan.] . . . The role of histamine in numerous allergic emergencies ought to guarantee to the products of this group a vast field of clinical applications. . . .

"From the pharmacological point of view we have been able to ascertain the existence of three groups of antihistaminic substances which can be associated 1) with the sympatholytic agents, 2) with both the parasympatholytics and sympatholytics, and 3) with histamine itself.

"In the first group belong the phenolic ethers (929F) and the derivatives of phenylethylenediamine (157F) studied at the Pasteur Institute; antergan, studied by Halpern [1942]; and antazoline, studied by Meier and Bucher [1946]. The substances of the second group, much more homogeneous from the chemical point of view, possess the structure common to spasmolytics and to atropine-like substances, and are effectively spasmolytic as well as antihistaminic (diphenhydramine, Loew [1945]). In the derivatives of α-aminopyridine which constitute the third group, the antihistaminic action has a high degree of specificity, lacking secondary effects. . . . Products of this group are represented by pyrilamine, but numerous other syntheses achieved along this route have equally resulted in products endowed with activity. . . .

"To conclude, if we were to return rapidly to the point from which we started, we would see that in travelling through the vast domain of pharmacology we have been led by a small group of biogenic amines of remarkably simple structure and these, like Ariadne's thread, have prevented us from losing our way in the labyrinth of physiological action and chemical constitution."

CONSEQUENCES IN THEORY
AND PRACTICE

Certain biogenic amines like adrenaline, noradrenaline, dopamine, acetylcholine, 5-hydroxytryptamine (serotonin), and histamine are known or are presumed to be involved in various diseases: the first two in hypertension and some vascular disorders, histamine in allergic conditions (asthma, hay fever, urticaria), acetylcholine and dopamine in Parkinson's disease, and 5-hydroxytryptamine in malignant carcinoid, a rare intestinal tumor. The problem has been to find drugs that antagonize the actions of these bodily substances and others that mimic their actions. Such drugs will perhaps be effective clinically. As Bovet points out, the antimetabolite hypothesis, stemming in the first instance from studies in vitamin science, was of inestimable help to him and his colleagues in designing new drugs acting upon the autonomic nervous system. This concept asserts that a substance whose chemical properties and molecular shape resemble those of a normal metabolite may modify the functions of that metabolite. The relationship has been likened to that of a lock (a metabolic reaction) and a specific key (the metabolite) which readily opens it; whereas, another key, notched in a slightly different fashion (the antimetabolite), will prevent insertion of the true key and may even jam the lock. The hypothesis in its present form dates from studies of the antagonism of sulfanilamide by para-aminobenzoic acid, but it has its antecedents in the chemotherapeutic concepts of Ehrlich (page 56), as well as the biochemical views of Emil Fischer (Nobel Laureate in Chemistry, 1902) and J. H. Quastel.

The modern search for synthetic autonomic drugs, as against those occurring naturally,' began in the laboratory of Bovet's teacher, Ernest Fourneau; this great chemist contributed to knowledge of many new classes of organic compound, and his name is memorialized in the "F" attached to the laboratory code-numbers of numerous compounds, such as the sympatholytic agent 929F. Today, research into the chemistry and pharmacology of drugs acting on the autonomic nervous system occupies the attention of a very large number of scientists. Bovet states, for example, that "after the initial group including Maderni, de Lestrange and Benoit in Fourneau's laboratory in Paris, Viaud, Horclois, Mossnier and Charpentier in French industry, Hartman and Hofman in Switzerland, Rieveschl, Scholtz, Huttrer and Roblin in the U. S. A., and Cavalini in Italy, approximately 500 chemists have accomplished in less than ten years about 5000 syntheses in the field of antihistaminics"! Production of these drugs represents an important sector of the pharmaceutical industry today.

Bovet's work deals essentially with the problem of the relation of chemical structure to biological activity, but with special reference to substances acting at autonomic structures. Two of these "action substances" are known to be concerned with transmission of the impulse generated in certain nerves: acetylcholine (page 191 ff.) and noradrenaline. Substances antagonizing the effects of these chemical mediators in pharmacological tests may prove useful clinically as "blocking agents." Thus, curare blocks the action of acetylcholine at the junction of the nerve fiber with the voluntary muscle that it ordinarily causes to contract. Synthetic curares, like succinylcholine, do the same and are an aid in surgery, producing deep relaxation of the voluntary muscles. Other naturally-occurring blocking agents are atropine, found in belladonna, and the alkaloids of ergot, a fungus that grows on rye and whose consumption (in bread made from the infected grain) led during the

Middle Ages to periodic mass poisonings (St. Anthony's fire). Atropine antagonizes the action of acetylcholine, and is used in the treatment of "colic" (intestinal spasm) as well as in ophthalmology for dilatation of the pupil; it is the "model" for other synthetic spasmolytic drugs. Ergot alkaloids interfere with the action of adrenaline, noradrenaline, and 5-hydroxytryptamine. Some of them have found a place in therapeutics, e.g. in obstetrics as uterine stimulants, and in the prevention of migraine headaches. No natural alkaloids antagonizing histamine are known, although certain steroid hormones can alleviate its actions; these are, however, not isosteres.

Bovet and his collaborators played a signal role in relieving us of our dependence upon nature for therapeutic agents effectively opposing a number of biogenic amines. Many other investigators have followed in the search for antimetabolites or blocking agents that will be useful in the treatment of high blood pressure and other vascular and cardiac disorders, atherosclerosis, cancer, and nervous and mental diseases. An especially productive series of compounds in this respect have been the phenothiazine derivatives. At first, these were synthesized for testing as antihistaminic agents, and this resulted in the selection of promethazine for this purpose. Others were then found to be effective in the treatment of Parkinson's disease (diethazine) and of mental disturbances including anxiety states and schizophrenia (chlorpromazine, promazine, trifluoperazine, and others).

Certain biogenic amines have also been found within the brain. This has brought many suggestions as to specific roles that these substances may play in the working of the central nervous system, although it must be kept in mind that to the present time only acetylcholine has been shown to act as a true mediator of nervous transmission in the brain. A most interesting contribution in this sphere was the accidental finding by A. Stoll in 1943 that the diethylamide of lysergic acid (LSD), a partially synthesized ergot alkaloid, has a pronounced hallucination-producing action when taken in very minute amounts. If it acts by antagonizing some important brain chemicals, then it should be possible 'eventually to identify these substances and to provide them in one way or another to persons suffering from "natural" hallucinations, as in schizophrenia. Interest in LSD in psychiatry has remained high also because of some claimed benefits from its use in addictions. Certain other hallucinogenic agents bear a close chemical resemblance to important biogenic amines found in the brain: mescaline (trimethoxyphenylethylamine) to dopamine (hydroxytyramine) and noradrenaline; and bufotenine and psilocybin to 5-hydroxytryptamine.

1 9 5 8
GEORGE WELLS BEADLE

(1903–   )

EDWARD LAWRIE TATUM

(1909–   )

"For the discovery that genes regulate certain definite chemical processes."

(The award for 1958 was shared with J. Lederberg; see below, pp.362-368.)

BIOGRAPHICAL SKETCHES

BEADLE

GEORGE WELLS BEADLE WAS BORN IN OCTOBER, 1903, IN WA-hoo, Nebraska. His schooling, up to the M.S. degree (1927), was in that state. His Ph.D. research was carried out at Cornell University, in the field of genetics. From 1931 to 1936 he conducted research at the California Institute of Technology in the same subject, with T. Dobzhansky, A. H. Sturtevant, and S. Emerson; and in 1935 he worked with B. Ephrussi at l'Institut de Biologie Physico-Chimique in Paris, on the eye pigments of the fruit fly. Beadle has pursued a career in university teaching and research at Harvard (1936-1937), Stanford (1937-1946), where he and Tatum worked together, and the California Institute of Technology (1946-1961). Since 1961 he has been president of the University of Chicago.

TATUM

EDWARD LAWRIE TATUM WAS BORN ON DECEMBER 14, 1909, AT Boulder, Colorado. His university training began at the University of Chicago, but most of it was taken at the University of Wisconsin, where his father headed the Department of Pharmacology. His undergraduate work was in chemistry, but his graduate studies, directed by E. B. Fred and W. H. Peterson, were in microbiology and biochemistry. He received the Ph.D. degree from the University of Wisconsin in 1932. After further study there and in Utrecht, Holland, Tatum taught and conducted research at Stanford University, except for a three-year interlude at Yale University. In 1957 he left his position as professor of biology at Stanford to become a member and professor at the Rockefeller Institute in New York City.

DESCRIPTION OF THE PRIZE-WINNING WORK

BEADLE*

"One line of investigation that was destined to reveal much about what genes do was started by Wheldale (later Onslow) in 1903. It began with a genetic study of flower pigmentation in snapdragons. But soon the genetic observations began to be correlated with the chemistry of the anthocyanin and related pigments that were responsible [for flower color].

"It became clear very soon that a number of genes were involved and that they acted by somehow controlling the onset of various identifiable and specific chemical reactions. Since an understanding of the genetics helped in interpreting the chemistry and *vice versa,* the anthocyanin work was well known to both geneticists and biochemists. It significantly influenced the thinking in both fields and thus had great importance in further developments.

"A second important line of investigation was begun even earlier

---

* From G. W. Beadle, "Genes and chemical reactions in Neurospora," *Les Prix Nobel en 1958.*

by the Oxford physician-biochemist Sir Archibald E. Garrod. At the turn of the century he was interested in a group of congenital metabolic diseases in man, which he later named, 'inborn errors of metabolism.' There are now many diseases described as such; in fact, they have come to be recognized as a category of diseases of major medical importance.

"One of the first inborn errors to be studied by Garrod was alcaptonuria, [a condition in which homogentisic acid, a normal product of the metabolism of tyrosine, appears in the urine, although it is normally not detectable there].

". . . It was his belief that alcaptonuria was the result of inability of affected individuals to cleave the ring of homogentisic acid as do normal individuals. He believed this to be due to absence or inactivity of the enzyme that normally catalyzes this reaction. This in turn was dependent on the absence of the normal form of a specific gene.

"Thus Garrod had clearly in mind the concept of a gene-enzyme-chemical reaction system in which all three entities were interrelated in a very specific way.

"I shall now shift to a consideration of an independent line of investigation that ended up with conclusions very much like those of Garrod and which led directly to the work with Neurospora that Tatum and I subsequently began.

"In 1933, Boris Ephrussi came to the California Institute of Technology to work on developmental aspects of genetics. During his stay he and I had many long discussions in which we deplored the lack of information about the manner in which genes act on development.

"It would be worthwhile, we believed, to attempt to remedy this situation by finding new ways experimentally to study *Drosophila melanogaster* [the fruit fly so intensively studied by T. H. Morgan]—which, genetically, was the best understood organism of the time.

"We first investigated the sex-linked eye-color mutant vermilion [cf. page 170] because of the earlier finding of Sturtevant that, in gynandromorphs [organisms of mixed sex], genetically vermilion eye tissue often fails to follow the general rule of autonomy [in this case, to develop the vermilion eye pigment].

"Gynandromorphs may result if, in an embryo that begins development as a female from an egg with two X chromosomes, one X chromosome is lost during an early cleavage, giving rise to a sector that has one X chromosome and is male. If the original egg is heterozygous for a sex-linked gene [i.e. bears a pair of contrasted genes], say vermilion, and the lost chromosome carries the normal allele, the male sector will be genetically vermilion, whereas the female parts are normal or wild type.

"Yet in Sturtevant's gynandromorphs in which only a small part of the body including eye tissue was vermilion, the appearance of that tissue was usually not vermilion but wild type—as though some substance had diffused from wild-type tissue to the eye and caused it to become normally pigmented.

"It was on the basis of this observation that Ephrussi and I transplanted vermilion eyes into wild type larvae. The result was as expected—the transplanted eyes were indeed wild type.

"We found only one other clear-cut non-autonomous eye character. This was cinnabar, a bright red color, like vermilion but differentiated by a second chromosome recessive gene.

"[The next experiments dealt with reciprocal transplants between the two mutants. The results were very puzzling because] a cinnabar eye in a vermilion host remained cinnabar, but a vermilion eye in a cinnabar host became wild type.

"To explain this result we formulated the hypothesis that there must be two diffusible substances involved, one formed from the other according to the scheme: $\rightarrow$ Precursor $\rightarrow v^+$ substance $\rightarrow cn^+$ substance $\rightarrow$ Pigment . . . where v^+ substance is a diffusible material capable of making a vermilion eye become wild type and cn^+ substance is capable of doing the same to a cinnabar eye. [The enzymes catalyzing these reactions would be under the control of genes.]

"What was later called the one gene-one enzyme concept was clearly in our minds at this time although as I remember, we did not so designate it."

[The precursor and diffusible substances formed from it by enzymic action were later identified through the work of many different laboratories. The precursor is the common amino acid tryptophan; v^+ substance is kynurenine, another amino acid; and cn^+ substance is 3-hydroxykynurenine.]

"Isolating the eye-pigment precursors of Drosophila was a slow and discouraging job. Tatum and I realized that this was likely to be so in most cases of attempting to identify the chemical disturbances underlying inherited abnormalities; it would be no more than good fortune if any particular example chosen for investigation should prove to be simple chemically. Alcaptonuria was such a happy choice for Garrod, for the chemistry had been largely worked out and the homogentisic acid isolated and identified many years before.

"Our idea—to reverse the procedure and look for gene mutations that influence known chemical reactions was an obvious [and simple one]: Select an organism like a fungus that has simple nutritional requirements. This will mean it can carry out many reactions by which amino acids and vitamins are made. Induce mutations by radiation or other mutagenic agents. Allow meiosis [the process of 'reduction division' of the cell, that results in sex cells having only a single set of chromosomes] to take place so as to produce spores that are genetically homogeneous. Grow these on a medium supplemented with an array of vitamins and amino acids. Test them by negative transfer to a medium with no supplement. Those that have lost the ability to grow on the minimal medium will have lost the ability to synthesize one or more of the substances present in the supplemented medium. The growth requirements of the deficient strain would then be readily ascertained by a systematic series of tests on partially supplemented media.

"In addition to the above specifications, we wanted an organism well suited to genetic studies, preferably one on which the basic genetic work had already been done.

"Tatum and I realized that Neurospora [a bread mold] was genetically an almost ideal organism for use in our new approach.

"We prepared more than a thousand single spore cultures on supplemented medium before we tested them. The 299th spore isolated gave a mutant strain requiring vitamin B_6 [pyridoxine] and the 1085th one required [vitamin] B_1 [thiamine, or aneurine]. We made a vow to keep going until we had 10 mutants. We soon had dozens.

"Because of the ease of recovery of all the products of a single meiotic process in Neurospora, it was a simple matter to determine whether our newly induced nutritional deficiencies were the result of mutations in single genes. If they were, crosses with the original should yield four mutant and four non-mutant spores in each spore sac. They did."

TATUM*

"After completing graduate work at Wisconsin I was fortunate in being able to spend a year studying at the University of Utrecht with F. Kögl, the discoverer of the growth factor biotin, and to work in the same laboratory with Nils Fries, who already had contributed significantly in the field of nutrition and growth of fungi.

"At this time, Professor Beadle was just moving to Stanford University, and invited me as a biochemist to join him in the further study of the eye-color hormones of *Drosophila,* which he and Ephrussi in their work at the California Institute of Technology and at Paris had so brilliantly established as diffusible products of gene-controlled reactions. During this, my first contacts with modern genetic concepts, . . . we were able to isolate the v^+ hormone in crystalline state from a bacterial culture supplied with tryptophan, and with A. J. Haagen-Smit to identify it as kynurenine. . . . It might be pointed out here that kynurenine has since been recognized to occupy a central position in tryptophan metabolism in many organisms aside from insects, including mammals and fungi.

"At about this time . . . we began our work with the mold *Neurospora crassa.*

"Our use of *Neurospora* for chemical genetic studies would . . . have been much more difficult, if not impossible, without the availability of synthetic biotin as the result of the work of Kögl and of du Vigneaud [Nobel Prize in Chemistry, 1955]. In addi-

---

* From E. L. Tatum, "A case history in biological research," *Les Prix Nobel en 1958.*

tion, the investigations of Nils Fries on the nutrition of *Ascomy-cetes* [a sub-group of fungi] were most helpful, as shown by the fact that the synthetic minimal medium used with *Neurospora* for many years was that described by him and supplemented only with biotin, and has ordinarily since been referred to as 'Fries medium.' It should also be pointed out that the experimental feasibility of producing the desired nutritionally deficient mutant strains depended on the early pioneering work of Roentgen [Nobel Prize in Physics, 1901], with x-rays, and on that of H. J. Muller [page 247], on the mutagenic action of x-rays and ultraviolet light on *Drosophila.* All that was needed was to put these various facts and findings together to produce in the laboratory with irradiation, nutritionally deficient (auxotrophic) mutant strains of *Neurospora,* and to show that each single deficiency produced was associated with the mutation of a single gene.

". . . Let us review the basic concepts involved in this work. Essentially these are (1) that all biochemical processes in all organisms are under genic control, (2) that these overall biochemical processes are resolvable into a series of individual stepwise reactions, (3) that each single reaction is controlled in a primary fashion by a single gene, or in other terms, in every case a 1:1 correspondence of gene and biochemical reaction exists, such that (4) mutation of a single gene results only in an alteration in the ability of the cell to carry out a single primary chemical reaction. The underlying hypothesis, which in a number of cases has been supported by direct experimental evidence, is that each gene controls the production, function and specificity of a particular enzyme. Important experimental implications of these relations are that each and every biochemical reaction in a cell of any organism, from a bacterium to man, is theoretically alterable by gene mutation, and that each mutant cell strain differs in only one primary way from the non-mutant parental strain.

"If the postulated relationship of gene to enzyme is correct, several consequences can be predicted. First, mutation should result in the production of a changed protein, which might be enzymatically inactive, of intermediate activity, or have otherwise detectably altered physical properties. The production of such proteins changed in respect to heat stability, enzymatic activity, or other properties such as activation energy, by mutant strains has indeed been demonstrated in a number of instances.

"A second consequence of the postulated relationship stems from the concept that the genetic constitution defines the potentialities of the cell, the time and degree of expression of which are to a certain extent modifiable by the cellular environment. The analysis of this type of secondary control at the biochemical level is one of the important and exciting new areas of biochemistry. This deals with the regulation and integration of biochemical reactions by means of feed-back mechanisms restricting the synthesis or activities of enzymes and through substrate-induced biosynthesis of enzymes. It seems probable that some gene mutations may affect biochemical activities at this level (modifiers and suppressors) and that chemical mutants will prove of great value in the analysis of the details of such control mechanisms."

CONSEQUENCES IN THEORY AND PRACTICE

The "one gene-one enzyme" concept was the product of a gradual evolution beginning with Garrod, but with contributions from many geneticists and biochemists before reaching fruition in the beautifully conclusive demonstrations by Beadle, Tatum, and their colleagues. There were immediate benefits to the study of intermediary metabolism, particularly with respect to the formation and breakdown of amino acids, vitamins, purines, and pyrimidines. This stimulation came not only from the theoretical advances, but also from the new technique worked out first with *Drosophila* and *Neurospora,* and soon extended to the bacteria *Escherichia coli* and *Acetobacter* species. The first auxotrophic mutants were obtained by a tedious process: irradiated bacterial cells were plated out (see page 237) on fully supplemented medium; individual colonies on the agar plate were then isolated and grown in the minimal medium, satisfactory for the parent stock of organisms; cultures that did not grow then had to be systematically supplemented with known growth-factors, until the specific requirements of the particular mutant became evident. New techniques soon brought simplified procedures of isolating and testing mutants;

contributions to this end were made by J. Lederberg and his wife, B. D. Davis, E. A. Adelberg, J. W. Myers, and others. In one method penicillin is incorporated into the agar medium; the antibiotic kills growing organisms, so that the rapidly growing non-mutant strain is eliminated, and the mutants that remain can be grown after removal of the antibiotic and after making suitable additions to the medium. The "replica plating technique" consists of preparing a "negative" by pressing an agar plate, containing many colonies, against a piece of sterilized velvet; the velvet can then be used to transfer replicas of the original to other plates made up with different growth-factor supplements.

The concepts of biochemical genetics have further significance for general biology and medicine. Tatum (loc. cit.) points out that in microbiology ". . . mutation has proven of primary importance in the improvement of yields of important antibiotics—such as in the classic example of penicillin, the yield of which has gone up from around 40 units per ml. of culture shortly after its discovery by Fleming to approximately 4000, as the result of a long series of successive experimentally produced mutational steps. On the other side of the coin, the mutational origin of antibiotic-resistant microorganisms is of definite medical importance. The therapeutic use of massive doses of antibiotics to reduce the numbers of bacteria which, by mutation could develop resistance, is a direct consequence of the application of genetic concepts.

"We may cite the probable mutational origin of resistance to chemotherapeutic agents in leukemic cells, and the increasing and effective simultaneous use of two or more chemotherapeutic agents in the treatment of this disease. In this connection it should be pointed out that the most effective cancer chemotherapeutic agents so far found are those which interfere with DNA synthesis. . . ."

Many biologically important compounds are formed by a series of consecutive step-wise reactions in each of which the product serves as the starting material for the next. According to present-day thought, such compounds were formed by non-biological reactions in past eons that witnessed the beginnings of life. The earliest organisms would then have obtained these "finished products" directly from the environment. But by a series of single mutations, enzymes catalyzing individual steps in the synthesis of these products would arise in the organism; the first to appear would be the enzyme catalyzing the very last stage in formation of a product. Organisms that underwent such mutation would have the selective advantage of greater and greater independence from the environment and its ready-made "metabolites."

In 1908 Garrod described four genetic defects of metabolism that had been observed in man; among them were alcaptonuria and albinism, the absence of pigment from skin, hair, and eyes. Since then scores of other such defects have been described. One of them, phenylpyruvic oligophrenia, or phenylketonuria, was described by the Norwegian biochemist A. Følling (1934) in certain mentally defective children who excreted large amounts of phenylpyruvic acid, a product of incomplete metabolism of the amino acid phenylalanine. This was the first metabolic defect with which mental deficiency was associated. Phenylketonuria has been extensively studied as a metabolic disorder and now, through dietary means, it has been possible in some cases to prevent the appearance of mental deficiency.

With the recognition that chromosomes contain deoxyribonucleic acid as the material basis of the genetic code, the science of heredity has drawn closer to biochemistry. Genetics can no longer be accused of dealing solely with "superficial characteristics" and morphology of organisms, for it is now concerned with the basic chemistry and physics of the reproduction of life.

JOSHUA LEDERBERG
(1925–   )

*"For his discoveries concerning genetic recombination
and the organization of the genetic apparatus of
bacteria."*

*(The award for 1958 was shared with G. W. Beadle and E. L. Tatum;
see above, pp. 352-361.)*

BIOGRAPHICAL SKETCH

JOSHUA LEDERBERG WAS BORN ON MAY 23, 1925, IN MONT-
clair, New Jersey. He was educated in the public school system of
New York City and at Columbia College, from which he was
graduated in 1944 with the B.A. degree in zoology. He began
medical studies at the College of Physicians and Surgeons (Columbia University), but interrupted them to carry on research under
E. L. Tatum at Yale University. He received the Ph.D. degree
from Yale in 1948. Instead of returning to medical studies, Lederberg continued his genetic research at the University of Wisconsin
(1947-1958) where he ultimately established a department of
medical genetics, and subsequently at the Stanford University
Medical School where he organized the Department of Genetics
and became its first chairman. His wife is a scientist in the same
field.

DESCRIPTION OF THE PRIZE-WINNING
WORK*

"For many years bacteria were considered biologically exceptional organisms with no genes, nuclei, or sex, although the recognition of their biochemical similarities to other forms of life constituted one of the main foundations of comparative biochemistry. Over the last decade evidence has accumulated which has led to the satisfying conclusion that bacteria are not biologically unique but possess genetic and behavior systems more or less analogous to those of other forms, including nuclei, genes, and in certain instances even true sexual mechanisms for recombination of unit characters.

"Historically, this change in our thinking in regard to bacteria stems from the pioneer concepts of Lwoff (1938) and Knight (1936) relating the nutritional requirements of microorganisms to an evolutionary loss of synthetic abilities. If such losses in microorganisms were based on mutation and selection as required by modern concepts of evolution, the capacities for synthesis of essential nutrilites [basic food ingredients] in microorganisms should be determined by genes, which should be subject to mutation, as are most genes in other organisms. Such considerations led Beadle and Tatum (1941) to the successful production by irradiation of nutritionally deficient or biochemical mutants in . . . *Neurospora,* and to the establishment of the genic basis of biochemical reactions. . . .

"The next step in the evolution of our concepts of bacterial genetics was the experimental application of the *Neurospora* techniques to the production of biochemical mutants in these simpler organisms. The first nutritionally deficient (auxotrophic) mutants were produced in 1944 by x-ray treatment of *Escherichia coli* and *Acetobacter melanogenum.* . . . Subsequently, auxotrophic mutants

---

* The first quotation is from J. Lederberg and E. L. Tatum, "Sex in bacteria: genetic studies, 1945-1952," *Science,* Vol. 118 (1954), pp. 169-175. The second quotation is from Lederberg, "A view of genetics," *Les Prix Nobel en 1958.* The last is from Lederberg, "Genetic transduction," *American Scientist,* Vol. 44 (1956), pp. 264-280.

have been obtained in almost every species of bacteria investigated. . . .

"After establishment of this functional analogy between genes of bacteria and those of sexual forms, the next step logically was to ask if the analogy could be carried further, and if a mode of inheritance of bacterial characters similar to the Mendelian process in higher types could be detected. [Attempts to answer this question had been made as early as 1908, but without success. The availability of auxotrophic mutants, that is, strains whose specific nutritional requirements could act as markers,' made it possible to test for recombination of hereditary units in bacteria. It was found that a given deficiency acted quite independently of others and, by successive mutational treatment of *E. coli* strain K-12, stocks of the organism were obtained with more than one mutation.]

". . . In this way, for example, cultures Y-10, requiring threonine, leucine, and thiamine, and [cultures] 58-161, requiring biotin and methionine, were obtained. For simplicity in considering its capacity for synthesis of the factors concerned, strain 58-161 can be represented as biotin$^-$ methionine$^-$ threonine$^+$ leucine$^+$ thiamine$^+$ ($B^-M^-T^+L^+B_1^+$), while strain Y-10 would similarly be represented as $B^+M^+T^-L^-B_1^-$. In this representation, in analogy with other organisms such as *Neurospora,* the genes determining alternative characters (B^+ and B^- for example) are considered allelic.

"Accordingly, a sexual process in a mixed culture of these two strains would involve reshuffling the indicated alleles at these five loci. If this were at random, any recombination might be expected, and might have been looked for. However, recombination to give a nutritionally independent type (prototroph) would be most easily detected, since it alone would grow on minimal medium, whereas any dependent types, including both parental strains, would not.

"Experimental tests were carried out . . . by growing the two strains either separately or together in complete media, then centrifuging out the cells, washing repeatedly to remove growthfactors, and plating mixtures of the washed cells into minimal agar. The results were striking in that about 100 colonies developed for each 10^9 cells examined, and on re-isolation and purification these maintained their prototrophic character. Similarly treated single cultures of each strain gave no colonies on the minimal medium. This would be expected on the basis of the low frequency of mutation of each character to independence (*ca.* 1 in 10^7 cells) since the derivation of a prototroph from a triply deficient strain would then occur with a frequency of 1 in 10^{21} cells.

"The simplest explanation for these results therefore appeared to be that gene recombination took place to give the prototroph $B^+M^+T^+L^+B_1^+$. . . . Other possibilities . . . were made unlikely by various experimental tests which established the homogeneity and uniqueness of the derived prototrophs.

"Thus the results of experiments of the type described above are satisfactorily explained only as resulting from a sexual mating process, followed by reassortment or segregation of genetic material. Repetition and extension of these experiments in a considerable number of laboratories during the last five years have amply confirmed the reality of the essential phenomenon and the validity of this conclusion."

*　　*　　*

"Later, more fertile strains [of *E. coli*] were discovered which have been most helpful to further analysis. This has shown that typical multinucleate vegetative bacteria unite by a conjugation bridge through which part or all of a male genome [a single set of chromosomes] migrates into the female cell. The gametic [i.e. germ] cells then separate. . . . When fertilization is prematurely interrupted [by agitating the suspension of bacteria in a Waring blendor briefly], the chromosome may be broken so that only anterior markers appear among the recombinants. All of the genetic markers [identified, as explained above, by a specific nutritional requirement] are arranged in a single linkage group and their order can be established either by timing their passage during fertilization or by their statistical association with one another among the recombinants. Finally, the transfer of genetic markers can be correlated with the transfer of DNA as inferred from the lethal effect of the radioactive decay of incorporated P^{32} [shown by F. Jacob and E. L. Wollman, in 1958].

"Sexual recombination is one of the methods for analyzing the gene-enzyme relationship. The studies so far are fragmentary but they support the conception that the gene is a string of nucleotides which must function as a coherent unit in order to produce an active enzyme."

* * *

"[Other modes of recombination of characters, that is, of altering the genetic constitution, in bacteria than sexual fertilization are now known. One of these was first announced by F. Griffith in 1928, but was described in detail and evaluated only in 1944, by O. T. Avery, C. M. MacLeod, and M. McCarty at the Rockefeller Institute. The virulent pneumococcus bacterium is encased in an envelope, or capsule, consisting of polysaccharide. Each serological type of the organism depends for its specificity upon a characteristic polysaccharide. When grown on a solid (agar) medium, some types have a capsule that gives a 'smooth' appearance to the colonies; others are of the 'rough' type. Griffith] prepared a vaccine with heat-killed smooth type and injected it into mice that also received some live, rough cells. Neither vaccine nor cells alone produced disease, but in a few cases when they were given together there was a virulent infection and live smooth cells could be isolated, and their serotype depended upon the serotype of the bacteria used for preparation of the vaccine, not on that of the live cells. This demonstrated conversion of one type of cell to the other.

"[The report by Avery and his colleagues] stated that the material active in transforming the pneumococcus from rough to smooth type was a form of DNA, already recognized in chromosomes and thought to be involved in the hereditary process. [Griffith's results were explained by the 'transduction' hypothesis: the DNA which is transferred was thought to correspond to a viable part of chromosomes of one type of pneumococcus, and this would be transferred to the other variant. Confirmatory data were then obtained with influenza bacillus *Hemophilus influenzae*.]

"A second mode of transduction, mediated by bacterial viruses rather than chemically extracted DNA [as in the case of Avery's experiments] was discovered independently of the pneumococcus researches in the course of studies on *Salmonella*. . . . This group of bacteria is of medical interest because of their connection with diseases such as food-poisoning and enteric and typhoid fever. However, they are closely related to *Escherichia coli*. . . .

". . . The term 'transduction' was introduced at this point for the hypothesis that genetic fragments were being transmitted from one strain to another, via cell-free filtrates, as seemed to occur in the pneumococcus, too. However, *Salmonella* proved to be far more amenable to genetic study than the pneumococcus, and generalizations on this transduction could be based on studies with 30 or 40 different markers in a relatively short time. . . . [The activity was connected with] particles about 0.1 micron in diameter and hence just beneath microscopic visibility . . . These particles were later identified as bacteriophage, or bacterial virus. [In genetic transduction in *Salmonella*] bacteriophage acts as passive carrier of the genetic . . . fragments.

"So far, no definite case of transduction has been reported for higher organisms. Claims that DNA from tumor cells would induce tumors in normal mouse tissues are controversial but they do illustrate the impact of transduction on experimental cancer research. . . . The representation of genic differences in chemically purifiable DNA is the closest approach to the reduction of genetics to biochemistry, an enterprise which can challenge the skills and imagination of specialists in a dozen sciences."

CONSEQUENCES IN THEORY AND PRACTICE

Tatum's and Lederberg's choice of the K-12 strain of *E. coli* was a stroke of great and good fortune. Not only did this organism possess clear-cut genetic markers—the auxotrophic mutants—but the strain turned out to be of the very few able to undergo recombination.

In 1929 Sir MacFarlane Burnet and M. Mackie suggested that a bacterial virus (phage), or its precursor (prophage), exists as part of the hereditary material of the bacterial cell. The Lederbergs proved this in 1953 by showing that a prophage segregates as a typical chromosomal marker in sexual recombination. Thus, bacteria exhibit four processes whereby the genetic material is altered: (1) absorption of dissolved DNA provided in the medium, resulting in the "transformation" as in the pneumococcus; (2) incorporation of DNA from an infecting phage (transduction); (3) recombination of the genetic materials of two cells in contact with one another; and (4) chemical change in the organism's DNA, or mutation. The last is, of course, a well known phenomenon in higher organisms.

Most of the hereditary material of *Escherichia coli* is borne on a single chromosome. However, one exceptional material was an infectious particle called "F," which determines the organism's capacity to function as a male partner in fertilization. Although it has never been separated from the cells, F appears to be genic material localized in the cytoplasm. Another mutant *Hfr* is derived from F+ (male) strains, and is much more fertile in crosses with F− (female) than is the standard F+. Lederberg interprets the *Hfr* mutant as arising from fixation of the F particle to a particular chromosomal site, resulting in the disappearance of infectivity of the male character. He suggests that the chromosomal location of the F particle (i.e. in *Hfr*) is analogous to prophage, whereas the plasmagene F would correspond to the vegetative phage within the cell.

The analysis of bacterial genetics and the new understanding of the nature of the genic materials have contributed to our appreciation of the unity of living things, with the bacteria now recognized as having a greater role to play in the study of the comparative biology of sex. The discovery of genetic transduction provides the possibility of controlling the bacterial genotype experimentally; inasmuch as this would signify the achievement of control over the nature of intracellular DNA, the findings could have very broad significance for biology, especially in regard to problems of differentiation of cells including tumor cells.

1 9 5 9
SEVERO OCHOA
(1905–   )

ARTHUR KORNBERG
(1918–   )

"For their discoveries of the mechanisms of the biologic synthesis of ribonucleic and deoxyribonucleic acids."

BIOGRAPHICAL SKETCHES

OCHOA

SEVERO OCHOA WAS BORN ON SEPTEMBER 24, 1905, AT LUARCA, Spain. He was educated at Málaga College in Spain, receiving the B.A. degree in 1921. He became very interested in biology through reading the papers of Santiago Ramón y Cajal, and decided to study medicine at the University of Madrid. During this period he was assistant to Dr. Juan Negrin and, for a short time, worked in Glasgow under Dr. D. N. Paton. After graduating with the M.D. degree in 1927, he went to Otto Meyerhof's laboratory in Heidelberg where he carried out research on the biochemistry and physiology of muscle. From Germany Ochoa went to England, spending some fruitful years at Oxford University with Professor R. A. Peters, and working on the function of thiamine. In 1941 he went to Washington University in St. Louis, Missouri, where he worked with Carl and Gerty Cori, but in the next year he left

for the New York University School of Medicine, where he is now
professor of biochemistry and chairman of the department. He
adopted United States citizenship in 1956. In a later extension of
the work on synthesis of ribonucleic acid, described below, Ochoa
and his colleagues have succeeded in growing virus outside the
living cell.

KORNBERG

ARTHUR KORNBERG WAS BORN ON MARCH 3, 1918, IN BROOK-
lyn, New York. He attended the City College of New York from
1933 to 1937, graduating B.S. in chemistry, and then went to
Rochester University to study medicine. He received the M.D.
degree in 1941, and interned the next year at the Strong Memorial
Hospital in Rochester, New York. He became a commissioned
officer in the United States Public Health Service, discharging his
responsibilities in research at the National Institutes of Health in
Bethesda, Maryland. Except for a stint as a medical officer in the
Coast Guard, a year in Ochoa's department at New York University (1946), and another year at Washington University, St.
Louis, with the Coris, he remained in Bethesda until 1951. After a
year with Dr. H. A. Barker at the University of California at
Berkeley, he went to St. Louis once more, shortly becoming chairman of the Department of Microbiology at the Washington University School of Medicine. It was here that Kornberg carried out
the experiments that led to the Nobel Prize-winning work. In
1959, he went to Stanford University School of Medicine as ex-
ecutive head of the Department of Biochemistry.

DESCRIPTION OF THE PRIZE-WINNING
WORK

OCHOA*

"The nucleic acids have a considerable biological importance
because of their role in cell growth and in the transmission of
hereditary characters. As first suggested by the pioneering work

---

* From S. Ochoa, "Enzymatic synthesis of ribonucleic acid," *Les Prix Nobel en*
1959.

of [T.] Caspersson and [J.] Brachet the former function is performed by ribonucleic acid (RNA) through its participation in the biosynthesis of proteins. The second is carried out by deoxyribonucleic acid (DNA), the main component of the nuclear chromosomes. It is of interest, however, that in certain viruses such as tobacco mosaic, influenza, and poliomyelitis virus, which consist of RNA and protein, RNA is the carrier of genetic information.

". . . Little was known until recently of the mechanism of synthesis of the giant molecules of the nucleic acids themselves. We owe our present information to the discovery of enzymes capable of catalyzing the synthesis of RNA and DNA in the test tube from simple, naturally occurring precursors.

"In 1955 we isolated a bacterial enzyme capable of catalyzing the synthesis of high molecular weight polyribonucleotides [i.e. RNA-like material] from nucleoside diphosphates [see page 66] with release of orthophosphate [H_3PO_4, in the acid form]. The reaction, which requires magnesium ions and is reversible, can be formulated by the equation

$$nX{-}R{-}P{-}P \; \underset{\phantom{Mg^{++}}}{\overset{Mg^{++}}{\rightleftharpoons}} \; (X{-}R{-}_{\!l}P)_n + nP$$

where R stands for ribose, P–P for pyrophosphate [pyrophosphoric acid is $H_4P_2O_7$], P for orthophosphate, and X for one or more bases including, among others, adenine, hypoxanthine, guanine, uracil, or cytosine. [In the equation n represents the number of units combining to form the product.] In the reverse direction the enzyme brings about a cleavage of polyribonucleotides by phosphate, i.e. a phosphorolysis to yield ribonucleoside diphosphates. The reaction is similar to the reversible synthesis and cleavage of polysaccharides, catalyzed by phosphorylase; for this reason the new enzyme was named polynucleotide phosphorylase. Because of its reversibility, the reaction leads to an incorporation or 'exchange' of orthophosphate into the terminal phosphate group of nucleoside diphosphates. It was through this exchange that polynucleotide phosphorylase was discovered by the use of radioactive phosphate. In our early work with [M.] Grunberg-Manago, polynucleotide phosphorylase was partially purified . . . from the microorganism *Azotobacter vinelandii*. The enzyme has the unique feature of catalyzing not only the synthesis of RNA from mixtures of the four naturally occurring ribonucleoside diphosphates, but also that of non-naturally occurring polyribonucleotides containing only one, two, or three different kinds of nucleotides in their chains. The nature of the product depends on the kind and variety of the nucleoside diphosphate substrates utilized for the synthesis.

"In joint experiments with L. A. Heppel it has been established that the synthetic polyribonucleotides conform in all respects to the structural pattern of natural RNA. Thus, it was found by degradation with alkali, or such enzymes as snake venom and spleen phosphodiesterase or pancreatic ribonuclease, that they consist of linear chains in which the component nucleoside units are linked to one another through 3', 5'-phosphodiester bridges.

"Although large variations in the relative proportions of the different nucleoside diphosphate substrates have a rather marked influence on the nucleotide composition of the resulting polymer, when synthetic RNA is prepared from equimolar mixtures of adenosine, guanosine, uridine, and cytidine diphosphate, the nucleotide composition of the product is very similar to that of natural *Azotobacter* RNA. . . . It is noteworthy that the base ratios differ widely from unity in spite of the fact that equimolar concentrations of the nucleoside diphosphate precursors were used.

"The synthetic polyribonucleotides also resemble natural RNA in size. Their molecular weight varies between about 30,000 and one to two millions. The sedimentation constant of samples of synthetic RNA was similar to that of RNA isolated from whole *Azotobacter* cells. Polynucleotides containing only one kind of nucleotide unit, such as polyadenylic or polycytidylic acid, are often of very large size and confer high viscosity to their solutions. It is possible to follow the course of synthesis visually by the marked increase in viscosity [internal friction of the solution, with, in this case, an increased resistance to flow] that takes place on incubation of nucleoside diphosphates with a few micrograms of enzyme.

"To study the mechanism of action of polynucleotide phosphorylase it was essential to obtain highly purified preparations of the enzyme. . . . The purification . . . after chromatography is some six hundred fold over the initial extract of *Azotobacter* cells.

"It appears justified to conclude that polynucleotide phosphory-lase may be unable to start the synthesis of a polynucleotide chain from nucleoside diphosphates as the only reactants and that the presence of an oligonucleotide [a short chain of nucleotides] to serve as nucleus for growth of new polynucleotide chains is prob-ably indispensable. If the enzyme could be obtained completely free of oligonucleotide primer material, it might prove to be com-pletely inactive in the absence of added oligonucleotides.

"Polynucleotide phosphorylase is widely distributed in bacteria. The enzyme has been partially purified from microorganisms other than *Azotobacter vinelandii* and polyribonucleotides have been synthesized with these enzyme preparations. Indications have also been obtained for the presence of the enzyme in green leaves. On the other hand, it has been difficult to detect the enzyme in animal tissues. . . .

"The occurrence of polynucleotide phosphorylase in nature ap-pears to be widespread enough to warrant the assumption that this enzyme may be generally involved in the biosynthesis of RNA.

"Since RNA is the genetic material of some viruses, the work reviewed in this lecture may help to pave the way for the artificial synthesis of biologically active viral RNA and the synthesis of viruses. These particles are at the threshold of life and appear to hold the clue to a better understanding of some of its most funda-mental principles."

KORNBERG*

"[Much evidence has been adduced in recent years favoring the view] that it is DNA which not only directs the synthesis of the proteins and the development of the cell but that it must also be the substance which is copied so as to provide for a similar de-velopment of the progeny of the cell for many generations. DNA, like a tape recording, carries a message in which there are specific instructions for a job to be done. Also, like a tape recording, ex-

---

* From A. Kornberg, "The biologic synthesis of deoxyribonucleic acid," *Les Prix Nobel en 1959*.

act copies can be made from it so that this information can be used again and elsewhere in time and space.

"Are these two functions, the expression of the code (protein synthesis) and the copying of the code (preservation of the race) closely integrated or are they separable? What we have learned from our studies over the past five years and what I shall present is that the replication of DNA can be examined and at least partially understood at the enzymatic level even though the secret of how DNA directs protein synthesis is still locked in the cell."

[Kornberg first describes the structure of DNA as known at that time: analysis of DNA prepared from many different sources had shown that the number of purine and pyrimidine bases were always equal. In 1953 J. D. Watson and F. H. C. Crick interpreted these and other facts, particularly those derived from the x-ray crystallographic measurements made by M. H. F. Wilkins and his colleagues, as evidence for a structure in which two very long polynucleotide strands are wound about each other in a helical manner. They suggested that these two spirals are held together by hydrogen bonds between adenine and thymine as well as between cytosine and guanine, i.e. between 6-amino and 6-oxo bases, respectively (see page 399 ff.). The concept of 'base-pairing' has been fundamental to all studies ot DNA chemistry since then.]

"I feel now, as we did then, that for an effective approach to the problem of nucleic acid biosynthesis it was essential to understand the biosynthesis of the simple nucleotides and the coenzymes and to have these concepts and methodology well in hand. It was from these studies that we developed the conviction that an activated nucleoside 5'-phosphate is the basic biosynthetic building block of the nucleic acids. [Kornberg points to the numerous roles of adenosine triphosphate (ATP), just such an activated nucleotide, in the synthesis of coenzymes and in the activation of fatty acids and amino acids preparatory to their entry into certain paths of metabolism. These 'high energy' triphospate forms are known for other nucleosides also, such as uridine, cytidine and guanosine.]

". . . It was postulated that the basic building block [of DNA] is a deoxynucleoside 5'-triphosphate which is attacked by the 3'-hydroxyl group at the growing end of a polydeoxynucleotide chain; inorganic pyrophosphate is eliminated and the chain is lengthened by one unit. The results of our studies on DNA synthesis . . . are in keeping with this type of reaction.

"First let us consider the enzyme and comment on its discovery. Mixing the triphosphates of the four deoxynucleosides which commonly occur in DNA with an extract of thymus or bone-marrow or of *Escherichia coli* [as sources of synthesizing enzyme] would not be expected to lead to the net synthesis of DNA. Instead, as might be expected, the destruction of DNA by extracts of such cells and tissues was by far the predominant process and one had to resort to the use of more subtle devices for detection of such a biosynthetic reaction. We used a C^{14}-labeled substrate of high specific radioactivity and incubated it with ATP and extracts of *Escherichia coli,* an organism which reproduces itself every 20 minutes. The first positive results represented the conversion of only a very small fraction of the acid-soluble substrate [the nucleoside triphosphate] (50 or so counts out of a million added). While this represented only a few $\mu\mu$ moles [$1/10^{12}$ of a mole] of reaction, it was something. Through this tiny crack we tried to drive a wedge and the hammer was enzyme purification. . . . Our best preparations are several thousand-fold enriched with respect to protein over the crude extracts, but there are still contaminating quantities of one or more of the many varieties of nuclease and diesterase [degradative enzymes] present in the coli cell. The occurrence of what appears to be a similar DNA-synthesizing system in animal cells as well as in other bacterial species has been observed [by F. J. Bollum and V. R. Potter, and by C. G. Harford and Kornberg].

"When all four triphosphates are present, but when DNA is omitted, no reaction at all takes place. What is the basis for this requirement? Does the DNA function as a primer in the manner of glycogen [p. 258] or does it function as a template in directing the synthesis of exact copies of itself? We have good reason to believe that it is the latter. . . . I would like to emphasize that it is the capacity for base pairing by hydrogen bonding between the pre-existing DNA and the nucleotides added as substrates that accounts for the requirement for DNA.

"From collaborative studies with Dr. Howard K. Schachman

[on the physical properties of the synthetic material] it can be said that the enzymatic product is indistinguishable from high-molecular weight, double-stranded DNA isolated from nature. It has sedimentation coefficients in the neighborhood of 25, reduced viscosities of 40 deciliters per gram and, on the basis of these measurements, it is believed to be a long, stiff rod with a molecular weight of about 6 million. Upon heating DNA, the rod collapses and the molecule becomes a compact, randomly coiled structure; it may be inferred that the hydrogen bonds holding the strands together have melted. . . . Similar results are found upon cleavage of the molecule by pancreatic deoxyribonuclease."

[Additional evidence for the double-stranded structure of synthetic DNA came from the use of analogues of the nitrogen bases, such as 5-methylcytosine, 5-bromocytosine, hypoxanthine, and the unusual but naturally occurring compound hydroxymethylcytosine (replacing cytosine in the DNA of certain *E. coli* bacteriophages). The results of these studies were readily interpretable on the basis of base-pairing by hydrogen bond formation. A third line of evidence came from the determination of the composition of enzymatically synthesized DNA.]

"[It was found that] the characteristic ratio of adenine-thymine pairs to guanine-cytosine pairs of a given DNA primer is imposed rather faithfully on the product that is synthesized. Whether these measurements are made with isotopic tracers when the net DNA increase is only 1% or if it is 1000% the results are the same. . . . It has not been possible to distort these base ratios by using widely differing molar concentrations of substrates or by any other means.

"We believe that DNA is the genetic code; the four kinds of nucleotides make up a four-letter alphabet and their sequence spells out the message. At present we do not know the sequence; what Sanger [Frederick Sanger, Nobel laureate in chemistry, 1958] has done for peptide sequence in protein remains to be done for nucleic acids. The problem is more difficult, but not insoluble. [With four different nucleotides, sixteen possible kinds of dinucleotide, or nearest neighbor, sequences are possible in the structure of DNA. Studies of synthetic DNA show that:]

"1) All 16 possible dinucleotide sequences are found in each case.

"2) The pattern of relative frequencies of the sequences is unique and reproducible in each case and is not readily predicted from the base composition of the DNA.

"3) Enzymatic replication involves base pairing of adenine to thymine and guanine to cytosine and, most significantly:

"4) The frequencies also indicate clearly that the enzymatic replication produces two strands of opposite direction, as predicted by the Watson and Crick model."

CONSEQUENCES IN THEORY
AND PRACTICE

The modern studies of the synthesis of nucleic acids support the concept of a fundamental hierarchy of reactions: DNA → RNA → protein. That is, DNA, the genetic material, directs the synthesis of the body's enzymes and other tissue proteins through the mediation of RNA. The double-stranded nature of DNA ensures the ordered reproduction of DNA in new cells, for each strand acts as a template for the formation of its complement. The DNA and RNA polymerases, the subject of Ochoa's and Kornberg's Prize-winning work, appear to act in the same fashion on their respective substrates. A small amount of DNA must be present to get the former enzyme to work, and then the "primer" is copied. The enzymatically synthesized material has been examined in greater detail than at the time of Kornberg's early work as described above; there is now evidence for some differences from natural DNA, for example, in regard to the effect of heat on its solutions. Although RNA polymerase can initiate the synthetic reaction without a primer, when one is present it acts as a template. H. G. Khorana and his associates have prepared short-chain polydeoxyribonucleotides in the chemical laboratory and have used them as primers with the RNA polymerase of E. coli. Polythymidylic acid served as template in this way for the formation of polyriboadenylic acid.

Most of the cell's RNA is in the cytoplasm, and only a little in the nucleus. Actually there are many different types of RNA, but they have been classified in three main groups according to their biological function. The first type consists of RNA formed with the help of a cellular DNA template. This "messenger"-RNA bears the necessary information to order the sequence in which amino acids line up for incorporation into protein. The individual amino acids are "activated" and then accepted by a low-molecular-weight "soluble"-RNA, or "transfer"-RNA. In this form, which consists of a distinct RNA species for each amino acid, the latter is borne to the ribosome, a small intracellular particle in which the actual process of protein synthesis takes place. The ribosomal-RNA links the amino acids together in the order "instructed" by the messenger-RNA. The ribosome possesses the shape and groups that are needed to bring together all the reacting molecules.

The demonstration of enzymes that catalyze the synthesis of nucleic acids in vitro provided an entirely new approach to the problems of the biology and chemistry of these substances. One of these problems has to do with the differences between nucleic acids synthesized in vivo and in vitro; in the former, after all, ready-made DNA template is available within the cell.

Knowledge of the precise primary structure (nucleotide sequence) of various nucleic acids is necessary for a complete understanding of their function and, fortunately, has been growing rapidly as new chemical and enzymatic methods of analysis are developed. This is a part of the problem of "breaking the genetic code," that is, determining the deoxyribonucleotide sequences that ultimately order specific amino acids into the cellular machinery for synthesizing protein. Understanding the RNA code and knowing how to prepare synthetic polyribonucleotides should eventually make it possible to direct the synthesis of specific proteins outside the body.

Where Beadle, Tatum, and Lederberg focussed attention on the biological mechanisms involving nucleic acids in the life of the cell and the organism, Ochoa and Kornberg were able to reveal the hitherto unknown enzymes that make possible the present fundamental attacks on the problems of cell growth and the transmission of genetic information.

1 9 6 0

FRANK MACFARLANE BURNET

(1899–)

PETER BRIAN MEDAWAR

(1915–)

"For their discovery of acquired immunological tolerance."

BIOGRAPHICAL SKETCHES

BURNET

SIR FRANK MACFARLANE BURNET WAS BORN ON SEPTEMBER 3, 1899, at Traralgon, Victoria, in Australia. From 1916 to 1922 he studied medicine at the University of Melbourne, and then began his training in pathology. Convinced by C. H. Kellaway, the director of the Walter and Eliza Hall Institute for Medical Research in Melbourne, that he should devote himself to biological research, he went to the Lister Institute in London on a fellowship and began studies on bacteriophage that were to occupy him intensively for many years. After earning the Ph.D. degree he returned to Australia (1928) as Kellaway's assistant, and haś remained there ever since, except for a further year in England. This was in 1932-1933 when he worked in Sir Henry Dale's group at the National Institute for Medical Research, where the influenza virus had been discovered. Burnet worked out the technique of cultivating virus in living chick embryos, a method that has been

379

used since then in every virology laboratory. At the Hall Institute his earlier work included studies of staphylococcus, psittacosis, herpes, and poliomyelitis. Elected a fellow of the Royal Society in 1942, he has received its Royal Medal for his work in virology and immunity. He was director of the Hall Institute, following Kellaway, until his retirement in 1965.

MEDAWAR

PETER BRIAN MEDAWAR WAS BORN ON FEBRUARY 28, 1915, IN Rio de Janeiro, the son of a naturalized British subject. He studied zoology at Oxford under Professor J. Z. Young (now at University College, London) and after graduation began to work in the School of Pathology at Oxford, directed by Sir Howard Florey. In 1944 he became a University Lecturer in zoology at Oxford, but left three years later to assume the post of Mason Professor of Zoology at the University of Birmingham. His earlier work at Oxford on the mechanism of skin graft reactions was continued in Birmingham with studies of acquired tolerance to skin grafts in cattle. In 1951 Medawar went to University College, London, as the Jodrell Professor of Zoology. When Sir Charles Harington retired in 1962, Medawar was appointed to his position as the director of the National Institute for Medical Research, at Mill Hill, London. He was elected to the Royal Society in 1949 and received its Royal Medal in 1959. He has written books entitled *The Uniqueness of the Individual* and *The Future of Man*.

DESCRIPTION OF THE PRIZE-WINNING WORK

MEDAWAR*

"Immunological tolerance may be described as a state of indifference or non-reactivity towards a substance that would normally be expected to excite an immunological response. The term first came to be used in the context of tissue transplantation immunity, i.e. of the form of immunity that usually prohibits the

---

* From P. B. Medawar, "Immunological tolerance," *Les Prix Nobel en 1960*.

grafting of tissues between individuals of different genetic make-up; and it was used to refer only to a non-reactivity caused by exposing animals to antigenic stimuli before they were old enough to undertake an immunological response. For example, if living cells from a mouse of strain CBA are injected into an adult mouse of strain A, the CBA cells will be destroyed by an immunological process, and the A-line mouse that received them will destroy any later graft of the same origin with the speed to be expected of an animal immunologically forearmed. But if the CBA cells are injected into a foetal or newborn A-line mouse, they are accepted; more than that, the A-line mouse, when it grows up will accept any later graft from a CBA donor as if it were its own.

"In 1945, R. D. Owen made the remarkable discovery that most twin cattle are born with, and may retain throughout life, a stable mixture—not necessarily a fifty-fifty mixture—of each other's red cells; it followed, then, that the twin cattle must have exchanged red-cell precursors and not merely red cells in their mutual transfusion before birth. This is the first example of the phenomenon we came to call immunological tolerance. . . . A few years later R. E. Billingham and I, with the help of three members of the scientific staff of the Agricultural Research Council, showed that most dizygotic cattle twins [fraternal twins; that is, twins developing from separate, fertilized ova] would accept skin grafts from each other, and that this mutual tolerance was specific, for skin transplanted from third parties was cast off in the expected fashion. We did not set out with the idea in mind of studying the immunological consequences of the phenomenon described by Owen; on the contrary, we had been goaded by Dr. H. P. Donald into trying to devise a foolproof method of distinguishing monozygotic [uniovular, or identical, twins; those developing from a single fertilized ovum] from dizygotic twins, an enterprise that seemed reasonable enough against the rather thorough background of knowledge we already possessed about the behaviour of skin grafts in experimental animals. It was F. M. Burnet and F. Fenner who first read a general significance into Owen's discovery and who wove it into a general hypothesis of the immunological response which counted the phenomenon of tolerance among its theoretical consequences.

". . . It proved impossible to distinguish between the two kinds of twins by skin grafting, but the causal connexion between Owen's phenomenon and our own was obvious, and we were now confident of our ability to make adult animals accept tissue homografts [grafts of tissue from the same species] by reproducing in the laboratory the very state of affairs that had come about by natural accident in twin cattle. Billingham, L. Brent and I eventually succeeded in doing so, and our first report on the matter was published in 1953. . . . It is now known that chimerism [the type of phenomenon discovered by Owen (see above), in which there occurs a 'mixture' of tissues in a given part of the organism —in his example, a mixture of red cell types in each of the bovine twins] can occur naturally, though rarely, in twin sheep, and more rarely still in twin human beings; in twin chickens it is probably the general rule. That chimerism should occur in man is clear proof that the principle of tolerance applies to human beings as well as to laboratory animals, and human chimeric twins can accept grafts of each other's skin.

"The main points that emerged from our analysis of the tolerant state were these. In the first place, tolerance must be due to an alteration of the host, not to an antigenic adaptation of the grafted cells, for grafts newly transplanted in adult life have no opportunity to adapt themselves, and the descendants of the cells injected into foetal or newborn animals can be shown by N. A. Mitchison's methods to retain their antigenic power. Once established, the state of tolerance is systemic; if one part of the body will tolerate a foreign graft, so will another. . . . The stimulus that is responsible for instating tolerance is an antigenic stimulus—one which, had it been applied to older animals, would have caused them to become sensitive or immune. . . . The state of tolerance is specific in the sense that it will discriminate between one individual and another, for an animal made tolerant of grafts from one individual will not accept grafts from a second individual unrelated to the first; but it will not discriminate between one tissue and another from the same donor. . . . These various tissues do indeed differ in their antigenic make-up, but not, apparently in respect of antigens that play an important part in transplantation immunity.

"Tolerance can be brought promptly and permanently to an end by an experimental device. [Referring to the experiment described in the first paragraph] imagine an A-line mouse which is tolerant of CBA tissue and which carries a CBA skin graft as outward evidence that it is so. The tolerated CBA graft can be destroyed within a week by injecting into its host lymphoid cells from A-line mice which have reacted upon and rejected CBA tissues in the expected fashion. . . . The inference [is] that tolerance is due to a central failure of the mechanism of immunological response and not to some intercession at a peripheral level.

". . . Does the maintenance of the tolerant state depend upon the continuing presence of the antigen that provoked it? . . . So far as transplantation immunity is concerned, no completely confident answer can be given until all the antigens that excite it can be extracted in a sufficiently potent form; but with 'tolerance' of foreign proteins and red cells, it does indeed seem that antigen must continue to be present, even though in quantities below the threshold of direct estimation, if a fully non-reactive state is to be maintained. . . . Tolerance is not an all-or-nothing phenomenon: every degree of tolerance is to be found, from that which allows a graft to live just perceptibly longer than would be expected of it in a normal animal to that in which the graft is permanently accepted by and incorporated into its host."

BURNET*

"I like to think that when Medawar and his colleagues showed that immunological tolerance could be produced experimentally the new immunology was born. This is a science which to me has far greater potentialities both for practical use in medicine and for better understanding of living process than the classical immunochemistry which it is incorporating and superseding."

[Burnet points out that the vertebrate organism recognizes its own components. In the immunological sense the organism avoids making antibodies to its own proteins, although it will produce antibodies against cells or proteins from another organism. Thus,

* From F. M. Burnet, "Immunological recognition of self," *Les Prix Nobel en 1960*.

it distinguishes between its own constituents—"self-components"
—and those deriving from another creature.] "For me, acquired
immunological tolerance means simply that the content of self-
components in the body has been enlarged by an experimental
manipulation.

"The production of antibody is not the only, nor I believe the
most important, manifestation of immunity but for reasons both
historical and of experimental convenience antibody is likely to
remain the touchstone of immunological theory. Any formulation
of theory must cover the nature of antibody and lay down the conditions under which it will or will not be produced.

"Bovine serum albumin [the major component of serum pro-
teins] is antigenic in a rabbit, rabbit serum albumin is not. Both
have presumably the same function in their proper species and the
difference responsible for antigenicity can be regarded genetically
as an example of neutral polymorphism. Superficially at least the
differences seem to have no relevance to survival. Serum albumin is
a well defined protein but no laboratory has yet attempted to ascertain its full chemical structure. . . . Insulin is a very poor antigen—
otherwise we could not use bovine insulin successfully for the
treatment of diabetes. Nevertheless it can function as an antigen in
man.

"Following Sanger's work it is well known that species differences between insulin involve primarily a group of three amino
acid residues. . . .

"The immunological difference between beef insulin and human
insulin, which is presumably responsible for the antigenicity of
the former in some human beings, is thus limited to a very small
portion of the whole molecule.

"This consideration of insulin as the only available antigen
whose chemical structure is known leads to a conclusion which
could be supported by many other pieces of evidence, viz. that an
antigenic determinant has very much the quality of a gene. Its existence can only be recognised in virtue of its *difference* from something else of the same general quality. A protein or other type
of macromolecule is antigenic because it carries one or more chemical configurations (antigenic determinants) which differ from any

configurations of the same general quality that are present in the animal being immunized.

"There is evidence . . . that an antigenic determinant, like the active patch on an antibody molecule with which it combines, is small (perhaps 100-200 Å²) [one Ångstrom is one ten-millionth of a millimeter] and that to be active it must be part of an appropriate carrier molecule. There is no evidence as to how many potential antigenic determinants there are in an insulin molecule. One could guess that there were some hundreds of different patterns produced by knots of 3-5 amino acids accessible on the surface of the molecule, any one of which might serve as an antigenic determinant, but until we know more about the requirements for antigenicity it could be a much smaller number. In practice, of course, all these potential determinants have the same structure as the corresponding substance in the immunized animal and are therefore inert.

"If my last statement is correct and I believe most immunologists would accept it, then it allows us to pose the basic problem of immunology in a specific form. How can an immunized animal recognise the difference between an injected material like insulin or serum albumin from another species and its own corresponding substance?

". . . Their recognition in the sense that we are using the word requires that there be available in the body a large volume of accessible 'information' with some superficial analogies to a dictionary. In other words, there must be something against which a configuration can be compared and a decision made whether it corresponds or not.

"If the small specifically patterned area of an antibody molecule is constructed of a small segment or knot of a polypeptide chain, we could legitimately simplify matters by regarding all specific antibody patterns as being four letter words, axqb, e.g., corresponding each to an antigenic determinant represented by the same upper case letters AXQB. We could generate the type of information we require in the alphabetical analogue by first requiring a computer to produce say 10^7 random four letter combinations [using a suitably enlarged alphabet]. The combinations are scrutinized as they are produced by a team of English speakers who eliminate every combination which forms an English four letter word. All other combinations are stored in the computer's memory to be called into activity whenever the corresponding upper case group is fed into the machine.

"Translated into biological terms this requires some process of randomization to provide the primary array of complementary steric patterns. The elimination of self-reactive patterns would by hypothesis result when pre-natal contact with self-components occurred. The residue would be available to react with and 'recognise' foreign configurations entering during the period of independent life.

"Two suggestions have been made as to the carriers of the patterns. [N. K.] Jerne postulated the circulating globulins, [D. W.] Talmage and I both preferred mesenchymal (lymphoid) cells. I believe that circulating globulin can be categorically eliminated in view of the phenomena of graft-versus-host reactions and that any attempt to give an observable basis to the concept must be concerned with the immunologically competent cell.

"I . . . define [such a] cell as one which is specifically stimulated to some reaction (either observable or in principle observable) by contact with an appropriate antigenic determinant. [Burnet then illustrates his definition by an experimental demonstration of the graft-versus-host reaction. Normal fowl leucocytes (the graft) are inoculated on to the chorioallantoic membrane of chick embryos (the host). The four eggs inoculated in this experiment are of identical genetic background. After inoculation they are re-incubated for another four days, and then the embryos and their membranes are examined.] . . . Two of the membranes show no lesions, the others between 100 and 200 well defined opaque foci about a millimetre across. These lesions mark areas of cellular proliferation in which both the embryonic (host) cells and the mature (donor) cells and their descendants play a part. The foci represent an immunological response initiated by individual immunologically competent cells [of the chick embryo membranes]; antibody production is not involved. We believe that the difference between positive and negative membranes is due to the presence of a single antigenic determinant in the embryos showing lesions and its absence in the negative ones. There are• several interesting features about these foci.

"First—they are immunological in character. Second—they are produced by *normal* lymphocytes from completely normal birds. Third—each lesion is almost certainly induced by a single cell but only about $1/10^4$ lymphocytes can do so. Fourth—the lesion is initiated either immediately or within a few hours of depositing the cells on the membrane.

"Any cellular theory of immunity demands the presence of cell receptors which, by making an antibody-like union with antigenic determinant, can provoke reaction of one sort or another. The difference between the grades of reactivity could well depend on the number and accessibility of these receptors."

CONSEQUENCES IN THEORY AND PRACTICE

The Nobel Prize has been awarded on several occasions for contributions to knowledge of immunity and of immunological individuality (cf. pp. 46, 51, 91, 146). In the past the Prize-winning work had dealt with the problem of the body's defences against foreign organisms and cells. In 1960 the Committee considered that the discovery that the body can be made under certain conditions to accept a transplant of foreign tissue was a major scientific advance. Burnet regards the discovery as ushering in "the new immunology," a science based on recognition of two important points: (1) the immunological pattern of the body, i.e. the type of antigens it makes, is genetically determined, and (2) the capacity to bring about an immunological reaction evolves gradually in the fetus and does not reach the "adult" stage until many weeks after birth. At that time the organism reacts to foreign matter, but does not produce antibodies to its own proteins except in very rare instances. Medawar (op. cit.) points out that "Burnet was the first to realize that this is not a state of affairs to be taken for granted, but something which calls for a special explanation."

The special explanation was, in fact, a generalized theory of immunity. In 1949, together with his colleague F. Fenner, Burnet presented the theory that the body's recognition of its own components is not an inherited feature, but one that develops slowly during fetal life. If this were true, one could conclude that foreign substances (antigens) introduced into the organism early enough in development would be accepted just as the body's own antigens are. Later on, when the immune mechanism had matured, the same antigens would be treated as "self-components," and there would be no immune reaction.

The actual proof of Burnet's theory of immunological tolerance acquired during fetal life came from Medawar's laboratory. In 1953 Medawar, Rupert Billingham, and Leslie Brent published a report of their experiments with mice (see above). At about the same time N. Hasek in Czechoslovakia provided additional evidence for the theory through experiments with chicks, although his work had originated from an entirely different theoretical background.

The application of acute immunological tolerance in medicine is only now in its earlier stages. The new knowledge is currently being used largely in biological experimentation, as in cancer and genetic research. Applications in medicine and surgery are already recognized but many practical difficulties still stand in the way. For example, if transplantation of a healthy organ into a body containing a defective one is to be successful, then the normal immune mechanisms must be overcome so that the foreign organ will be "tolerated." In this field there have been some initial successes with kidney-grafting. The recipient must first be treated with cortisone and other powerful drugs to reduce the immune reaction, and also with x-ray to cause "immunological paralysis." These measures tend to offset rejection of the "foreign" kidney. In addition the patient must take antibiotics as a defence against infection. It is not difficult to speculate on the significance for medicine of successful techniques for the transplantation of kidney and other organs.

Other applications of the new immunology are in the treatment of certain allergic states, where the body may have an exaggerated immune reaction, and of radiation damage, where the immunity-providing mechanisms have been deranged. More recently Burnet has offered tentative explanations of cancer and ageing on the basis of knowledge of acquired immunity.

REFERENCE

Medawar, P. B. (ed.). "Transplantation of tissues and organs," *British Medical Bulletin,* Vol. 21 (1965).

1961
GEORG VON BEKESY
(1899–   )

"For his discoveries concerning the physical mechanisms of stimulation within the cochlea."

BIOGRAPHICAL SKETCH

GEORG VON BEKESY WAS BORN ON JUNE 3, 1899, IN BUDAPEST, Hungary. His father was a diplomat and so he had his early schooling in many different places, including Munich, Istanbul, Budapest, and Zurich. At the University of Berne he studied chemistry, but took his Ph.D. degree in physics at the University of Budapest. He worked at the Hungarian Telephone Research Laboratory, a division of the post office, where he was concerned mainly with problems of long-distance communication but found sufficient time to investigate the function of the ear in transmitting sound. He spent one year in the laboratory of Siemens and Halske AG, Berlin. From 1939-1946 he held a simultaneous university position in Budapest as professor of experimental physics. He emigrated in 1946, going first to Stockholm where he worked at the Royal Caroline Medical Institute and at the Royal Institute of Technology. In the following year he went to work at the Psycho-acoustic Laboratory of Harvard University. Although his major physiological work has been on hearing, he has made important inroads into other special senses, such as vision, taste, and olfaction.

DESCRIPTION OF THE PRIZE-WINNING WORK*

"After the first World War, the only place in Hungary that had some scientific instruments left and was willing to let me use them was the research laboratory of the Post Office. . . . At that time, many of the important telephone lines went through Hungary and there were constant complaints that Hungary did not keep its lines in order. The method used to test a telephone line was to put an A.C. voltage on a line, beginning in Budapest, let the current go to the different capitals, and then feed it back to Budapest and compare the input with the output voltage for different frequencies. A single measure of the speech frequency range took more than 20 minutes. A few minutes after the measurement was completed, the lines were apt to be out of order again.

"I wanted to find a method that could complete the test in a second. The idea was that, when a musician tests his violin by plucking a string, he can tune it immediately. Theoretically, by plucking a telephone line it should be possible to obtain instantly all the data that are obtained by the cumbersome 20-minute test. Therefore, I transmitted a click through the line by switching in a small D. C. voltage and then listening and observing the returning signal. It turned out that the operator's switch always had some D.C. potential difference, and before long I was able to tell precisely in which city a disturbance of the lines had occurred just by listening to the clicks.

"Because of its simplicity, this click method has attained primary importance in research on the inner ear. In those days it was generally assumed by the medical profession that the mechanical properties of the tissues of the ear changed rapidly after death, and that there was virtually no possibility of determining the mechanical properties of the inner ear of man. Since it was clear to me from the beginning that if I started to make measurements of the inner ear it would take 2 or 3 years to collect the required data, I wanted to know, as precisely as possible, how fast the

---

* From G. von Bekesy, "Concerning the pleasures of observing, and the mechanics of the inner ear," *Les Prix Nobel en 1961.*

tissues disintegrate. With the click method measurements can be made with such great precision that changes in elasticity or friction as small as 1 or 2 per cent can be detected. My studies of the tissues of the ear centered first on the eardrum, because the drum is so thin that a change in any part of the ear would result in drying or loosening there.

"In the investigation of the tissue, the tendons of the stapes [the stirrup-shaped moveable bone in the middle ear that transmits sound vibrations to the inner ear] and tympanic muscles [tympanum = the eardrum] of anesthetized animals were severed, and changes in the properties of the eardrum were observed during and following the animal's death. If the relative humidity was kept at 100 per cent, even at room temperature there was only an insignificant change, and that mostly in the friction. . . . After these preliminary observations, the road was open to measure the mechanical properties of the cochlea in man and to compare it with the cochleas of different animals.

". . . The great anatomical discoveries by Corti [1851], Kölliker [1852], and Hasse [1862] had already made it clear that the vibrating tissue most important for hearing is the basilar membrane of the inner ear, because the cells on which the nerve endings terminate are seated on this membrane. [When a sound reaches the ear, the eardrum is caused to vibrate. The movement is transmitted by a set of tiny bones in the middle ear, including the stapes mentioned above, through the oval 'window' to the fluid of the inner ear, or cochlea. The cochlea is coiled in a spiral, and is internally divided in the longitudinal direction by the basilar membrane, whose cells are the ultimate sensing device, transmitting the mechanical energy that was initially set up by the vibration of air molecules at the outer ear into electrical energy of the nerve impulse.] . . . How does the basilar membrane vibrate when the eardrum is exposed to a sinusoidal [regular, undulating] sound pressure? Since nobody could see these vibrations, a number of theories developed. . . . And naturally, as time went on, all the possible mechanical vibrations were suggested. We had resonating systems, traveling waves, standing waves, and even no waves at all—just a bulged membrane.

"I took a tuning fork and touched its stem to any materials I could find—threads, chains, springs, membranes, human skin, fluid surfaces—and with a stroboscope [an instrument for detecting the transmitted vibrations and their frequency] observed the vibrations. 1 think my most exciting discovery was the observation that, if the frequency of the vibrations was high enough, all objects that had internal elasticity showed traveling waves. The waves traveled from the vibrator [the tuning fork] to the edge of the object, from which they were more or less reflected back. Therefore, I could see no physical reason whatsoever why the basilar membrane—a gelatinous mass imbedded in fluid—should not also have traveling waves when one section of it was put in motion by alternating pressure.

"The next problem was extremely difficult. . . . [Of the many conceivable types of wave, which ones] are present in the inner ear, and which one contributes to the stimulation of the auditory end organs? . . . It was essential to find out whether one of the waves exceeded the others in magnitude to the extent that, at least for a first approach, the others could be neglected. I well remember the crucial night when I finally became convinced that, at least over the lower frequency range, the ordinary bending of the basilar membrane furnished an adequate description of the vibrations that stimulate the nerve endings. To appreciate that night, you have to remember that the whole inner ear of a guinea pig is about as large as a drop of water at the end of an eye dropper."

[Von Bekesy now turned his attention to characterizing the vibrations of the basilar membrane under a wide variety of conditions, and determining the various physical constants in order to construct a mechanical model based on the essential variable factors. In the course of this research he found that vibration of the eardrum sets up a wave that travels along the basilar membrane from the base, near the oval window, to the apex or tip of the spiral. He observed that with different frequencies of sound the shape of the vibration curve along the basilar membrane is nearly constant, so that frequencies must be detected other than by the shape of the traveling wave. In fact, the wave shows variable amplitudes at different points of its travel. For high-pitched sounds (short wave-lengths, high frequency) the crest of the largest wave occurs near the base of the cochlea, whereas for low-pitched

sounds (long waves, low frequency) this crest is near the apex. Thus, the tone of the sound is characterized by the particular location of the nerve cells of the membrane that are stimulated by sufficiently large amplitudes of the traveling wave.]
"Since the essential variables and their magnitudes were now in hand, it was now possible to think about building an enlarged model of the cochlea. . . . This was done by [H. G.] Diestel [in 1954] in the widely known laboratory of Erwin Meyer in Göttingen. After some modification, the final version of the model consists of a plastic tube filled with water, and a membrane 30 cm in length; when it is stimulated with a vibration it shows traveling waves of the same type as those seen in the normal human ear. The usable frequency range is two octaves.

"Since this development went along so easily, I decided to go one step further and make a model of the inner ear with a nerve supply. An attempt to use a frog skin as a nerve supply had at an earlier time proved to be impractical, and so I simply placed my arm against the model. To my surprise, although the traveling waves ran along the whole length of the membrane with almost the same amplitude, and only a quite flat maximum at one spot, the sensations along my arm were completely different. I had the impression that only a section of the membrane, 2 to 3 cm long, was vibrating. When the frequency of the vibratory stimulus was increased, the section of sensed vibrations traveled toward the piston . . . which represents the stapes footplate of the ear; and when the frequency was lowered, the area of sensation moved in the opposite direction. The model had all the properties of a neuro-mechanical frequency-analyzing system, in support of our earlier view of the frequency analysis of the ear. My surprise was even greater when it turned out that two cycles of sinusoidal vibration are enough to produce a sharply localized sensation on the skin, just as sharp as for continuous stimulation. This was in complete agreement with the observations of [F.] Savart, who found that two cycles of a tone provide enough cue to determine the pitch of the tone [1840]."

CONSEQUENCES IN THEORY
AND PRACTICE

Von Bekesy has examined the function of each part of the hearing apparatus and his audiologic studies have defined its physical properties, from the mechanical movements of the vibrating eardrum to the electrical potential set up when the sensory cells of the cochlea are stimulated. Where his predecessors have described acoustic events, he has recorded them and applied to them the most up-to-date theory of communications engineering with which he was first imbued in his early work at the telephone company in Budapest. Considering that the amplitude of vibration of air particles need be only a tiny fraction of an atomic diameter in order to be detected by the ear as sound, one can appreciate the sensitivity required in instruments for studying the movements in the inner ear. The invention of the amplifier tube necessarily played an important role in facilitating von Bekesy's measurements, but this factor was more than matched by his great ingenuity in devising apparatus and miniaturising the scale of measurement, as in the use of microscope magnification for stroboscopy. He also invented diagnostic instruments. For example, with the audiometer that bears his name, the otologist can make tests to distinguish between deafness caused by functional loss in the cochlea, as in Menière's disease, and that caused by a defect in the auditory nerve.

In his work with the mechanical model of the inner ear, von Bekesy observed that the whole arm is made to vibrate but only a small part is recognized as vibrating; from this he concluded that nervous inhibition must be playing an important role. Indeed, it was found that every local stimulus applied to the skin causes strong inhibition around the place of stimulation; this appears to hold also for the ear and the retina. In this way von Bekesy has been attracted to the study of various special senses. Recently he has investigated the sense of smell.

The publication of Helmholtz's *Die Lehre von den Tonempfindungen* in 1863 established the principle of physical research in the physiology and psychology of hearing, but there was little progress for decades. Indeed, von Bekesy succeeded in solving problems that have been outstanding in acoustic physiology for a century, such as how the ear performs a frequency analysis. He bears the distinction of being a physicist winning the Nobel Prize in physiology and medicine.

1 9 6 2

FRANCIS HARRY COMPTON CRICK

(1916–)

JAMES DEWEY WATSON

(1928–)

MAURICE HUGH FREDERICK WILKINS

(1916–)

"For the discovery of the molecular structure of nucleic acids and its significance for the transfer of information in living material."

BIOGRAPHICAL SKETCHES

CRICK

FRANCIS HARRY COMPTON CRICK WAS BORN ON JUNE 8, 1916, at Northampton, England. He received his early education there and in London. At University College he studied physics and mathematics, obtaining his B.Sc. degree in 1937. His work towards the Ph.D. degree was interrupted by the Second World War, during which he worked as a scientist in the British Admiralty. In 1947 he returned to university to commence studies in biology at Cambridge at the Strangeways Research Laboratory, and soon after at the Medical Research Council Unit, now known as the Laboratory of Molecular Biology (under the direction of M. F. Perutz). Registering once again as a student, he received his Ph.D. in 1954 for research on the x-ray diffraction of polypeptides and proteins. It was during this period that he and J. D. Watson collaborated in their proposal of the structure of DNA and the mechanism of its replication. In 1960-1961 Crick was a fellow of Churchill College at Cambridge. His more recent interests have been in the field of protein synthesis and genetic coding.

WATSON

JAMES DEWEY WATSON WAS BORN IN CHICAGO ON APRIL 6, 1928. He obtained his schooling in that city as well as his B.S. degree in zoology from the University of Chicago (1947). He studied the effect of x-rays on multiplication of bacterial virus at the University of Indiana, in the laboratory of S. E. Luria, and received his Ph.D. degree there in 1950. In Bloomington he developed his interest in genetics through contact with H. J. Muller and T. M. Sonneborn. He then worked in Copenhagen and at Cambridge (in the Cavendish Laboratory, where he met Crick). After two years at the California Institute of Technology and another visit to Cambridge, he was appointed to the faculty of Harvard University in 1956, where he has been professor of biology since 1961. His research there has dealt with the role of nucleic acids in the synthesis of protein.

WILKINS

MAURICE HUGH FREDERICK WILKINS WAS BORN ON DECEMBER 15, 1916, of Irish parents, in Pongaroa, New Zealand. He took his schooling in Birmingham, England, and his university degree in physics at Cambridge. From 1938 to 1940 he carried on research there in the Department of Physics, on solid-state luminescence. His Ph.D. thesis was based on this work. During the

Second World War he worked on radar instrumentation and then (under M. L. E. Oliphant) on separation of uranium isotopes in Birmingham, and at the Manhattan Project in Berkeley, California. After the War, Wilkins turned to problems of biology, first at St. Andrew's University, Scotland, and then at King's College, London, with Professor J. T. Randall. It was at King's College that he began his studies of x-ray diffraction of DNA that led to the concept of the double-helical structure. He has been director of the Biophysical Research Unit there since 1955. In 1963 he was appointed professor of molecular biology.

DESCRIPTION OF THE PRIZE-WINNING WORK

WATSON AND CRICK*

"I arrived in Cambridge in the fall of 1951. Though my previous interests were largely genetic, Luria had arranged for me to work with John Kendrew. I was becoming frustrated with phage experiments and wanted to learn more about the actual structures of the molecules which the geneticists talked about so passionately. . . .

"But almost as soon as I set foot in the Cavendish Laboratory I knew I would never be of much help to [Kendrew]. For I had already started talking with Francis Crick . . . [and] my fate was sealed. For we quickly discovered that we thought the same way about biology. The center of biology was the gene and its control of cellular metabolism. The main challenge in biology was to understand gene replication and the way in which genes control protein synthesis. It was obvious that these problems could be logically attacked only when the structure of the gene became known. This meant solving the structure of DNA. Then this objective seemed out of reach to the interested geneticists. But in our cold, dark Cavendish lab, we thought the job could be done, quite possibly within a few months. Our optimism was partly based on Linus

---

* The first quotation is from J. D. Watson, "The involvement of RNA in the synthesis of proteins," *Les Prix Nobel en 1962*. The second is from Watson and F. H. C. Crick, "A structure for deoxyribose nucleic acid," *Nature* (London), Vol. 171 (1953), pp. 737-738.

Pauling's feat [with R. B. Corey, of deducing in 1951 the manner of coiling of peptide chains]. . . . We also knew that Maurice Wilkins had crystalline x-ray diffraction photographs from DNA, and so it must have a well-defined structure. There was thus an answer for somebody to get.

"During the next 18 months . . . we frequently discussed the necessity that the correct structure have the capacity for self-replication. And in pessimistic moods we often worried that the correct structure might be dull. That is, it would suggest absolutely nothing. . . .

"The finding of the double helix [structure of DNA] thus brought us not only joy but great relief. It was unbelievably interesting and immediately allowed us to make a serious proposal for the mechanism of gene duplication. Furthermore, this replication scheme involved thoroughly understood conventional chemical forces. Previously, some theoretical physicists, among them Pascual Jordan, had proposed that many biological phenomena, particularly gene replication, might be based on long-range forces arising from quantum mechanical resonance interactions. Pauling thoroughly disliked this conjecture and firmly insisted that known short-range forces between complementary surfaces would be the basis of biological replication.

"The establishment of the DNA structure reinforced our belief that Pauling's arguments were sound and that long range forces, or for that matter any form of mysticism, would not be involved in protein synthesis. But for the protein replication problem mere inspection of the DNA structure then gave no immediate bonus. This, however, did not worry us since there was much speculation that RNA, not DNA, was involved in protein synthesis."

*   *   *

"We wish to suggest a structure for the salt of deoxyribose nucleic acid (D.N.A.). This structure has novel features which are of considerable biological interest.

"[It] has two helical chains each coiled round the same axis; . . . each chain consists of phosphate di-ester groups joining [deoxyribose residues through the third and fifth carbon atoms of the sugar]. The two chains (but not their bases) are related by a dyad [system of paired units] perpendicular to the fibre axis. Both chains follow right-handed helices, but owing to the dyad the sequences of the atoms in the two chains run in opposite directions. . . . The bases are on the inside of the helix and the phosphates on the outside. . . . The sugar [is] roughly perpendicular to the attached base. There is a residue on each chain every 3.4Å. [one Ångstrom unit $= 10^{-8}$ centimeter]. . . . The structure repeats after 10 residues on each chain, that is, after 34Å. The distance of a phosphorus atom from the fibre axis is 10Å. As the phosphates are on the outside, cations have easy access to them.

"The novel feature of the structure is the manner in which the two chains are held together by the purine and pyrimidine bases. The planes of the bases are perpendicular to the fibre axis. They are joined together in pairs, a single base from one chain being hydrogen-bonded to a single base from the other chain. . . . One of the pair must be a purine and the other a pyrimidine for bonding to occur. . . .

"[On the basis of an assumption about the chemical form of the bases] only specific pairs of bases can bond together. These pairs are: adenine (purine) with thymine (pyrimidine), and guanine (purine) with cytosine (pyrimidine).

"In other words, if an adenine forms one member of a pair, on either chain, then on these assumptions the other member must be thymine; similarly for guanine and cytosine. The sequence of bases on a single chain does not appear to be restricted in any way. However, if only specific pairs of bases can be formed, it follows that if the sequence of bases on one chain is given, then the sequence on the other chain is automatically determined.

"It has been found experimentally [by Zamenhof, Brawerman and Chargaff, and by Wyatt in 1952] that the ratio of the amounts of adenine to thymine, and the ratio of guanine to cytosine, are always very close to unity for deoxyribose nucleic acid.

"The previously published X-ray data on deoxyribose nucleic acid are insufficient for a rigorous test of our structure. So far as we can tell, it is roughly compatible with the experimental data, but it must be regarded as unproved until it has been checked against more exact results.

". . . The specific pairing we have postulated immediately suggests a possible copying mechanism for the genetic material."

WILKINS*

[Soon after the end of the Second World War Wilkins moved, with Professor J. T. Randall, from St. Andrews, Scotland, to London, where he set to work in the Medical Research Council Biophysics Research Unit at King's College.] "By this time the work of [T.] Caspersson and [J.] Brachet had made the scientific world generally aware that nucleic acids had important biological roles which were connected with protein synthesis. The idea that DNA [deoxyribonucleic acid] might itself be the genetic substance was, however, barely hinted at. Its function in chromosomes was supposed to be associated with replication of the protein chromosome thread. The work of Avery, MacLeod, and McCarty [see p. 366], showing that bacteria could be genetically transformed by DNA, was published in 1944, but even in 1946 it seemed almost unknown, or if known its significance was often belittled.

"It was fascinating to look through microscopes at chromosomes in cells, but I began to feel that as a physicist I might contribute more to biology by studying macromolecules isolated from cells. I was encouraged in this by Gerald Oster, who came from Stanley's virus laboratory and interested me in particles of tobacco mosaic virus. As Caspersson had shown, ultraviolet microscopes could be used to find the orientation of ultra-violet absorbing groups in molecules as well as to measure quantities of nucleic acids in cells. . . . While examining oriented films of DNA prepared for ultraviolet dichroism studies, I saw in the polarising microscope extremely uniform fibres giving clear extinction [i.e. reduced transparency] between crossed nicols [i.e. the fibres rotated polarized light and reduced the amount of light passing through the films]. I found the fibres had been produced unwittingly while I was manipulating DNA gel. Each time that I touched the gel with a glass rod and removed the rod, a thin and

---

* From M. H. F. Wilkins, "The molecular configuration of nucleic acids," *Les Prix Nobel en 1962.*

almost invisible fibre of DNA was drawn out like a filament of spider's web. The perfection and uniformity of the fibres suggested that the molecules in them were regularly arranged. I immediately thought the fibres might be excellent objects to study by X-ray diffraction analysis. I took them to Raymond Gosling, who had our only X-ray equipment (made from war-surplus radiography parts). . . . Almost immediately, Gosling obtained very encouraging diffraction patterns. One reason for this success was that we kept the fibres moist. We remembered that, to obtain detailed X-ray patterns from proteins, Bernal had kept protein crystals in their mother liquor. It seemed likely that the configuration of all kinds of water-soluble biological macromolecules would depend on their aqueous environment. We obtained good diffraction patterns with DNA made by [R.] Signer and [H.] Schwander (1949), which Signer brought to London to a Faraday Society meeting on nucleic acids and which he generously distributed so that all workers, using their various techniques, could study it.

". . . Great interest was aroused [by the diffraction patterns]. In our laboratory, Alex Stokes provided a theory of diffraction from helical DNA. Rosalind Franklin . . . made very valuable contributions to the X-ray analysis. In Cambridge, at the Medical Research Council laboratory where structures of biological macromolecules were studied, my friends Francis Crick and Jim Watson were deeply interested in DNA structure. Watson was a biologist who had gone to Cambridge to study molecular structure. He had worked on bacteriophage reproduction and was keenly aware of the great possibilities that might be opened up by finding the molecular structure of DNA. Crick was working on helical protein structure and was interested in what controlled protein synthesis. . . . The X-ray data from DNA were not so complete that a detailed picture of DNA structure could be derived without considerable aid from stereochemistry. It was clear that the X-ray studies of DNA needed to be complemented by precise molecular model building. In our laboratory we concentrated on amplifying the X-ray data. In Cambridge, Watson and Crick built molecular models.

"The sharpness of the X-ray diffraction patterns of DNA

showed that DNA molecules were highly regular—so regular that DNA could crystallize. The form of the patterns gave clear indications that the molecule was helical, the polynucleotide chains in the molecular thread being regularly twisted. It was known, however, that the purines and pyrimidines of various dimensions were arranged in irregular sequence along the polynucleotide chains. How could such an irregular arrangement give a highly regular structure? This paradox pointed to the solution of the DNA structure problem and was resolved by the structural hypothesis of Watson and Crick."

CONSEQUENCES IN THEORY
AND PRACTICE

The discovery of the double helix structure of DNA was based upon the achievements of Wilkins and his colleagues in obtaining good x-ray diffraction pictures of the fibers that Signer had first donated, followed by many other preparations of DNA; their analysis and interpretation of these photographs; and the brilliant deductions made by Watson and Crick. The structure has been likened to a pair of intertwined helical staircases, the steps (nitrogen bases) being of four kinds; the intertwining actually consists of a pairing of the bases, so that where adenine occurs at a particular level in one of the two helical strands, thymine is found at the corresponding level in the other, and vice versa. Similarly, guanine and cytosine are paired. The sequence of bases appears to be random, but it is now being interpreted as the genetic code, transferring information for the synthesis of specific RNA molecules, and ultimately of specific protein molecules. This was the subject of Crick's Nobel Prize speech. But if the rule of complementary pairing holds, then whatever the sequence of purines and pyrimidines in one strand, the sequence of the other is determined. This means that as the double helix unwinds, each strand can serve as the template for the other, so that the original polynucleotide chains are reproduced. Thus, the Watson-Crick hypothesis of the structure of DNA provides for the role of this molecule in preserving encoded hereditary information and also for its "self-reproduction." The feat for which the Nobel Prize was awarded in 1962 is regarded by many as the greatest discovery in modern biology.

In his Nobel award speech Crick stated: "It now seems certain that the amino acid sequence of any protein is determined by the sequence of bases in some region of a particular nucleic acid molecule. Twenty different kinds of amino acid are commonly found in protein, and four main kinds of base occur in nucleic acid. The genetic code describes the way in which a sequence of twenty or more things is determined by a sequence of four things of a different type.

"It is hardly necessary to stress the biological importance of the problem. It seems likely that most if not all the genetic information in any organism is carried by nucleic acid—usually by DNA, although certain small viruses use RNA as their genetic material. It is probable that much of this information is used to determine the amino acid sequence of the proteins of that organism. . . . This idea is expressed by the classic slogan of Beadle: 'one gene— one enzyme', or, in the more sophisticated but cumbersome terminology of today, 'one cistron—one polypeptide chain'. [The cistron is a large loop of the DNA helix, containing a block of coded information.]

"Let us assume that the genetic code is a simple one and ask how many bases code for one amino acid. This [coding] can hardly be done by a pair of bases, as from four different things we can only form 4 x 4 (= 16) different pairs, whereas we need at least twenty and probably one or two more to act as spaces or for other purposes. However, triplets of bases would give us 64 possibilities. It is convenient to have a word for a set of bases which codes one amino acid and I shall use the word 'codon' for this.

"In a cell in which DNA is the genetic material it is not believed that DNA itself controls protein synthesis directly. [Probably] the base sequence of the DNA . . . is copied onto RNA, and this special RNA then acts as the genetic messenger and directs the actual process of joining up the amino acids into polypeptide chains. The breakthrough in the coding problem has come from the discovery, made by Nirenberg and Matthaei [in 1961], that one can use synthetic RNA for this purpose. In particular, they found that polyuridylic acid—an RNA in which every base is uracil—will promote the synthesis of polyphenylalanine when added to a cell-free system which was already known to synthesize polypeptide chains. Thus, one codon for phenylalanine appears to be the sequence UUU (where U stands for uracil). . . ." *

At present, largely through the work going on in the laboratories of Nirenberg in Bethesda, Maryland, and Ochoa, in New York, about fifty "letters" are known. The code in different organisms is thought to be similar, if not identical. Evidence of this similarity would be equally evidence of the fundamental unity of living things. The elucidation of the detailed sequences in DNA clarifies the genetic code, just as protein structure is being assessed, on a greater and greater scale, in terms of its amino acid sequences. This means that one can expect within a few years not only detailed knowledge of the genetic code, but also experimental means of altering the encoded information to produce variations of polypeptide structures that will, in effect, mean the directed synthesis of new, laboratory-designed proteins, as well as "old" ones such as insulin and other protein or polypeptide hormones, and even enzymes. At the same time we shall gain a better understanding of the interaction of heredity and environment, of mutations and their consequences for enzyme synthesis, and, perhaps, even new insights into the origin of life.

---

* F. H. C. Crick, "On the genetic code," *Les Prix Nobel en 1962.*

1 9 6 3
JOHN CAREW ECCLES
(1903–)

ALAN LLOYD HODGKIN
(1914–)

ANDREW FIELDING HUXLEY
(1917–)

"For their discoveries concerning the ionic mechanisms involved in the excitation and inhibition in the peripheral and central portions of the nerve cell membrane."

BIOGRAPHICAL SKETCHES

ECCLES

JOHN CAREW ECCLES WAS BORN IN MELBOURNE, AUSTRALIA, on January 27, 1903. He studied medicine at Melbourne University, receiving his degree in 1925, and then continued his studies at Oxford in physiology, in Sherrington's department. His Ph.D. thesis (1929) dealt with excitation and inhibition in the nervous system. He remained at Oxford until 1937, when he was appointed director of a medical research laboratory in Sydney. In 1944 he went to the University of Otago, New Zealand, as professor of physiology. Here he studied synaptic transmission in the central nervous system. He returned to Australia once again, in 1952, to become the professor of physiology at the newly founded Australian National University in Canberra. Eccles was elected to fellowship in the Royal Society in 1941, and received its Royal Medal in 1962. He is a fellow of the Royal Society of New Zealand, and has been president of the Australian Academy of Science.

HODGKIN

Alan Lloyd Hodgkin was born in Banbury, Oxfordshire, on February 5, 1914. He was educated at Greshams School and Holt, going on to Cambridge in 1932 where he studied science. His graduate studies dealt with the physiology of nerve and eventually led to an invitation to work at the Rockefeller Institute, in Gasser's laboratory. During his stay in the United States (1937-1938) he worked for a while at Woods Hole Marine Biological Laboratory, with K. S. Cole. During the Second World War he was a scientific officer in the Air Ministry, working on airborne radar. In 1945 he returned to Cambridge to teach physiology. A. F. Huxley was among his students. Hodgkin was elected to the Royal Society in 1948. In 1951 he became a Foulerton Research Professor of the Society, and in 1958 he won its Royal Medal. He was a member of the Medical Research Council of Great Britain from 1959 to 1963.

HUXLEY

Andrew Fielding Huxley was born in London on November 22, 1917. After his early schooling there, he entered Cambridge in 1935, specializing at first in the physical sciences, but then changing to physiology. In 1939 he carried out his first research project when he joined A. L. Hodgkin at the Plymouth Marine Biological Laboratory. At the beginning of the Second World War he was a medical student, but he left this to join the operational research group of the Anti-Aircraft Command, for two years, and then the Admiralty for the remainder of the War. In 1946 he returned to Cambridge where he held various posts and carried on research until 1960. Since then he has been Jodrell Professor of Physiology and head of the department at University College, London. He was elected to the Royal Society in 1955.

DESCRIPTION OF THE PRIZE-WINNING WORK

HODGKIN*

"Trinity College, Cambridge, which I entered in 1932, has a long-standing connexion with neurophysiology. As an undergraduate I found myself interested in nerve and was soon reading books or papers by Keith Lucas, [E. D. Lord] Adrian, [A. V.] Hill, and Rushton, all of whom are, or were, fellows of Trinity. . . . My reading introduced me to Bernstein's membrane theory, in the form developed by Lillie and I thought it would be interesting to test their assumptions by a simple experiment. A central point in the theory is that propagation of the impulse from one point to the next is brought about by the electric currents which flow between resting and active regions. On this view, the action potential is not just an electrical sign of the impulse, but is the causal agent in propagation. Nowadays the point is accepted by everyone, but at that time it lacked experimental proof. By a roundabout route I came across a fairly simple way of testing the idea. The method depended on firing an impulse at a localised block, and observing the effect of the impulse on the excitability of the nerve just beyond the block. It turned out that the impulse produced a transient increase in excitability over a distance of several millimetres, and that the increase was almost certainly caused by electric currents spreading in a local circuit through the blocked region. More striking evidence for the electrical theory was obtained later, for instance when it was shown that the velocity of the nerve impulse could be changed over a wide range by altering the electrical resistance of the external fluid.

---

* From A. L. Hodgkin, "The ionic basis of nervous conduction," *Les Prix Nobel en 1963*.

". . . In 1938 . . . I had the good fortune to spend a year in Gasser's laboratory at the Rockefeller Institute in New York. Before leaving Cambridge, I had found by a lucky accident that it was quite easy to isolate single nerve fibres from the shore crab, *Carcinus maenas*. This opened up several interesting lines and I became increasingly impressed with the advantages of working on single nerve fibres. *Carcinus* fibres are very robust, but they are at most 1/30 millimeter in diameter, and for many purposes this is inconveniently small. There was a good deal to be said for switching to the very much larger nerve fibres which J. Z. Young had discovered in the squid and which were then being studied by Cole and Curtis in Woods Hole. Squids of the genus *Loligo* are active creatures, one or two feet long, which can swim backwards at high speed by taking water into a large cavity and squirting out a jet through a funnel in the front of the animal. The giant nerve fibres, which may be as much as a millimeter in diameter, run in the body wall and supply the muscles that expel water from the mantle cavity. Although these fibres are unmyelinated, their large size makes them conduct rapidly and this may be the teleological reason for their existence. It should be said that large nerve fibres conduct faster than small ones because the conductance per unit of the core increases as the square of the diameter whereas the electrical capacity of the surface increases only as the first power. . . .

"Early in 1938, K. S. Cole asked me to spend a few weeks in his laboratory at Woods Hole where squid are plentiful during the summer. I arrived in June 1938 and was greeted by a sensational experiment, the results of which were plainly visible on the screen of the cathode-ray tube. Cole and Curtis had developed a technique which allowed them to measure changes in the electrical conductivity of the membrane during the impulse; when analysed, their experiments proved that the membrane undergoes a large increase in conductance which has roughly the same time course as the electrical change. This was strong evidence for an increase in ionic permeability but the experiment naturally did not show what ions were involved, and this aspect was not cleared up until several years after the war. At first sight, Cole and Curtis's results seemed to fit in with the idea that the membrane broke down during activity, as Bernstein and Lillie had suggested. However, there was one further point which required checking. According to Bernstein, activity consisted of a momentary breakdown of the membrane,.and on this view the action potential should not exceed the resting potential. Huxley and I started to test this point early in 1939. We measured external electrical changes from *Carcinus* fibres immersed in oil with a cathode ray tube, d.c. amplifier and cathode followers as the recording instrument. The resting potential was taken from the steady potential between an intact region and one depolarized by injury or by isotonic potassium chloride. To our surprise we found that the action potential was often much larger than the resting potential, for example 73 mV for the action potential as against 37 mV for the resting potential. . . . We were extremely suspicious of these results with external electrodes, and before they could be published both of us were caught up in the war. . . .

"At the end of the war, the position was that several of Bernstein's assumptions had been vindicated in a striking way, but that in one major respect the classical theory had been shown to be wrong. By 1945 most neurophysiologists agreed that the action potential was propagated by electric currents, and that it arose at the surface membrane; it was also clear that the resting potential was at least partly due to the E. M. F. [electromotive force] of the potassium concentration cell. On the other hand, there was impressive evidence that in both crab and squid fibres the action potential exceeded the resting potential by 40-50 mV. This was obviously incompatible with the idea that electrical activity depended on a breakdown of the membrane; some process giving a reversal of E. M. F. was required.

"There were several attempts to provide a theoretical basis for the reversal, but most of these were speculative and not easily subject to experimental test. A simpler explanation, now known as the sodium hypothesis, was worked out with Katz and Huxley, and tested during the summer of 1947. The hypothesis, which probably owed a good deal to the classical experiments of Overton [in 1902], was based on a comparison of the ionic composition of the axoplasm of squid nerve with that of blood or sea water. As in Bernstein's theory, it was assumed that the resting membrane is selectively permeable to potassium ions and that the potential across it arises from the tendency of these ions to move outward from the more concentrated solution inside a nerve or muscle fibre. In the limiting case, where a membrane which is permeable only to potassium separates axoplasm containing 400 mM-K from plasma containing 20 mM-K [the concentrations of K, the potassium ion, in axoplasm and in plasma], the internal potential should be 75 mV negative to the external solution. This value is obtained from the Nernst relation [between the potential of a 'potassium cell,' and the concentrations or activities of potassium ions inside and outside the fibre].

"From Bernstein's theory it might be assumed that when the membrane broke down . . . the action potential could not exceed the resting potential and would in fact be less by at least 8 mV. . . . By assuming that the active membrane undergoes a large and selective increase in the permeability to sodium [and that] the membrane is much more permeable to sodium than to any other ion, the potential should approach that given by the Nernst formula [for a 'sodium cell.' This value would be] +58 mV for the 10-fold concentration ratio observed by [H. B.] Steinbach and [S.] Spiegelman [in 1943] and accounts satisfactorily for the reversal of the 50 mV commonly seen in intact axons.

"A simple consequence of the sodium hypothesis is that the magnitude of the action potential should be greatly influenced by the concentration of sodium ions in the external fluid. For the active membrane should no longer be capable of giving a reversed E. M. F. if the concentration of sodium is equalised on the two sides of the membrane. The first quantitative tests were made by [B.] Katz in the summer of 1947. They showed that the action potential, but not the resting potential, was reduced by replacing external sodium chloride with choline chloride or with glucose.

"It was also shown that a solution containing extra sodium increased the overshoot by about the amount predicted [from the Nernst equation for sodium]. This is a particularly satisfactory result, because it seems most unlikely that an increase beyond the normal could be brought about by an abnormal solution.

"The effect of varying external sodium concentration has now been studied on a number of excitable tissues: for example frog muscle, myelinated nerve, Purkinje fibres of the heart [M. H. Draper and S. Weidmann, 1951], and crustacean nerve [J. C. Dalton, 1958]. In all these cases the results were very similar to those in the squid axon.

"[Hodgkin concludes his lecture with a description of a new method: perfusion of axons. The basic technique had been worked out by others at Woods Hole and at Plymouth. It depends upon the fact, known since 1937,] that most of the axoplasm in giant nerve fibres can be squeezed out of the cut end. . . . Until fairly recently no one paid much attention to the electrical properties of the thin sheath which remained after the contents of the nerve fibre had been removed. Since extrusion involves flattening the axon with a glass rod or roller it was natural to suppose that the membrane would be badly damaged by such a drastic method. However in the autumn of 1960 [P. F.] Baker and [T. I.] Shaw recorded action potentials from extruded sheaths which had been refilled with isotonic solution of a potassium salt. On further investigation [with Hodgkin's collaboration] it turned out that such preparations gave action potentials of the usual magnitude for several hours, and that these were abolished, reversibly, by replacing K with Na in the internal solution. . . . The resting potential and action potential vary with the internal concentrations of K and Na in a manner which is consistent with the external effect of these ions."

HUXLEY*

". . . By the time I was taking physiology seriously, in my final year in 1938-39 [at Trinity College, Cambridge, Hodgkin] was one of my teachers . . . and my first introduction to research was the short period that we spent together at the Marine Biological Laboratory at Plymouth in the summer of 1939, when we succeeded in recording the resting and action potentials of the giant nerve fibre of the squid with an internal microelectrode. This work was brought to a stop by the war, but we joined up again at

---

* From A. F. Huxley, "The quantitative analysis of excitation and conduction in nerve," *Les Prix Nobel en 1963.*

Cambridge early in 1946, and almost the whole of my share in the work for which the prize was given was done jointly with him during the succeeding five or six years.

"The measurements on which [the ionic theory of the nerve impulse] was based were made by a feed-back method which has become known as the 'voltage clamp'. [Two electrodes made of fine silver wires are thrust down the axis of the fibre for a distance of about 30 mm., with care not to touch or scrape the inside of the membrane. One electrode together with an external electrode in the sea water bathing the fibre records the membrane potential. The other electrode is used to pass current through the membrane to another external electrode. The size of this current is regulated by a feed-back amplifier in such a way that the membrane potential can be changed suddenly and held, or 'clamped,' at the new level. The two circuits are connected so that] any accidental change of membrane potential is almost completely annulled by the current that the amplifier sends through the membrane.

"[Using the 'voltage clamp' method we were able to show] that when the normal potential difference across the membrane is increased by 40 mV (inside made more negative), the currents are very small. They are . . . always inwards . . . But where the inside of the fibre is made more positive by an equal amount. . . . the currents are of a large order of magnitude; further, if the fibre is in sea water . . . there is a conspicuous early phase in which the direction of the current is against the change of membrane potential. If it were not for the feedback, this current would drive the inside of the fibre still more positive, that is to say, it would produce the rising phase of an action potential. . . . The evidence derived from quite different experiments that Professor Hodgkin has already presented thus suggested that the inward phase of current was carried predominantly by sodium ions, moving under the influence of concentration differences and the potential difference across the membrane. If so, it should disappear when the external sodium concentration is lowered by an appropriate amount. [Experiment showed] that this is the case.

"On this interpretation, the early phase of current should actually be reversed if the external sodium concentration is made low enough or if the internal potential is made high enough. This does actually occur. . . . [In a family of curves derived from experiments in which the membrane currents are measured when the internal potential is clamped at various levels, some voltages cause an early phase of inward current, while higher voltages show an outward current. The record made at 117 mV showed neither,] and it is therefore taken to be very close to the sodium equilibrium potential, at which the current carried by sodium is zero. [That is to say, at this voltage] the electrical potential difference across the membrane just balances the tendency of the sodium ions to diffuse from the higher concentration outside to the lower concentration inside. This potential was found to vary with the sodium concentration in the external fluid, and indeed in exactly the way required by Nernst's equation. This result is perhaps the strongest evidence for the sodium theory, and it justified us in separating the current into two components, the earlier of which is carried predominantly by sodium ions. . . . There is evidence . . . that the late outward current is carried by potassium ions. Perhaps the most convincing is the equivalence that we found between the potassium efflux [outflow], measured with radioactive potassium, and the outward current [Hodgkin and Huxley, 1953].

"The computations [of membrane potentials under various conditions, sodium and potassium conductances, and their temporal relations were for some time] done by hand. This was a laborious business: a membrane action potential took a matter of days to compute, and a propagated action potential took a matter of weeks. But it was often quite exciting. For example, when calculating the effect of a stimulus close to the threshold value, one would see the forces of accommodation—inactivation of the sodium channel, and the delayed rise of potassium permeability—creeping up and reducing the excitatory effect of the rapid rise of sodium permeability. Would the membrane potential get away into a spike, or die in a subthreshold oscillation? Very often my expectations turned out to be wrong, and an important lesson I learnt from these manual computations was the complete inadequacy of one's intuition in trying to deal with a system of this degree of complexity.

"Later on, we extended the range of our calculated responses by using the electronic computers EDSAC I and EDSAC II in the Mathematical Laboratory of Cambridge University.

"The agreement between these computed responses and the potential changes that can be recorded from real nerve fibres is certainly encouraging, but I would not like to leave you with the impression that the particular equations we produced in 1952 are definitive. . . . Both Hodgkin and I feel that these equations should be regarded as a first approximation which needs to be refined and extended in many ways in the search for the actual mechanism of the permeability changes on the molecular scale."

ECCLES[*]

"The body and dendrites of a nerve cell [see p. 36-37] are specialized for the reception and integration of information which is conveyed as impulses that are fired from other nerve cells along their axons. . . . Impinging on [the surface of the nerve cell] are numerous small knoblike endings of fine fibres which are, in fact, the terminal branches of axons from other nerve cells. Communication between nerve cells occurs at these numerous areas of close contact or *synapses,* the name first applied to them by Sherrington, who laid the foundations of what is often called synaptology. . . .

"The high resolving power of electron-microscopy gives essential information on those structural features of synapses that are specially concerned with [the] chemical phase of transmission. [Photographs made in this way reveal] the membrane, about 70 Å thick, that encloses the expanded axonal terminal or *synaptic knob.* These knobs contain numerous small vesicular structures, the *synaptic vesicles* that are believed to be packages of the specific chemical substances concerned in synaptic transmission. Some of these vesicles are concentrated in zones on the membrane that fronts the *synaptic cleft* which is [a] remarkably uniform space about 200 Å across. . . .

---

[*] From J. C. Eccles, "The ionic mechanism of postsynaptic inhibition," *Les Prix Nobel en 1963.*

"The simplest example of synaptic action is illustrated [by the example of] a single synchronous synaptic bombardment [which reaches a motoneurone and] diminishes the electric charge on the cell membrane. A rapid rise to the summit [of the wave of depolarization] is followed by a slower, approximately exponential, decay. This depolarization becomes progressively larger . . . as the number of activated synapses increases, there being in fact a simple summation of the depolarization produced by each individual synapse. . . . When above a critical size, the synaptic depolarization evokes . . . the discharge of an impulse, just as occurs in peripheral nerve. The only effect of strengthening the synaptic stimulus . . . was the earlier generation of the impulse, which in every case arose when the depolarization reached 18 mV. The synapses that in this way excite nerve cells to discharge impulses are called *excitatory synapses,* and the depolarization potentials that excitatory synapses produce in the postsynaptic membrane are called *excitatory postsynaptic potentials* or *EPSPs.* There has now been extensive investigation of a wide variety of nerve cells in the central nervous system, and in every case synaptic transmission of impulses is due to this same process of the production of EPSPs, which in turn generate impulse discharge when attaining a critical level of depolarization.

"[Eccles goes on to speak of] a second class of synapses that oppose excitation and tend to prevent the generation of impulses by excitatory synapses; hence they are called *inhibitory synapses.* There is general agreement that these two basic modes of synaptic action govern the generation of impulses by nerve cells. . . . Activation of inhibitory synapses causes an increase in the postsynaptic membrane potential. The *inhibitory postsynaptic potential* or *IPSP* is virtually a mirror image of the EPSP. The effects of individual inhibitory synapses on a nerve cell summate in exactly the same way as with the excitatory synapses; and of course the inhibition of excitatory synaptic action is accounted for by the opposed action on the potential of the postsynaptic membrane.

"The effects produced in the size and direction of the IPSP by varying the initial membrane potential correspond precisely to the changes that would be expected if the currents generating the

IPSP were due to ions moving down their electrochemical gradients. . . . These currents would be caused to flow by increases in the ionic permeability of the subsynaptic membrane that are produced under the influence of the inhibitory transmitter substance. . . .

"Experimental investigations on the ionic mechanisms [require special techniques when working with mammalian nerves]. . . . The procedure of electrophoretic injection of ions out of [a microelectrode whose tip has been carefully thrust into the body of the cell] has been employed to alter the ionic composition of the postsynaptic cell. . . .

"In conclusion [one can summarize] the detailed events which are presumed to occur when an impulse reaches a presynaptic terminal, and which we would expect to see if electron-microscopy can be developed to have sufficient resolving power. Some of the synaptic vesicles are in close contact with the membrane and one or more are caused by the impulse to eject their contained transmitter substance into the synaptic cleft. Diffusion across and along the cleft, as shown, would occur in a few microseconds for distances of a few hundred Ångstroms. [A speed of 100 Å per microsecond = 1 cm./sec.] Some of the transmitter becomes momentarily attached to the specific receptor sites on the postsynaptic membrane with the consequence that there is an opening up of fine channels across this membrane, i.e. the subsynaptic membrane momentarily assumes a sieve-like character. The ions, chloride and potassium, move across the membrane thousands of times more readily than normally; and this intense ionic flux gives the current that produces the IPSP and that counteracts the depolarizing action of excitatory synapses, so effecting inhibition."

CONSEQUENCES IN THEORY AND PRACTICE

The chief cation of the body fluids is sodium (Na^+), that of muscle, nerve, and other tissues is potassium (K^+). Conversely, the concentration of sodium in these tissues is less than in the extracellular fluids, and the concentration of potassium is lower in plasma than in cells. These facts were long known to physiologists, and provided the basis for a theory of the propagation of the nerve impulse as an electrical wave down the fiber. Julius Bernstein, at the University of Halle in Germany, proposed in 1902 that the resting potential of the cell may derive from the differential concentration of potassium on the two sides of the axonal membrane, maintained by the permeability characteristics of the membrane. According to his hypothesis, when the nerve impulse arrives at a particular spot this permeability alters so that excessive sodium ions from the external fluid rush into the fiber and cause the potential to fall to zero. This becomes the stimulus for similar changes in the adjacent regions of the fiber, so that the impulse moves rapidly down the length of the axon. The question was: how to detect ionic changes of such small absolute values and occurring in periods measurable in thousandths of a second?

In the course of his studies of the nervous system of cephalopods (e.g. octopus, squid, cuttlefish) J. Z. Young reported on the presence of "giant" nerve fibers in these species, as much as 0.5 mm. across. His suggestion that they might prove useful to the nerve physiologist was taken up by teams in the United States—K. S. Cole and H. J. Curtis, working at Woods Hole, on Cape Cod— and in England—Hodgkin and Huxley, among others, working at Plymouth and Cambridge. By 1939 these two groups had been able to measure the membrane potential of the giant axons by pushing an extremely fine electrode down the center of the fiber and connecting this wire to their measuring system. In his Nobel Prize speech Hodgkin asks how we do without giant nerve fibers. "The answer is that vertebrates have developed myelinated axons in which the fibre is covered with a relatively thick insulating layer over most of its length, and the excitable membrane is exposed only at [intervals, at] the nodes of Ranvier. In these fibres, conduction is saltatory and the impulse skips from one node to the next."

After the Second World War, when Hodgkin and Huxley were able to return to their neurophysiological research, they adopted additional techniques. Among these was the use of micropipettes devised by Ling and Gerard (then at the University of Chicago). These instruments were smaller than one two-thousandth of a millimeter in diameter at the tip and could be inserted into the interior of a cell without injury, the membrane sealing itself around the pipette. Once inside, the pipette can be used to inject minute volumes of solutions, to carry an electrical current, or to record the potential of the cell. The "voltage clamp" technique, described above, had been devised by Cole and G. Marmont at Woods Hole, and was later adopted and developed by Bernhard Katz, working with Hodgkin and Huxley. The micropipette and microelectrode techniques have been extensively applied by Eccles and his colleagues to study motor neurones of spinal cord and of the synapses there and elsewhere in the central nervous system. In particular they have demonstrated that the process of synaptic transmission in the spinal cord is analogous to transmission of the impulse from motor nerve to muscle fiber, our knowledge of which stems from the fundamental experiments on chemical transmission of the nerve impulse carried out by Otto Loewi and Sir Henry Dale.

The appreciation of the fundamental chemical and physical events in the action of nerves that stems from the Nobel Prize-winning work has increased our understanding of related events in other organs as well, notably the heart and kidney. But above all it can be expected that this knowledge will be found applicable to the study of the action of many neurones acting in concert, as in brain function, as well as to the fundamental investigation of diseases of the nervous system.

1 9 6 4
KONRAD BLOCH
(1912–   )

FEODOR LYNEN
(1911–   )

*"For their discoveries concerning the mechanism and
regulation of cholesterol and fatty acid metabolism."*

BIOGRAPHICAL SKETCHES

BLOCH

KONRAD EMIL BLOCH WAS BORN IN NEISSE, GERMANY, ON
January 21, 1912. He studied chemical engineering at the Technische Hochschule in Munich, but left Germany for the United
States in 1936, where he studied for the Ph.D. degree in biochemistry at Columbia University under the late Rudolf Schoenheimer.
He received the degree in 1938 for his work in metabolism, using
compounds that had been "labeled" with deuterium, at that time
a highly novel technique. He joined the faculty of Columbia University, and later that of the University of Chicago. In 1954 he
became Higgins Professor of Biochemistry at Harvard University.

LYNEN

FEODOR LYNEN WAS BORN IN MUNICH ON APRIL 6, 1911. HE
received his university education in that city, studying with H.
Wieland from 1935 to 1937. He joined the Department of Chemistry of the University of Munich in 1942. In 1947 he was made
professor of chemistry there. In 1951 he discovered the identity
of "active acetate" to be acetyl-coenzyme A, and subsequently characterized the metabolic unit involved in the biosynthesis of terpenes, carotenoids, and steroids as isopentenyl pyrophosphate.
This was simultaneous with a similar report from K. Bloch's laboratory. He has also conducted research on the metabolism of fatty
acids and on the function of biotin. Since 1954 he has been the
director of the Max Planck Institute for Cell Chemistry in his
native city. He received the first "Otto Warburg Medal" of the
German Chemical Society (1963).

DESCRIPTION OF THE PRIZE-WINNING
WORK

BLOCH*

"The biological synthesis of the steroids became an experimental
area nearly twenty years ago when it was demonstrated that these
substances are constructed by the interaction of numerous small
molecules [shown by David Rittenberg and Rudolf Schoenheimer
in 1937 at Columbia University in New York], and that it is acetic
acid which furnishes the building blocks for ergosterol in yeast
[R. Sonderhoff and H. Thomas in 1937] and for cholesterol in
animal tissues [Bloch and Rittenberg in 1942]. In the years following, the role of acetate as the prime sterol precursor has been
consolidated and the direction of research has gradually shifted

---

* The first section is from K. Bloch, "The biological synthesis of cholesterol,"
Vitamins and Hormones, Vol. 15 (1957), pp. 119 ff. The second is taken from
an article by S. Chaykin, J. Law, A. H. Phillips, T. T. Tchen, and K. Bloch,
"Phosphorylated intermediates in the synthesis of squalene," *Proceedings of the
National Academy of Science* (U. S. A.), Vol. 44 (1958), pp. 998-1004.

toward the identification of the numerous intermediates on the path from acetate to cholesterol.

". . . When acetic acid was first shown to be the carbon source of the steroid molecule, the known metabolic reactions of acetic acid were few and there were none of obvious relevance to steroid biogenesis. At that time, the elongation of 2-carbon chains [such as that of acetate] by condensation to acetoacetate was reasonably well established, but no evidence existed for the participation of acetate in the synthesis of extended or branched chains, or of cyclic structures. A chemical analysis of biosynthetic C^{14}-cholesterol [i.e. cholesterol with some of its carbon atoms 'labeled' with radioactive carbon] was then undertaken with the aim of ascertaining how many of the carbon atoms of the C_{27}-steroid skeleton were furnished by acetate [H. N. Little and Bloch, 1950]. It was also hoped that the labeling pattern which emerged would throw some light on the nature of the condensation process. While this work was in progress, the role of acetate as the principal carbon source for the steroids was convincingly demonstrated by an independent study on ergosterol formation in [a mutant of *Neurospora* that requires acetate for growth. R. C. Ottke, Nobel Prizewinner E. L. Tatum, I. Zabin and Bloch collaborated in this work]. The laborious analysis of the cholesterol molecule by stepwise degradation of the carbon skeleton was nevertheless continued [by the British investigators J. W. Cornforth and G. Popjak], and with results which amply justified these efforts. Thus, the first experimental suggestion that the sterols may arise by ring closure from an acyclic polyisoprenoid precursor [a compound made up of several 5-carbon, branched-chain isoprene units] came from the distribution pattern of the two carbon atoms of acetic acid in the . . . side chain of cholesterol. Later, when the terpenoid precursor [the terpenes are complex compounds, represented by certain odoriferous essential oils of plants, vitamin A, squalene (a compound first found in shark liver oil, hence its name), and sterols] was shown to be squalene [by R. G. Langdon and Bloch in 1953] and various cyclization schemes [i.e. hypotheses to explain the chemical steps whereby the open-chain compound squalene folds to form the four condensed rings of cholesterol] were under discussion, the isotopic framework again furnished the critical information for distinguishing between alternative reaction mechanisms [R. B. Woodward and Bloch, 1953].

". . . The recognition that lanosterol, one of the alcohols from wool fat, is structurally related to both cholesterol and the cyclic triterpenes [L. Ruzicka, Nobel Prize Winner in chemistry, and his colleagues showed this in 1952] has aided in rationalizing the origin of the tetracyclic steroids from an acyclic triterpenoid chain.

"[The transformation of squalene into lanosterol] occurs presumably in a single step, but the building of the triterpenoid chain and the demethylation of lanosterol to cholesterol must be composites of numerous individual reactions. . . . The present indications are that many of the intermediates still missing between acetate and squalene and between lanosterol and cholesterol occur in amounts far too small to be identified by the traditional methods of organic chemistry.

"It seemed until recently that all conceivable approaches toward the identification of the biologically active isoprene unit had been exhausted and had ended inconclusively. However, the problem has now entered a new and promising stage with the isolation of mevalonic acid, the acetate-replacing factor for *Lactobacillus casei*. Mevalonic acid, the lactone of β,δ-dihydroxy-β-methylvaleric acid, [has been tested as a prescursor of cholesterol and found to be highly effective, although under the same conditions compounds that are closely related were virtually inert as precursors]. The remarkable activity of mevalonic acid suggests that it is closely related in structure to the active isoprenoid intermediate. . . . In the author's laboratory, a soluble enzyme system from yeast has been found to catalyze the conversion of mevalonic acid to squalene as the sole product in the presence of [adenosine triphosphate, divalent manganese ions] and reduced pyridine nucleotide. A. preparation of mevalonic acid labeled by tritium at the δ-carbon atom yielded squalene without loss of heavy hydrogen. This suggests that the condensing unit has the same oxidation level as mevalonic acid, i.e. the squalene chain appears to be formed by direct interaction of CH_2 groups, a condensation of an entirely novel type. . . .

"Structural similarities between the terpenes and the sterols

Some Intermediates in the Biosynthesis of Cholesterol

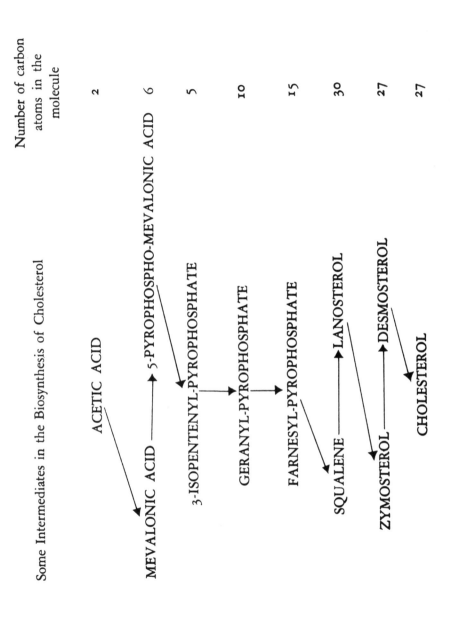

	Number of carbon atoms in the molecule
ACETIC ACID	2
MEVALONIC ACID	
5-PYROPHOSPHO-MEVALONIC ACID	6
3-ISOPENTENYL-PYROPHOSPHATE	5
GERANYL-PYROPHOSPHATE	10
FARNESYL-PYROPHOSPHATE	15
SQUALENE	30
LANOSTEROL	
ZYMOSTEROL	
DESMOSTEROL	27
CHOLESTEROL	27

were early recognized and made the basis for the suggestion that the two classes of compounds are biogenetically related. This hypothesis received its first support when [H. J.] Channon [in 1926] showed that the feeding of squalene . . . produced increased levels of sterols in the liver of the rat. The subject was not further explored experimentally until isotopic tracers permitted the demonstration [by Langdon and Bloch] that a hydrocarbon indistinguishable from squalene is synthesized from acetate by mammalian tissues. Furthermore, isotopic carbon from biosynthetically prepared squalene was found to be incorporated into cholesterol with high efficiency."

[The distribution of the respective carbon atoms of acetate in cholesterol was initially postulated to occur in a particular fashion. This has now been verified by several groups of researchers for specific cholesterol-carbons.] "The degradation and isotopic analysis of the entire ring system of cholesterol has recently been completed by Cornforth and Popjak. With this remarkable achievement, the long series of investigations on the distribution of acetate carbons in the steroid molecule has come to a successful conclusion."

*   *   *

"Investigations in this laboratory on the mechanism of squalene synthesis from mevalonic acid have proceeded along two lines: (1) certain structural features of the 'isoprenoid' condensing unit have been defined by experiments using heavy hydrogen as a tracer, and (2) yeast extracts have been fractionated with the aim of accumulating intermediates between mevalonic acid and squalene. The experiments with D_2O [heavy water, i.e. water containing the heavy isotope of hydrogen, deuterium] and T-labeled [T = tritium, the radioactive isotope of hydrogen] mevalonic acid have led to the principal conclusions that the new carbon-carbon bonds between two isoprenoid units are formed by the interaction of two methylene groups and that the carboxyl groups of mevalonic acid are probably removed in a concerted process with simultaneous elimination of the tertiary hydroxyl groups. As to the requirements for the over-all process, it could be shown that in yeast extracts the co-factors for squalene synthesis from mevalonic acid are adenosine triphosphate, divalent manganese ions, and re-duced pyridine nucleotide. To account for the requirements of adenosine triphosphate and manganese, the formation of phos-phorylated intermediates was postulated [in 1957]. The subsequent demonstration of an enzyme system that catalyzes the reaction mevalonic acid + adenosine triphosphate → phosphomevalonic acid + adenosine diphosphate confirmed this hypothesis. Phos-phomevalonic acid is efficiently converted to squalene and appears to be the first product in the over-all transformation. Evidence has been presented that [it] is a phosphate ester and, as will be shown later, can be assumed to be 5-phosphomevalonic acid. We have also reported briefly that adenosine triphosphate is still re-quired for the further metabolism of phosphomevalonic acid, sug-gesting the existence of additional phosphorylation steps. We now wish to describe a second and a third phosphorylated inter-mediate (II and III) which are formed during the conversion of mevalonic acid to squalene.

"In order to characterize compounds II and III, a series of ex-periments were carried out using [forms of mevalonic acid, phos-phomevalonic acid and adenosine triphosphate variously labeled with carbon-14 and/or phosphorus-32]. By combining various labeled substrates and labeled or unlabeled adenosine triphosphate [in incubation experiments, the] properties of compounds II and III were established.

"[The results suggest] that compound II is mevalonic acid-5-pyrophosphate . . . [and that compound III is] Δ³-isopentenol pyrophosphate."

LYNEN*

"With the discovery of mevalonic acid in the laboratory of K. Folkers [at Merck Sharp and Dohme, Inc., in the United States], the study of the biosynthesis of terpenes and steroids from acetic acid has entered upon a new phase. After Tavormina, Gibbs and Huff had shown that cell-free extracts of liver could convert radioactive mevalonic acid into cholesterol, there appeared a rapid

---

* From F. Lynen, H. Eggerer, U. Henning, and I. Kessel, "Farnesyl-pyrophosphat und 3-Methyl-Δ³-butenyl-1-pyrophosphat, die biologischen Vorstufen des Squa-len," *Angewandte Chemie*, Vol. 70 (1958), pp. 738-742.

series of publications in which the incorporation of mevalonic acid into squalene, carotenoids, mono- and triterpenes, or rubber was described. It was therefore clear that 'active isoprene' was formed from mevalonic acid, this 'active isoprene' serving as the building block in the biosynthesis of terpenes and related natural products. The existence of such a common building-block had to be expected on the basis of the 'isoprene-rule', which L. Ruzicka, in his pioneering investigations on the chemical constitution of terpenes, had recognized and formulated.

"With regard to the enzyme systems concerned here, the conversion of mevalonic acid into squalene has been most exhaustively studied. One can hardly question the fact that the results thus far obtained are of the greatest importance for the problem of the biosynthesis of terpene. Above all, there is the question of the manner in which the molecules of the building-block are joined together to form longer chains of carbon atoms. . . .

"The question of the biological precursor of farnesyl-pyrophosphate [the phosphorylated intermediary form of farnesol, just such an elongated chain (of 15 carbon atoms),] was answered by inhibition-experiments. If, to the reaction mixture containing carbon-14-labeled mevalonic acid-5-phosphate, magnesium ions, adenosine triphosphate and yeast enzyme, M/200 iodoacetamide is added, the formation of farnesyl-pyrophosphate ceases. In its place appears another intermediary product, which can be separated [from other materials] by high-voltage electrophoresis. . . . The radioactive material could be eluted [i.e. washed off] from papers on which the electrophoresis was carried out, using dilute ammonia, and by subsequent preparative paper chromatography [another separation procedure] in ethanol-water-concentrated ammonia (8:1:1) as the solvent it could be obtained pure. As chemical investigation has shown, it behaves like 3-methyl-$\triangle^3$-butenyl-(1)-pyrophosphate or, more briefly, isopentenyl-pyrophosphate. . . .

"Still not understood are the reactions whereby 5-phosphomevalonic acid, together with adenosine triphosphate, is converted by dehydration and decarboxylation to isopentenyl pyrophosphate. As Rilling, Tchen and Bloch conjectured, on the basis of the insignificant introduction of deuterium into squalene when the reaction was run in heavy water, the decarboxylation takes place in a concerted reaction together with the elimination of the tertiary hydroxyl group. The role of adenosine triphosphate in this reaction is still not precisely understood.

"We have just as little certainty about the chemical processes upon which the formation of squalene from farnesyl-pyrophosphate is based. According to our experiments the enzyme that is involved is tightly bound to the particles of the yeast extract or to the microsomes of the liver homogenate. Reduced triphosphopyridine nucleotide is needed for the reaction."

CONSEQUENCES IN THEORY AND PRACTICE

Cholesterol is an ubiquitous constituent of animal tissues, and is characterized chemically by four rings of carbon atoms, fused together, with various other attached groups that specify the particular steroid compound and its physiological activity: cholesterol itself, the sex hormones, the bile acids, and the adrenal cortical hormones. The plant world forms other members of this class of compound, such as ergosterol, a substance analogous to the cholesterol of the animal kingdom. Vitamin D is derived from certain steroids by ultraviolet irradiation. Because of these fascinating relationships, it had long been believed that when the mechanism of formation of cholesterol would be known, the biological synthesis of the related hormones and vitamins would also be understood. As Bloch points out, it was in 1937 that the origin of cholesterol and ergosterol in small molecules, particularly acetic acid, was discovered. This was accomplished by using isotopic atoms in the composition of acetic acid in order to "label" that molecule and to permit identification later on of those acetic acid-derived atoms in the finished sterol product. In 1942-1945 Bloch and Rittenberg (the latter, now professor of biochemistry at the College of Physicians and Surgeons of Columbia University) showed the origin of cholesterol and fatty acids in acetic acid. Eleven years later Langdon and Bloch identified squalene as an intermediate in cholesterol biosynthesis. In 1958, Bloch and Lynen simultaneously identified a phosphorylated compound made up of

5 carbon atoms, isopentenyl pyrophosphate, as a precursor of the sterols. Feodor Lynen has contributed much to an understanding of the steps that lie between self-condensation of this intermediate to form larger and larger molecules, eventually attaining the 30-carbon structure of squalene. Bloch has since studied the transformation of this substance, which is an open-chain compound, into the cyclic steroid structures leading to cholesterol. The work of these investigators might not have led so steadily to the untangling of the mystery of cholesterol's formation in the cell but for the yeoman work of J. W. Cornforth and G. J. Popjak in England. These investigators employed acetate labeled with radioactive carbon in order to trace the location of particular atoms of this precursor in biologically synthesized cholesterol. Their painstaking work specified the origin of each carbon of cholesterol as to its derivation from the methyl or carboxyl group of acetic acid, respectively. When this "mapping" had been done for the side chain of cholesterol, the distribution of the two carbons of acetic acid suggested that the sterols might arise from an open-chain compound with the polyisoprenoid structure, which folds to form the complex ring structure.

Acetic acid enters metabolism by being phosphorylated and converted to the "active" form. As already mentioned (p. 311), Lynen discovered in 1951 that this was a condensed product of acetate and coenzyme A, the pantothenic acid-containing substance that Lipmann and his co-workers had described. In 1958 it was found that the conversion of acetyl-coenzyme A to fatty acids, long-chain structures, requires the B vitamin biotin as a participant in the reaction. Through the work of many laboratories, including that of Lynen, it is now known that biotin enables the acetyl-coenzyme A to take up a molecule of carbon dioxide to form malonyl-coenzyme A (i.e. a 3-carbon compound is now formed from the 2-carbon acetic acid, both attached to coenzyme A), and that this substance is actually the source of the carbons in the fatty acid, although the carbon dioxide is lost as the malonate is about to be attached to the incipient fatty acid chain. Lynen has shown that the biotin takes up a molecule of carbon dioxide to form 1'-N-carboxybiotin. This is known colloquially to biochemists as "active CO_2," and it then participates in the conversion of acetyl- to malonyl-coenzyme A.

Many disorders of metabolism of the lipides are known. Atherosclerosis has figured prominently among these, because of the association with heart disease. But fat metabolism is upset in diabetes mellitus; and various types of lipide ("fatty") disorders are known, such as xanthomatosis and the sphinglipidoses. A detailed, intimate knowledge of the manner in which specific lipides are formed and broken down in the body can be expected to aid in the treatment of these various disturbances of metabolism. We already have compounds that can inhibit the biological formation of cholesterol in the body at one stage or another, and help reduce the concentration of that substance in the blood and elsewhere. Unfortunately, these compounds are too toxic to be used clinically, but their action certainly gives hope that other similarly acting materials will become available in the future for non-toxic drug use. Although obesity is not a disease, one can look for a greater appreciation of the metabolic factors in this condition which has been called the major nutritional problem in the United States.

REFERENCE

Cornforth, J. W., and Popjak, G. J. "The biochemistry of cholesterol," *New Scientist,* Vol. 24 (1964), pp. 220-221.

1 9 6 5
FRANÇOIS JACOB
(1920–   )

ANDRÉ LWOFF
(1902–   )

JACQUES MONOD
(1910–   )

"For their discovery of a previously unknown class of genes whose function is to regulate the activity of other genes."

BIOGRAPHICAL SKETCHES

JACOB

FRANÇOIS JACOB WAS BORN AT NANCY IN 1920. IN 1938 HE registered as a student in the Faculty of Medicine, Paris, with the aim of training in surgery but, in 1940, he left France in one of the last Allied ships before the beginning of the Occupation. After military service in North Africa and France, he completed his medical training and then chose a research career at the Pasteur Institute in Paris under Lwoff. He obtained his science doctorate

432

from the Sorbonne in 1954, with a thesis on lysogeny. After joining the Pasteur Institute he received promotions that gradually
gave him positions of greater research responsibility and, in 1960,
he became the chief of the Department of Microbial Genetics. He
was appointed professor of cellular genetics at the Collège de
France in 1964. In that year he helped to set up the European Organization for Molecular Biology, and was the first head of the
Council.

LWOFF

ANDRÉ MICHEL LWOFF WAS BORN AT AULNAY-LE CHATEAU
(Allier) on May 8, 1902. His parents had not long before emigrated from Russia to France, where his father became director of
a mental hospital. Lwoff obtained his medical (1927) and science
(1932) doctorates in Paris. Since 1925 he and his wife have been
collaborators in research at the Pasteur Institute. In 1938 he became head of the Department of Microbial Physiology there, and
in 1959 he was appointed professor of microbiology at the Sorbonne. He has received many honors, including election to membership in the Royal Society and the National Academy of Sciences
(U.S.A.). In 1962 he was president of the International Association of Societies of Microbiology.

MONOD

JACQUES LUCIEN MONOD WAS BORN IN PARIS ON FEBRUARY 9,
1910. He completed his first science degree in 1931, and received
his Doctorate in Natural Sciences in 1941 (Paris). During this
interval he taught in the Department of Zoology at the University
of Paris, and also spent a year at the California Institute of Technology as a Rockefeller Fellow in 1936. He joined the Pasteur
Institute staff in 1945 and soon became head of the Department of
Microbial Physiology. In 1954 he was appointed director of cellular biochemistry. He received university recognition through appointment as professor of metabolic chemistry at the Faculty of
Sciences, Paris, in 1957. Monod is an accomplished musician.

DESCRIPTION OF THE PRIZE-WINNING
WORK

LWOFF *

"Lysogeny occupies a privileged position at the cross roads of normal and pathological heredity, of genes and viruses. The study of lysogenic bacteria has modified our conceptions, concerning the origin, nature, biology and physiology of bacteriophages [bacterial viruses] and posed the problem of cellular immunity. . . .

"In 1925, Eugène Wollman put forward the hypothesis that some genes could perhaps have a certain stability and be transmitted from cell to cell by the external medium [in contrast to the only type of transfer known at that time: nuclear inheritance in sexual reproduction]. Discussing in 1928 the transmission of bacterial properties through the external medium which he referred to as *paraheredity,* Wollman expressed the prophetic view that such transmissions could be due to genes; thus, the nature of the future transforming principles [see p. 366] was foreseen. Wollman also compared phages to lethal genes [those causing the death of the organism bearing them, or at least those organisms homozygous for such genes] and concluded that one has to distinguish *true viruses,* that is, parasitic germs, foreign to their host, and *elements of cellular origin* able to be transmitted either hereditarily or through the medium. These views were severely criticized by [J.] Bordet and [E.] Renaux [in 1928] who remarked that if bacteriophages were really 'materialized hereditary properties', it was difficult to understand how they could be responsible for lytic processes [that disrupt the infected bacterium].

"The Wollman's gene conception was well in advance of its time and, until 1950–51, remained unaccepted or ignored with one exception. In 1936, [F. M.] Burnet and [D.] Lush, discussing the origin of the induced resistance towards a phage brought by the infection with another phage, noted that the resistance, the changed character, is transmitted indefinitely to the descendants and remarked that the change could come either from an altered

---

* From A. Lwoff, "Lysogeny," *Bacteriological Reviews,* Vol. 17 (1953), pp. 269–337.

genetic constitution of the bacterium or be directly induced by the associated phage at each division. The distinction would disappear, however, according to Wollman's hypothesis that regarded phage as a gene reintroduced into the genetic make-up of the organism.

"In 1934, the Wollmans [Eugène and Elisabeth], convinced of the validity of their gene theory of the phage, started their work on lysogeny.

"Lysogeny is the hereditary power to produce bacteriophage. *A lysogenic bacterium is a bacterium possessing and transmitting the power to produce bacteriophage.* Each bacterium of a lysogenic strain gives rise to a lysogenic clone.

". . . A given lysogenic bacterium may produce one or several types of phages. When a nonlysogenic bacterium is infected and lysogenized with a given phage, the lysogenic strain produces the original phage. Thus, lysogenic bacteria perpetuate a specific structure. But when a lysogenic bacterium is disrupted [as by lysozyme, an enzyme discovered by Sir Alexander Fleming] no infectious particles are released. Lysogeny is perpetuated in the form of a noninfectious structure. This specific noninfectious structure, endowed with genetic continuity, is called prophage. *Prophage is the form in which lysogenic bacteria perpetuate the power to produce phage.* Its multiplication is correlated with bacterial reproduction. It seems to be located at a specific site of a bacterial chromosome and to behave in crosses as a bacterial gene. . . .

"The proportion of lysogenic bacteria which produces phages spontaneously is variable. Shall we consider this situation as a statistician, draw mortality curves, calculate the probability for a given bacterium to produce bacteriophage in the interval of two divisions, and be satisfied with a formula expressing the state of health of the bacterial population in terms of Greek symbols? Or, acting as a biologist, a biochemist, or as the sorcerer's apprentice, shall we attempt to intervene in the course of events which transform an innocuous particle into a virus? . . ."

[The second question was, of course, rhetorical. Lwoff certainly "intervened." He used a technique that his colleagues had planned to introduce in this work—the study of individual bacteria rather than a large population with "averaged-out" characteristics.]

". . . The Wollmans realized that the solution of the problems concerning lysogeny would come from experiments with single bacteria and secured a micromanipulator. But their work was tragically interrupted in 1943 when [they] were arrested in the Pasteur Institute, deported to Germany and disappeared in one of the Vernichtungslagern. . . . [In 1950, Lwoff and A. Gutmann described the results they had obtained with the single-organism technique.]

"The observation of a number of bacterial microclones of *B. megatherium* developing in microdrops had shown that in some clones, a high proportion of up to 10/10 bacteria lysed and liberated phages, whereas in others only one bacteria in 100 to 200 produced phage. This strongly suggested that phage production was controlled by external factors . . . by some changes of the medium induced by the bacterial metabolism. After a large number of experiments, it was finally discovered that irradiation with UV (ultraviolet) light was followed by phage formation in almost the entire bacterial population [this was the work of Lwoff, L. Siminovitch and N. Kjeldgaard, in 1950]; forty-five minutes after irradiation, the bacteria lysed and liberated bacteriophages. Evidently, UV light induces the development of prophage into bacteriophage. The synthesis of a particle possessing the characteristic traits of a virus from a particle possessing the behavior of a gene can therefore be induced and studied under defined conditions . . ."

JACOB AND MONOD *

"It has been known for a long time . . . that the synthesis of individual proteins may be provoked or suppressed within a cell, under the influence of specific external agents, and more generally that the relative rates at which different proteins are synthesized may be profoundly altered, depending on external conditions. Moreover, it is evident from the study of many such effects that their operation is absolutely essential to the survival of the cell.

"It has been suggested in the past that these effects might result from . . . complementary contributions of genes on the one hand, and some chemical factors on the other in determining the final structure of proteins. This view, which contradicts at least partially the 'structural gene' hypothesis, has found as yet no experimental

---

* From F. Jacob and J. Monod, "Genetic regulatory mechanisms in the synthesis of proteins," *Journal of Molecular Biology*, Vol. 3 (1961), pp. 318–356.

support. . . . Taking, at least provisionally, the structural gene hypothesis in its strictest form, let us assume that the DNA message contained within a gene is both necessary and sufficient to define the structure of a protein. The elective effects of agents other than the structural gene itself in promoting or suppressing the synthesis of a protein must then be described as operations which control the rate of transfer of structural information from gene to protein. Since it seems to be established that proteins are synthesized in the cytoplasm, rather than directly at the genetic level, this transfer of structural information must involve a chemical intermediate synthesized by the genes. This hypothetical intermediate we shall call the structural messenger.

". . . Let us . . . consider what properties would be required of a cellular constituent, to allow its identification with the structural messenger. These qualifications, based on general assumptions and on [experimental] results, would be as follows: (1) The 'candidate' would be a polynucleotide. (2) The fraction would presumably be very heterogeneous with respect to molecular weight. However, assuming a coding ratio of 3 [nucleotide residues to each amino acid in the protein to be synthesized] the average molecular weight would not be lower than 500,000. (3) It should have a base composition reflecting the base composition of DNA. (4) It should, at least temporarily or under certain conditions, be found associated with ribosomes, since there are good reasons to believe that ribosomes are the seat of protein synthesis. (5) It should have a very high rate of turnover. . . .

"It is immediately evident that none of the more classically recognized cellular RNA fractions meets these very restrictive qualifications. . . .

"However, a small fraction of RNA, first observed by [E.] Volkin and [L.] Astrachan (1957) in phage infected E. coli, and recently found to exist also in normal yeasts [by M. Yčas and W. S. Vincent in 1960] and coli [by F. Gros, H. Hiatt, W. Gilbert, C. G. Kurland, R. W. Riseborough and J. D. Watson in 1961], does seem to meet all the qualifications listed above.

"This fraction (which we shall designate 'messenger RNA' or M-RNA) amounts to only about 3% of the total RNA; it can be separated from other RNA fractions by column fractionation or

sedimentation. [It has] a minimum molecular weight of 300,000.
. . . The rate of incorporation of [radioactive phosphorus into this
fraction, a measure of its rate of synthesis] is extremely rapid. [In
fact, it is] several hundred times faster than any other RNA fraction. [Its base composition corresponds to that of DNA of the
structural gene.]·

"The best defined systems wherein the synthesis of a protein is
seen to be controlled by specific agents are examples of enzymatic
adaptation, this term being taken here to cover both enzyme induction, i.e. the formation of enzyme electively provoked by a substrate, and enzyme repression, i.e. the specific inhibition of enzyme
formation brought about by a metabolite. Only a few inducible and
repressible systems have been identified both biochemically and
genetically to an extent which allows discussion of the questions in
which we are interested here. In attempting to generalize, we will
have to extrapolate from these few systems. Such generalization is
greatly encouraged, however, by the fact that lysogenic systems,
where phage protein synthesis might be presumed to obey entirely different rules, turn out to be analysable in closely similar
terms. . . .

"Most of the fundamental characteristics of the induction effect
have been established in the study of the 'lactose' system of *Escherichia coli* [which functions in the fermentation of lactose, or
milk sugar, by that organism].

"Wild type *E. coli* cells grown in the absence of a galactoside
contain about 1 to 10 units of galactosidase per mg dry weight,
that is, an average of 0.5 to 5 active molecules per cell or 0.15 to
1.5 molecules per nucleus. Bacteria grown in the presence of a
suitable inducer contain an average of 10,000 units per mg dry
weight. This is the induction effect.

"A primary problem, to which much experimental work has
been devoted, is whether this considerable increase in specific activity corresponds to the synthesis of entirely 'new' enzyme molecules,
or to the activation or conversion of pre-existing protein precursors.
It has been established by a combination of immunological and isotopic methods that the enzyme formed upon induction: (a) is
distinct, as an antigen, from all the proteins present in uninduced
cells; (b) does not derive any significant fraction of its sulfur

[work done at the Pasteur Institute in 1953–1955] or carbon [work of B. Rotman and S. Spiegelman in the United States in 1954] from pre-existing proteins.

"The inducer, therefore, brings about the complete *de novo* synthesis of enzyme molecules which are new by their specific structure as well as by the origin of their elements. The study of several other induced systems has fully confirmed this conclusion, which may by now be considered as part of the *definition* of the effect.

"Since the specificity of induction or repression is not related to the structural specificity of the controlled enzymes, and since the rate of synthesis of different enzymes appears to be governed by a common element, this element is presumably not controlled or represented by the structural genes themselves. . . .

"If this inference is correct, mutations which affect the controlling system should not behave as alleles [i.e. corresponding or paired genes on homologous chromosomes] of the structural genes. In order to test this prediction, the structural genes themselves must be identified. The most thoroughly investigated case is the lactose system of *E. coli*. . . . [Three types of mutants, each with a different set of enzymic characteristics as a result of the action of their respective genes, are considered:]

"(1) Galactosidase mutations: [symbolized as] $z^+ \rightleftarrows z^-$ [and signifying] loss of the capacity to synthesize active galactosidase (with or without induction).

"(2) Permease mutations: $y^+ \rightleftarrows y^-$ expressed as the loss of the capacity to form [the enzyme 'acetylase'].

"(3) Constitutive mutations: $i^+ \rightleftarrows i^-$ expressed as the ability to synthesize large amounts of galactosidase *and* acetylase in the absence of inducer."

[The location of the mutant genes in these types has been determined by the recombination technique using *E. coli* K12, the strain that Tatum and Lederberg used so effectively in their own research. Not only were the z and y genes located in relation to others on the chromosome, but they were confirmed as the structural genes for galactosidase and acetylase, respectively. Furthermore, it was found that the z and y genes belong to different loops of the folded chromosome.]

[In regard to the i^+ gene, its function seems to be the determination of the synthesis of a repressor substance that is inactive or absent in the i^- alleles and which therefore permit the formation of galactosidase and acetylase constitutively. One piece of evidence for this is the fact that substances that inhibit induction of galactosidase by exogenous galactosides have no such action in mutants of the type $i^- z^+ y^+$.]

"A direct and specific argument comes from the study of one particular mutant of the lactose system. This mutant (i^s) has lost the capacity to synthesize *both* galactosidase and [another enzyme in the system, namely permease. This would seem to indicate a deletion of the structural genes, making the mutant $z^- y^-$. But it cannot be so because the mutant] recombines, giving Lac^+ types, with all the z^- and y^- mutants. [In further studies of crosses, the i^s mutant proved to have unique properties which are] exceedingly difficult to account for except by the admittedly very specific hypothesis that mutant i^s is an allele of i where the *structure* of the repressor [synthesized through the action of the mutated gene i^s] is such that it cannot be antagonized by the inducer any more. . . .

"[A major conclusion from the work on induced enzymes was the defining of] a new type of gene, which we shall call a 'regulator gene'. A regulator gene does not contribute structural information to the proteins which it controls. The specific product of a regulator gene is a cytoplasmic substance [such as that formed under the influence of the gene i^+], which inhibits information transfer from a structural gene (or genes) to protein. In contrast to the classical structural gene, a regulator gene may control the synthesis of several different proteins: the one-gene one-protein rule does not apply to it. [In addition] one expects to find that the genetic control of repressible systems also involves regulator genes. [Experiments on the repression of synthesis of three enzymes, tryptophan synthetase, the arginine-synthesizing system of enzymes, and alkaline phosphatase, are then reviewed.]

"The sum of these observations leaves little doubt that repression, like induction, is controlled by specialized regulator genes, which operate by a basically similar mechanism in both types of systems, namely by governing the synthesis of an intracellular substance which inhibits information transfer from structural genes to protein. . . .

"The specificity of operation of the repressor implies that it acts by forming a stereospecific combination with a constituent of the system possessing the proper (complementary) molecular config-uration. . . . The flow of information from gene to protein is inter-rupted when this element is combined with the repressor. This controlling element we shall call the *'operator'*. We should perhaps call attention to the fact that, once the existence of a specific re-pressor is considered as established, the existence of an operator element defined as above follows necessarily. . . .

"[Recombination studies of constitutive mutants involving the operator gene in the *Lac* system showed] that the $o^+ \rightarrow o^c$ muta-tions correspond to a modification of the specific, repressor-accept-ing structure of the operator . . . [and furthermore] that the operator governs an integral property of the genetic segment *ozy*, or of its cytoplasmic product. . . . *This genetic unit of co-ordinate expression* we shall call the *'operon'*.

"The existence of such a unit of genetic expression is proved so far only in the case of the *Lac* segment."

CONSEQUENCES IN THEORY AND PRACTICE

As Lwoff explains, prophage was one of the "previously un-known class of genes whose function is to regulate the activity of other genes." The phage enters the bacterial cell, becomes part of that cell's chromosome and, in doing so, temporarily retires its capacity to produce more phage. At the same time it endows the bacterium with immunity against any further invasion by the same type of virus. Production of new phage occurring spontaneously in only a few bacteria, could be initiated in *any* cell by irradiation with ultraviolet light or X-rays, or by treatment with nitrogen mustards or certain other chemical agents. Gene action could then be studied in the same manner as any other biochemical or physio-logical activity of the cell, indeed, by many of the same techniques.

These studies on lysogeny have been a crowning achievement of

Lwoff's extremely fruitful scientific work. In the 1920's he established his eminence as a student of the unicellular animalcules known as protozoa. In the 1930's he produced his treatise on biochemical evolution, the thesis being that evolution is accompanied by the gradual loss of enzymes so that higher organisms are more dependent upon the environment to provide ready-made nutrients and other metabolites. This view came into its own later on when research on the mode of origin of living matter began in earnest (cf. p. 314). Lwoff and his wife, Marguerite, also began during this period the study of the nutritional requirements of bacteria and established, among other things, the role of vitamins as co-factors of enzymic reactions in these organisms. This finding had most important repercussions in animal nutrition, as well as in chemotherapy with sulfonamides and other drugs.

In their classic paper on the regulation of protein synthesis, which has been quoted above, Jacob and Monod introduced many new concepts into genetics and established others that had been mooted for some years by investigators in this field of work, generally. For example, the structural-gene hypothesis, stating that the chromosomal DNA directs the synthesis of enzymes and other proteins, left unexplained why all proteins were not being constantly manufactured in the cell at steady rates of production, a situation that would be at complete variance with experience in bacterial, plant and animal biochemistry. How did known environmental factors, whether the presence of a substrate, irradiation with short or ultra-short rays, exposure to chemicals, or increase in the ambient temperature, affect the work of DNA? The solution to this restatement of the old "nature-nurture" problem in terms of macromolecular chemistry came from Jacob and Monod's comprehensive theory and experimental work, in which they postulated the existence of a second type of gene, the regulatory one. In a hereditary cluster which they called the operon, consisting of neighboring genes that control a particular sequence of reactions, there are included not only the structural genes but also the operator gene transmission of whose "message" to the former instructs them to "go ahead and make enzymes." But the operator gene can do this only if it is released from the inhibition exerted by a "repressor substance" manufactured regularly under the influence of another regulatory gene located at some distance along the chromosome from the operon. Hence, when E. *coli* is presented with, say, a galactoside this substrate neutralizes the action of the repressor substance, freeing the operator gene now to direct the structural genes to do their work. Jacob and Monod point out (op. cit.) "that the mechanisms of control in all these systems are negative, in the sense that they operate by inhibition rather than activation of protein synthesis, [and] that the control mechanisms operate [not at the cytoplasmic level by controlling the activity of the messenger-RNA but] at the genetic level, i.e. by regulating the activity of structural genes."

The Nobel Prize Winners have introduced many new concepts, along with fresh terminology to match. But their great contributions have been in experiment as well as in the realm of theory. Many unanswered questions remain about the genetic control mechanisms, such as the nature of repressor substances, extension of the work to other systems besides the *Lac* system of E. *coli,* and the applicability of the concepts to higher organisms. On this score, the Pasteur Institute group declares, "What is true for a microbe is also true for an elephant." Indeed, it has been suggested that repressors operate in embryonic differentiation, with "de-repression" occurring at various times and in different parts of the organism, allowing full expression to specific structural genes in development. It is conceivable that this happens in other ways. For example, a portion of our chromosomal DNA, needed only for a short time in embryonic growth might eventually be repressed and remain so unless an inducing agent neutralizes it, with the consequence that certain enzymes, or tissues proliferate to an unwanted extent, and result in disease. In this sense the findings of the French investigators are relevant to the cancer problem.

The 1965 award had an immediate and unexpected consequence in France. It opened up a public discussion of the social and political relations of science in that country. Why had France not produced any "Nobels" in science since 1935, when Pierre and Irène Curie had won the prize in physics? Why had scientists at the Pasteur Institute been the main recipients of the prizes in physiology or medicine in France?* How was it possible that the 1965 Prize Winners were so widely known and honored outside France, yet so long unrecognized in their own country? It can be expected that this open debate will have a salutary effect on future support of scientific investigation in France.

REFERENCES

Pollock, M. R. "1965 Nobel Prize for medicine," *Nature,* Vol. 208 (1965), pp. 1250–1252.

Stent, G. S. "1965 Nobel laureates in medicine or physiology," *Science,* Vol. 150 (1965), pp. 462–464.

---

* Laveran, Metchnikoff, Nicolle, Jacob, Lwoff and Monod. In addition, Bordet and Bovet had carried out some of their Prize-winning work at the Pasteur Institute in Paris, although they received the award later, when they were working elsewhere.

CLASSIFICATION OF AWARDS BY TOPIC

ELECTROPHYSIOLOGY

Einthoven	1924	Eccles	1963
Erlanger	1944	Hodgkin	1963
Gasser	1944	Huxley	1963

EMBRYOLOGY

| Spemann | 1935 |

ENDOCRINOLOGY

Kocher	1909		
Banting	1923	Kendall	1950
Macleod	1923	Hench	1950
Houssay	1947	Reichstein	1950

ENZYMOLOGY AND METABOLISM

Meyerhof	1922	Lipmann	1953
Warburg	1931	Theorell	1955
Szent-Györgyi	1937	Beadle	1958
Houssay	1947	Tatum	1958
Cori, C. F.	1947	Bloch	1964
Cori, G. T.	1947	Lynen	1964
Krebs	1953		

GENETICS AND MOLECULAR BIOLOGY

Morgan	1933		
Muller	1946	Watson	1962
Beadle	1958	Wilkins	1962
Tatum	1958	Jacob	1965
Lederberg	1958	Lwoff	1965
Crick	1962	Monod	1965

IMMUNITY AND IMMUNE MECHANISMS

von Behring	1901	Landsteiner	1930
Metchnikoff	1908	Burnet	1960
Ehrlich	1908	Medawar	1960
Richet	1913	Lwoff	1965
Bordet	1919		

445

INSECT VECTORS OF DISEASE

Ross	1902	Müller	1948
Nicolle	1928	Theiler	1951

MENTAL DISEASE

Wagner-Jauregg	1927	Moniz	1949

MICROBIOLOGY

von Behring	1901	Jacob	1965
Koch	1905	Lwoff	1965
Waksman	1952	Monod	1965
Lederberg	1958		

NUCLEIC ACIDS

Kossel	1910	Crick	1962
Ochoa	1959	Watson	1962
Kornberg	1959	Wilkins	1962

PARASITOLOGY

Ross	1902	Fibiger	1926
Laveran	1907	Wagner-Jauregg	1927

PHARMACOLOGY AND CHEMOTHERAPY

Dale	1936	Chain	1945
Loewi	1936	Florey	1945
Domagk	1939	Waksman	1952
Fleming	1945	Bovet	1957

PHOTOTHERAPY

Finsen	1903

PHYSIOLOGY (blood, digestion, heart, muscle)

Pavlov	1904	Minot	1934
Krogh	1920	Murphy	1934
Hill	1922	Heymans	1938
Meyerhof	1922	Cournand	1956
Einthoven	1924	Forssmann	1956
Whipple	1934	Richards	1956

PHYSIOLOGY (nervous system and sense organs)

Golgi	1906	Gullstrand	1911
Cajal	1906	Bárány	1914

PHYSIOLOGY (nervous system and sense organs) (*cont.*)

Sherrington	1932	Hess	1949
Adrian	1932	von Bekesy	1961
Dale	1936	Eccles	1963
Loewi	1936	Hodgkin	1963
Erlanger	1944	Huxley	1963
Gasser	1944		

SURGERY AND TRANSPLANTATION PROBLEMS

Kocher	1909	Burnet	1960
Carrel	1912	Medawar	1960

VIROLOGY

Nicolle	1928	Weller	1954
Theiler	1951	Lederberg	1958
Enders	1954	Lwoff	1965
Robbins	1954		

VITAMINS

Eijkman	1929	Doisy	1943
Hopkins	1929	Lipmann	1953
Szent-Györgyi	1937	Theorell	1955
Dam	1943	Lynen	1964

INDEX

M